Computer Simulation Techniques

Computer Simulation Techniques

Thomas H. Naylor
Professor of Economics
Duke University

Joseph L. Balintfy
Professor of Operations Research
Tulane University

Donald S. Burdick
Associate Professor of Mathematics
Duke University

Kong Chu
Associate Professor of Industrial Management
Georgia Institute of Technology

John Wiley & Sons, Inc., New York · London · Sydney

Library of Congress Catalog Card Number: 66-17622
Printed in the United States of America
ISBN 0 471 63060 8

Foreword

Professors Naylor, Balintfy, Burdick, and Chu have written a book which makes available to decision makers and analysts a spectrum of techniques and concepts in computer simulation. With computer simulation, one can gain insight into complex systems, build and test theories, and peer dimly, but explicitly into the future. The final choice of an action or a theory to fit reality still rests with the human involved, but computer simulation is capable of providing powerful assistance as an analytical tool.

Although several books have been written in the past three years on simulation techniques, this book, in my opinion, is notable because for the first time a single book has achieved a balanced, high-level treatment of computer simulation techniques, combining both theoretical and practical considerations. To be sure, no one book can cover an entire field or be everything to everyone, but the combined talents of the four authors have produced a consistent and comprehensive summary of computer simulation techniques not found in any book to date. Drawing from the academic areas of economics, business administration, and mathematics, the various chapters expose the reader to the state of the art, present theoretical foundations for techniques, describe in many instances "how to do it," and show areas where techniques need to be developed. Accordingly, this book will be of value to the researcher, practitioner, and teacher.

The original work for this book began at Tulane University, where Professor Balintfy offered a course in simulation in the School of Business Administration and where Professors Naylor and Chu were graduate students in economics. Later Professor Burdick from the mathematics department at Duke University joined the collaboration that produced this book.

Lest all of this sound as though this work encompasses the entire field of simulation and for all time, I quickly add—it is a simulation of computer simulation techniques as they exist today. Like all simulations, at best it reduces a complex subject to manageable proportions and serves to crystallize our understanding. Toward that goal, this book is a great addition to the literature.

C. JACKSON GRAYSON, JR.
DEAN OF THE SCHOOL OF
BUSINESS ADMINISTRATION,
TULANE UNIVERSITY

Preface

Since the advent of the digital computer in the early 1950's a plethora of new and powerful analytical tools have been created which have had a significant and lasting impact on a number of scientific disciplines. This book is about a special class of these new analytical tools known as computer simulation techniques. The literature describing particular applications of computer simulation as a mode of analysis is now quite extensive and includes such fields as medicine, physics, engineering, space technology, social sciences, business administration, and economics to mention only a few. Although the literature on particular applications of computer simulation has been successful in imparting general knowledge about computer simulation, it has not provided the kind of information which is necessary if one wants to know how to proceed in planning computer simulation experiments on systems which differ from the special cases cited in the literature. On the other hand, there is no shortage of technical articles and monographs dealing with certain specific problems related to computer simulation such as the generation of pseudorandom numbers and stochastic variates on a computer and the use of special purpose simulation languages. But with rare exception these technical papers have made little effort to consider the overall methodology of computer simulation. Although it is generally known that in order to design and carry out computer simulation experiments one must possess a minimal knowledge of mathematical statistics, probability theory, difference or differential equations, experimental design techniques, and computer programming, the literature on computer simulation for the most part has neglected to spell out in detail just how much knowledge and what type of knowledge of each of these subjects is required to conduct simulation experiments. There appears to be a real need for a book which has as its goal the development of a step-by-step methodology for planning, designing, and carrying out simulation experiments.

This book is an attempt at least partially to close this gap. The purpose of this book is to provide a detailed treatment of the methods and procedures involved in planning and designing computer simulation experiments as well as the theory on which these methods are based. Although most of the applications of computer simulation described in this book are related to business administration, economics, and operations research, the techniques described and the theory underlying these techniques are of a general nature and should be applicable to simulation experiments in a wide variety of different fields.

In developing a methodology for computer simulation of business and economic systems we shall outline many of the practical, theoretical, and philosophical problems which arise in planning and implementing simulation experiments. When solutions are known to exist to these problems, we shall describe them. But in other cases we shall merely point out the nature of problems which remain unresolved and require future research efforts.

It is assumed that the reader has had a basic calculus course and some mathematical statistics and probability theory and possesses a minimal knowledge of computer programming. Deficiencies in these prerequisites may easily be remedied by consulting the references which we have included on each of these topics.

In Chapter 1 we begin by defining the concept of "computer simulation" and relating it to the scientific method and scientific philosophy in general. The rationale underlying the use of computer simulation as a tool of analysis is set forth in this introductory chapter also. Chapter 2 contains a nine-step procedure which has been found to be useful in planning simulation experiments with business and economic systems. In the remainder of the book (Chapters 3 through 9), we elaborate on the nine steps outlined in Chapter 2, placing particular emphasis on those aspects of computer simulation which are not treated in existing textbooks.

In Chapter 3 we describe several alternative methods for generating pseudorandom numbers on a computer as well as a number of statistical tests for testing the "randomness" of pseudorandom numbers. Chapter 4 contains a collection of techniques, computer flow charts, and FORTRAN subroutines for generating stochastic variates from some of the better known probability distributions as well as empirical distributions. In addition this chapter describes methods for simulating Markov processes on a computer and generating correlated variates.

Chapters 5 and 6 consist of a set of computer models and flow charts for simulating business and economic systems. Queueing, inventory, and scheduling systems provide applications of computer models in Chapter 5, and Chapter 6 contains a collection of computer models based on economic theory and includes models of the firm and industry and the economy as a whole. Chapter 7 is a comparison of some of the so called special purpose simulation languages such as GPSS, SIMSCRIPT, GASP, DYNAMO, SIMULATE, and others. Chapters 8 and 9 deal with the problems of verification and experimental design, respectively. The problem of verifying the results of computer simulation studies is considered both from a practical and a philosophical point of view. The objective of Chapter 9 is to provide the reader with the background necessary to consult the existing literature on design of experiments so as to apply this literature to the design of computer simulation experiments.

Although it would be impossible to acknowledge all of the assistance that we have received in compiling this book, we do want to mention the contributions of certain individuals and organizations. We are indebted to the editors of *Management Science, IBM Systems Journal,* and *The Journal of Industrial Engineering* for permission to reprint material which was previously published in these journals. Geoffrey Gordon of the IBM Advanced Systems Division contributed an article describing GPSS and a GPSS program for one of our computer models. A GASP program and the results of a computer run for a multi-stage queueing model were provided by Philip J. Kiviat of The RAND Corporation. Gary McKay and Jerry Yurow gave us some of the benefits of their experience with DYNAMO models of the textile industry at the Technical Analysis Division, Institute for Applied Technology, National Bureau of Standards. Merrell Patrick and Thomas M. Gallie, directors of the Duke University Computer Center, provided us with the type of atmosphere in a computation center necessary for testing the computer models contained in this book. Daniel B. Killeen provided similar encouragement at the Tulane University Computer Center. Special mention should be made of the International Business Machines Corporation which granted permission to reproduce the "IBM Management Decision-Making Game" in Chapter 6. Chapters 5 and 6 are based in part on the results of two studies supported by the Duke University Council on Research entitled "Simulation of Economic Systems" and "A Computer Model of the Textile Industry in North Carolina." Partial support for the research on Chapter 9 was obtained by Donald S. Burdick from a grant to Duke University by the National Aeronautics and Space Administration (Grant No. 34-001-005). Earl Sasser and Lyman C. Dennis, II, of Duke University and Tulane University, respectively, contributed numerous helpful comments and criticisms of earlier versions of the manuscript. We are particularly appreciative of the tireless efforts of Mrs. Louise Keir who devoted long hours to typing countless revisions of a manuscript heavily infested with mathematical symbols. Miss Susan Wilkins also assisted with a portion of the typing.

Durham, North Carolina

THOMAS H. NAYLOR
JOSEPH L. BALINTFY
DONALD S. BURDICK
KONG CHU

Contents

Computer Simulation Techniques

Chapter 1 | Introduction to Computer Simulation

COMPUTER SIMULATION DEFINED

The verb "to simulate" is a term that has come into vogue recently in a number of scientific disciplines to describe the ancient art of model building. Although simulation has been applied to some extremely diverse forms of model building, ranging from Renaissance paintings and sculpture to scale models of supersonic jet airliners and computer models of cognitive processes, it has come to mean something quite specific to both physical scientists and behavioral scientists. The modern use of the word traces its origin to the work of von Neumann and Ulam in the late 1940's, when they joined the term "Monte Carlo analysis" to apply to a mathematical technique they used to solve certain nuclear-shielding problems that were either too expensive for experimental solution or too complicated for analytical treatment. Monte Carlo analysis involved the solution of a nonprobabilistic mathematical problem by simulating a stochastic process that has moments or probability distributions satisfying the mathematical relations of the nonprobabilistic problem.

With the advent of the high-speed computer in the early 1950's, simulation took on still another meaning because it had become possible to experiment with mathematical models (describing some system of interest) on a computer. For the first time the social scientists found that, like the physicists, they too could perform controlled, laboratorylike experiments; they, however, used electronic computers rather than physical devices such as a nuclear reactor. With the invention of computer simulation, countless applications came into being, but an even greater number of practical and theoretical problems were also created by this innovation. In this book we attempt to investigate a number of important applications of simulation in the areas of economics and operations research as well as suggest some alternative methods for solving some of the practical and theoretical problems involved in performing actual simulations.

Although we have used the word "simulation" quite freely in the preceding paragraphs to refer to a number of different things, let us try to give a more precise definition. Unfortunately, there is by no means a consensus among those people who use this term as to its exact meaning. For those who prefer a strictly formal definition of simulation, the one proposed by C. West Churchman may prove to be satisfactory. Recognizing the inherent inconsistencies and ambiguities in the present-day usage of the word, Churchman has defined simulation as follows:

"x simulates y" is true if and only if (a) x and y are formal systems, (b) y is taken to be the real system, (c) x is taken to be an approximation to the real system, and (d) the rules of validity in x are non-error-free [7, p. 12].

Although it is not as precise a definition, for the purposes of this book Shubik's definition of simulation appears to be more appropriate because it is typical of the more popular definitions.

A simulation of a system or an organism is the operation of a model or simulator which is a representation of the system or organism. The model is amenable to manipulations which would be impossible, too expensive or impractical to perform on the entity it portrays. The operation of the model can be studied and, from it, properties concerning the behavior of the actual system or its subsystem can be inferred [41, p. 909].

Simulation is, therefore, essentially a technique that involves setting up a model of a real situation and then performing experiments on the model. This definition of simulation is extremely broad, however, and may very well include such seemingly unrelated things as Link trainers, military war games, business management games, physical models of major river basins, econometric models, various electrical analog devices, and wind tunnel tests of aircraft. However, in this book we will be concerned with a much more narrow definition of simulation. First, although we will have occasion to mention simulations in such fields as psychology, medicine, engineering, etc., most of the simulations discussed in this book will deal with either the firm, the industry, the economy, or some component thereof. But the basic methodology proposed here would also be applicable to any scientific discipline.

Second, we will restrict our definition of simulation to experiments on logical and mathematical models only. Hence, all physical, verbal, pictorial, and analog models will necessarily be excluded from this book. However, one should not infer from our failure to include these other types of models that they are any less important than mathematical models, for such is not the case. In fact, the only inference that can be made at all is that the authors have simply elected to write a book on mathematical models.

Third, our primary interest lies in simulation experiments that can be performed on a digital computer. However, this does not preclude the possibility of using an analog computer or a hand calculator rather than a digital computer to implement the methods discussed here.

Fourth, we are not interested in experiments such as those found in microeconomic theory, which take place under conditions of complete certainty and static equilibrium and yield completely deterministic solutions. Instead we are interested in experiments that take place over extended periods of time under stochastic or dynamic conditions and whose solutions are not necessarily completely, deterministic by strictly analytical means.

Having imposed these four constraints on our original definition of simulation, we are now prepared to formulate the definition that will be used throughout this text. *Simulation is a numerical technique for conducting experiments on a digital computer, which involves certain types of mathematical and logical models that describe the behavior of a business or economic system (or some component thereof) over extended periods of real time.*

Before turning to the rationale underlying the use of computer simulation, it is necessary to define two important variants of simulation—operational gaming and Monte Carlo analysis.

The term "operational gaming" refers to those simulations characterized by some form of conflict of interest among players or human decision-makers within the framework of the simulated environment. "Players or decision-makers act within the simulated environment, and the experimenter, by observing them, may be able to test hypotheses concerning the behavior of the individuals and/or the decision system as a whole" [41, p. 910]. The two most widely used forms of operational gaming are military games and business management games. Military gaming is essentially a training device for military leaders which enables them to test the effects of alternative strategies under simulated war conditions. Business games are also a type of educational tool but for training (either present or future) managers or business executives rather than military leaders.

A business game is a contrived situation which imbeds players in a simulated business environment, where they must make management-type decisions from time to time, and their choices at one time generally affect the environmental conditions under which subsequent decisions must be made. Further, the interaction between decisions and environment is determined by a refereeing process which is not open to argument from the players [34, pp. 7–8].

On the other hand, Monte Carlo analysis is a simulation technique for problems having a stochastic or probabilistic basis [19]. Two different types of problems give rise to the use of this technique. First, there are those problems that involve some kind of stochastic process. Consumer demand, production lead time, and total investment for the economy are examples of economic variables which may be considered to be stochastic in nature. Monte Carlo methods have been developed for simulating most of the well-known probability distribution as well as any empirical distribution.

Second, certain completely deterministic mathematical problems cannot be solved easily (if at all) by strictly deterministic methods. However, it may be possible to obtain approximate solutions to these problems by simulating a stochastic process whose moments, density function, or cumulative distribution function satisfy the functional relationships or the solution requirements of the deterministic problem. Solutions to high-order (greater than second order) difference equations and multiple integral problems can often be obtained more rapidly than otherwise by the use of this method of numerical analysis.

A RATIONALE FOR COMPUTER SIMULATION

The fundamental rationale for using simulation in any discipline (whether it be economics or operations research or not) is man's unceasing quest for knowledge about the future. This search for knowledge and the desire to predict the future are as old as the history of mankind. But prior to the seventeenth century the pursuit of predictive power was limited almost entirely to the purely deductive methods of such philosophers as Plato, Aristotle, Euclid, and other. In a critical appraisal of the methodology of these philosophers, Hans Reichenbach labeled their search for predictive knowledge as "speculative philosophy."

Speculative philosophy sought to acquire a knowledge of generalities, of the most general principles that govern the universe. It was thus led to the construction of philosophic systems including chapters that we must regard today as naive attempts at a comprehensive physics, a physics in which the function of scientific explanation was assumed by simple analogies with experiences of everyday life. It attempted to account for the method of knowledge by a similar use of analogies; questions of the theory of knowledge were answered in terms of picture language rather than by logical analysis [25, p. 303].

However, in 1620 Sir Francis Bacon became the first in a series of philosophers to recognize the limitations of "speculative philosophy" as a methodology for predicting the future. Bacon published his dissent in a book entitled *Novum Organum*.

Bacon saw that reason alone does not have any predictive capacity; it gains it only in combination with observation. The predictive methods of reason are contained in the logical operations by means of which we construct an order into the observational material and derive conclusions. We arrive at predictions through the instrument of the logical derivation. Bacon recognized, furthermore, that if logical derivation is to serve predictive purposes, it cannot be restricted to *deductive logic;* it must include methods of *inductive logic* [35, p. 81].

Indeed, Bacon was the father of scientific philosophy. In its present day form scientific philosophy or the scientific method, as it is frequently called, consists of four well-known steps.

1. Observation of a physical system.
2. Formulation of a hypothesis (or in our case a mathematical model) that attempts to explain the observations of the system.
3. Prediction of the behavior of the system on the basis of the hypothesis by using mathematical or logical deduction, i.e., by obtaining solutions to the mathematical model or models.
4. Performance of experiments to test the validity of the hypothesis or mathematical model.

The reader may be a bit puzzled as to why we have gone to the trouble to reiterate the important attributes of the scientific method, when presumably a person would not have even considered reading this book unless he possessed more than a cursory knowledge of the merits of scientific investigation. The reason is quite straightforward. Sometimes it is simply not plausible to follow the four steps outlined above for a particular problem or system. When this is the case, some form of simulation may be a satisfactory substitute for the step (or steps) in the procedure which is causing the difficulty.

First, it may be either impossible or extremely costly to observe certain processes in the real world. For example, prior to the first manned orbital space flight by the United States or Soviet Russia, the National Aeronautics and Space Administration (NASA) had no actual data on the effects of such flights on humans, since no human being had ever experienced such a flight. Clearly, one alternative way of obtaining initial information about the effects of space flights on humans was to experiment with a large number of flights using human test pilots. This method was rejected because of the relatively high value placed on human life in this country. However, NASA quite successfully implemented an alternative—computer simulation of these flights and their effects on human test pilots. Thus each manned orbital flight achieved by NASA has been preceded by months and even years of experimentation with simulated flights. Other examples of processes in which it may be either impossible or prohibitively expensive to obtain data include: next year's sales figures for a firm, Gross National Product for the economy for the next five years, data on the frequency of machine breakdowns in a factory that has kept only limited records of information of this type, the performance of large-scale rocket engines, the effects of a proposed tax cut on the economy, the effects of an advertising campaign on total sales, the effect of a particular managerial decision policy on a firm's profits, and the effect of increasing the number of tollgates at the Lincoln Tunnel in New York. Yet in all these cases simulation can be used (and in many cases has been used) as an effective means of generating numerical data describing processes that otherwise would yield such information only at a very high cost, if at all.

Second, the observed system may be so complex that it is impossible to describe it in terms of a set of mathematical equations for which it is possible to obtain analytic solutions which could be used for predictive purposes. Most economic systems fall into this category. For example, it is virtually impossible to describe the operation of a business firm, an industry, or an economy in terms of a few simple equations. Simulation has been found to be an extremely effective tool for dealing with problems of this type and will be discussed in detail in Chapter 6. Another class of problems that leads to similar difficulties are large scale queueing problems involving multiple channels which are either parallel or in series (or both). Simulation models of queueing problems will be considered in Chapter 5.

Third, even though a mathematical model can be formulated to describe some system of interest, it may not be possible to obtain a solution to the model by straightforward analytical techniques and in turn make predictions about the future behavior of the system. Again, economic systems and complex queueing problems provide examples of this type of difficulty. Although it may be conceptually possible to use a set of mathematical equations to describe the behavior of a dynamic, multiprocess firm operating under conditions of complete uncertainty, present-day mathematics and computer technology are simply incapable of handling a problem of this magnitude. A classical operations research problem that has long defied analytical solution is the so called "job-shop problem." However, it may be possible to use these complicated mathematical models to simulate the system of interest. Although this approach does not guarantee either optimum or exact solutions to the model describing the system, it may be possible to experiment with a number of alternative solutions and decision rules to determine which solutions and decision rules are more useful in making predictions about the behavior of the system. In addition to the more general problems described above, there exist certain types of purely mathematical problems for which it is either impossible or extremely difficult to find solutions by strictly analytical methods. As was previously stated, computer simulation methods (including Monte Carlo) have proved to be efficient techniques of numerical analysis for solving high-order difference equations, complicated stochastic models, and multi-integral problems, as well as a variety of other mathematical problems.

Fourth, it may be either impossible or very costly to perform validating experiments on the mathematical models describing the system. It should be obvious to the reader that this problem is merely a mirror image of the first problem discussed regarding the implementation of the scientific method. In both cases there exists a problem of insufficient data. In the earlier case, there was insufficient data available for the purpose of formulating hypotheses about the system. However, in the present case, the problem lies in obtaining numerical data to verify the mathematical model and its solution. In fact, the only difference between these two problems is the use to which the scarce data are to be put. For example, in the first case we may be interested in simulating next year's sales data so as to *formulate* one or more hypotheses which are directly related to the firm's sales. However, in the fourth case we may be interested in simulating next year's sales data for an entirely different reason. That is, simulated data can also be used to *test* alternative *hypotheses* concerning the operation of the firm during the forthcoming year. Such hypotheses are usually called decision rules. In other words, the difficulties encountered in implementing steps one and four of the scientific method are in reality "two different sides of the same coin." In the first case simulated data are necessary to formulate hypotheses whereas in the latter case simulated data are required to test hypotheses.

Although the principal reason for choosing computer simulation may be its ability to overcome the aforementioned difficulties in implementing the scientific method, there are several other reasons for using simulation. It should be obvious that most of these additional reasons are not unrelated to the previous discussion. Furthermore, these reasons are by no means intended to be mutually exclusive.

1. Simulation makes it possible to study and experiment with the complex internal interactions of a given system whether it be a firm, an industry, an economy, or some subsystem of one of these.

2. Through simulation one can study the effects of certain informational, organizational, and environmental changes on the operation of a system by making alterations in the model of the system and observing the effects of these alterations on the system's behavior.

3. Detailed observation of the system being simulated may lead to a better understanding of the system and to suggestions for improving it, which otherwise would not be obtainable. "There is indeed a good deal of evidence that human beings have a great capacity for understanding the workings of complicated systems, and can find near optimum decision rules, operating procedures, etc., if they have enough experience with the system and it is stable enough" [28, p. 4].

4. Simulation can be used as a pedagogical device for teaching both students and practitioners basic skills in theoretical analysis, statistical analysis, and decision making. Among the disciplines in which simulation has been used successfully for this purpose include business administration, economics, medicine, and law.

5. Operational gaming "has been found to be an excellent means of stimulating interest and understanding on the part of the participant, and is particularly useful in the orientation of persons who are experienced in the subject of the game" [27, p. 2].

6. The experience of designing a computer simulation model may be more valuable than the actual simulation itself. The knowledge obtained in designing a simulation study frequently suggests changes in the system being simulated. The effects of these changes can then be tested via simulation before implementing them on the actual system.

7. Simulation of complex systems can yield valuable insight into which variables are more important than others in the system and how these variables interact.

8. Simulation can be used to experiment with new situations about which we have little or no information so as to prepare for what may happen.

9. Simulation can serve as a "preservice test" to try out new policies

and decision rules for operating a system, before running the risk of experimenting on the real system.

10. "Simulations are sometimes valuable in that they afford a convenient way of breaking down a complicated system into subsystems, each of which may then be modeled by an analyst or team which is expert in that area" [30, p. 373].

11. For certain types of stochastic problems the sequence of events may be of particular importance. Information about expected values and moments may not be sufficient to describe the process. In these cases Monte Carlo methods may be the only satisfactory way of providing the required information.

12. Monte Carlo simulations can be performed to verify analytic solutions.

13. Simulation enables one to study dynamic systems in either real time, compressed time, or expanded time.

14. When new components are introduced into a system, simulation can be used to help foresee bottlenecks and other problems that may arise in the operation of the system [30, p. 375].

15. "Simulation makes generalists out of specialists. Analysts are forced into an appreciation and understanding of all facets of the system, with the result that conclusions are less apt to be biased by particular inclinations and less apt to be unworkable within the system framework" [30, p. 375].

PROPERTIES OF SIMULATION MODELS

Before turning to the principal topic of this book, the design and application of computer simulation models of business and economic systems, it is appropriate that we specify exactly what we mean by a simulation model. The importance of models and model building as an integral part of scientific inquiry has been stated quite succinctly by Rosenblueth and Wiener [37, p. 316].

No substantial part of the universe is so simple that it can be grasped and controlled without abstraction. Abstraction consists in replacing the part of the universe under consideration by a model of similar but simpler structure. Models . . . are thus a central necessity of scientific procedure.

A scientific model can be defined as an abstraction of some real system that can be used for purposes of prediction and control. The purpose of a scientific model is to enable the analyst to determine how one or more changes in aspects of a modeled system may affect other aspects of the system or the system as a whole. In order to be useful a scientific model must necessarily embody elements of two conflicting attributes—realism and simplicity. On the one hand the model should serve as a reasonably close approximation to the real system and incorporate most of the important aspects of the system. On the other hand, the model must not be so complex that it is impossible to understand and manipulate. Unfortunately, realistic models are seldom simple, and simple models are seldom realistic. Since our primary interest in model building in this book is limited to mathematical models, we shall now concentrate on the design of mathematical models for computer simulation, rather than continue this somewhat general treatise on the philosophy of model building.

Mathematical models of economic systems consist of four well-defined elements: components, variables, parameters, and functional relationships [32, p. 898].

Components of economic models tend to vary widely depending on whether the economic system being simulated is an economy, an industry, a firm, or some component thereof. For example, major sectors such as the household, business, and government sectors have been used as components in a number of macroeconomic models. Among the models utilizing major sectors of the economy as components include those developed by Tinbergen [43], Clark [8], Klein [23, 24], Klein and Goldberger [25], Smithies [42], Liu [26], Friend and Taubman [18], and Duesenberry, Fromm, Klein, and Kuh [16]. However, only the Duesenberry et al. (Brookings-SSRC) model was actually a simulation model. The shoe, leather, and hide industries and the West Coast lumber industry were used as basic components in simulation studies by Cohen [11, 12] and Hoggatt and Balderston [3], respectively. The firm has served as a component in the simulation models of Bonini [5], Tonge [44], Chu [6], and Hoggatt [21, 22], to mention only a few. One of the most interesting simulation models developed thus far is the demographic model of Orcutt, Greenberger, Korbel, and Rivlin [32, 33], in which individuals and combinations of individuals are the basic components. This model represents one of the first successful attempts to use microcomponents for a model of the economy.

The variables that appear in economic models are used to relate one component to another and may be conveniently classified as exogenous variables, status variables, and endogenous variables.

Exogenous variables are the independent or input variables of the model and are assumed to have been predetermined and given independently of the system being modeled. These variables may be "regarded as acting upon the system but not being acted on by the system" [32, 33]. The direction of causality is assumed to flow one way from the exogenous variables to the system.

Exogenous variables can be classified as either controllable or non-controllable. Controllable (or instrumental) variables are those variables or parameters that can be manipulated or controlled by the decision makers or policy makers of the system. For example, a firm may be able to control the amount of raw material it purchases and the number of workers it employs at a particular period of time. Or the economic policy makers of a central government may be able to specify the rate of taxation or the amount and nature of governmental expenditures for a particular planning period. Noncontrollable variables are generated by the environment in which the modeled system exists and not by the system itself or its decision makers.

Status variables describe the state of a system or one of its components either at the beginning of a time period, at the end of a time period, or during a time period. These variables interact with both the exogenous and the endogenous variables of the system according to the assumed functional relationships of the system. The value of a status variable during a particular time period may depend not only on the values of one or more exogenous variables for some preceding period but also on the value of certain output variables in preceding periods. Whenever a component takes its input from a portion of its own output from a previous period a "feedback loop" is said to occur. Depending on the parameters of the functional equations, when lags are introduced into feedback loops, the values of the system's output variables may exhibit a tendency towards either damped or explosive oscillation. The status variables of a firm might include the level of cash, the level of inventory, and the level of current debt for a particular time period, as well as sales in some preceding period and advertising expenditures for some forthcoming period.

Endogenous variables are the dependent or output variables of the system and are generated from the interaction of the system's exogenous and status variables according to the system's operating characteristics. Endogenous variables for an industry might include total labor force, prices, total sales, and total production. Outputs for an individual might include marriage, death, having children, and divorce [32, 33].

Whether a particular variable should be classified as an exogenous variable, a status variable, or an endogenous variable depends on the purpose of the research. For example, national income may be regarded as an endogenous variable in a macroeconomic business cycle model but may legitimately be treated as an exogenous variable in microeconomic models concerned with predicting demand for a particular firm's products. Exogenous variables may be used in two different ways in simulation experiments. They may either be treated as given parameters (determined by either the environment or the decision makers), which of course have to be estimated first, and read into the computer as input data, or if they are stochastic variables, they may be generated internally by the computer by one of the methods discussed in Chapter 4.

In the language of experimental design, exogenous variables or parameters are classified as "factors." In conducting computer simulation experiments on a given system, we are concerned with the effects that different levels of various factors have on the endogenous variables of the system. That is, a computer simulation experiment consists of a series of computer runs in which we test empirically (using simulation data) the effects of alternative factor levels on the values of our endogenous variables.

The functional relationships describing the interaction of the variables and components of an economic model are twofold—identities and operating characteristics. Both identities and operating characteristics are used to generate the behavior of the system. Identities may take the form of either definitions or tautological statements about the components of the model. For the firm, total profit is defined as the difference between total revenue and total cost, and total assets are equal to total liabilities plus net worth. An operating characteristic is a hypothesis, usually a mathematical equation, relating the sytem's endogenous and status variables to its exogenous variables. Consumption and investment functions for an economy, demand functions for an industry, and production functions for a firm are examples of operating characteristics of economic systems. Operating characteristics for stochastic processes take the form of probability density functions. Unlike components and variables, which can be directly observed from the real system, the parameters of operating characteristics can only be derived on the basis of statistical inference. Needless to say, the accuracy of the results of a simulation depend to a great extent on the accuracy of these estimates of the system's parameters.

To illustrate the aforementioned system of classifying elements of mathematical models, consider the following two examples. The first model is a simple, single-channel, multistation, waiting line model for a firm [6]. The components of this model illustrated by Figure 1-1 consist of *orders* arriving at the firm and *processes* through which an order must pass before it is completed. The purpose of this model

Figure 1-1. A flow chart for a multiprocess firm.

is to relate the total time required for an order to pass through n processes to the arrival pattern of orders and the process time for each of the n processes. The model consists of the following variables, parameters, operating characteristics, and identities.

EXOGENOUS VARIABLES

AT_i = the time interval between the arrival of the ith order and the $(i - 1)$th order, where $i = 1, 2, \ldots, m$. $\qquad$ (1-1)

ST_{ij} = the process time for the ith order in the jth process, where $i = 1, \ldots, m$ and $j = 1, 2, \ldots, n$. $\qquad$ (1-2)

STATUS VARIABLES

WT_{ij} = the amount of time the ith order spends waiting to enter the jth process, where $i = 1, \ldots, m$ and $j = 1, \ldots, n$. $\qquad$ (1-3)

IDT_{ij} = the amount of time the jth process remains idle while waiting for the ith order to arrive, where $i = 1, \ldots, m, j = 1, \ldots, n$. $\qquad$ (1-4)

T_{ij} = the total time the ith order spends in the jth process, $i = 1, \ldots, m; j = 1, \ldots, n$. $\qquad$ (1-5)

ENDOGENOUS VARIABLE

T_i = the total time the ith order spends in the system; i.e., the time required to pass through all n processes. $\qquad$ (1-6)

PARAMETERS

$E(AT)$ = the expected time interval between orders. $\qquad$ (1-7)

$\mathrm{Var}(AT)$ = the variance of the time interval between orders. $\qquad$ (1-8)

$E(ST_j)$ = the expected process time for the jth process, $j = 1, 2, \ldots, n$. $\qquad$ (1-9)

$\mathrm{Var}(ST_j)$ = the variance of the process time for the jth process, $j = 1, 2, \ldots, n$. $\qquad$ (1-10)

OPERATING CHARACTERISTICS

$f(AT)$ = the probability density function for the time interval between orders. $\qquad$ (1-11)

$f(ST_j)$ = the probability density function for the process time for the jth process, $j = 1, \ldots, n$. $\qquad$ (1-12)

IDENTITIES

When the first order arrives at the firm, i.e., when $i = 1$, the following equations are assumed to describe the multiprocess system:

$$AT_1 = 0. \tag{1-13}$$

$$WT_{11} = 0, \ WT_{12} = 0, \ \ldots, \ WT_{1n} = 0. \tag{1-14}$$

$$IDT_{11} = 0, \ IDT_{12} = ST_{11}, \ \ldots, \ IDT_{1n} = \sum_{j=1}^{n-1} ST_{1j}. \tag{1-15}$$

$$T_{11} = ST_{11}, \ T_{12} = ST_{12}, \ \ldots, \ T_{1n} = ST_{1n}. \tag{1-16}$$

For subsequent arrivals, i.e., when $i = 2, 3, \ldots, m$, these equations must be modified accordingly. The T-equations become,

$$
\begin{aligned}
T_{i1} &= WT_{i1} + ST_{i1} & i = 2, \ldots, m \\
T_{i2} &= WT_{i2} + ST_{i2} & i = 2, \ldots, m \\
&\cdots\cdots\cdots\cdots \\
T_{in} &= WT_{in} + ST_{in} & i = 2, \ldots, m.
\end{aligned}
\tag{1-17}
$$

Whether waiting time or idle time occurs at a particular process depends on the sign of the following differences, where $i = 2, \ldots, m$:

$$
\begin{aligned}
DIF_1 &= T_{i-1,1} - AT_i \\
DIF_2 &= (T_{i-1,1} + T_{i-1,2}) - (AT_i + WT_{i1} + ST_{i1}) \\
&\cdots\cdots\cdots\cdots\cdots\cdots\cdots\cdots\cdots \\
DIF_n &= (T_{i-1,1} + T_{i-1,2} + \cdots + T_{i-1,n}) \\
&\quad - (AT_i + WT_{i1} + ST_{i1} + \cdots + WT_{i,n-1} + ST_{i,n-1}).
\end{aligned}
\tag{1-18}
$$

If DIF_j is positive for the jth process, then idle time will be zero, and waiting time can be calculated by

$$WT_{ij} = DIF_j \qquad i = 2, \ldots, m \qquad j = 1, \ldots, n. \tag{1-19}$$

If DIF_j is negative for a particular process, then waiting time will be zero, and idle time will be equal to

$$IDT_{ij} = -DIF_j \qquad i = 2, \ldots, m \qquad j = 1, \ldots, n. \tag{1-20}$$

If DIF_j is equal to zero for a particular process, then both waiting time and idle time will be equal to zero for that process.

This model of a multiprocess firm has a number of possible applications. For example, it can be used to test the economic feasibility of alternative process designs for the firm. Suppose that by purchasing a new piece of equipment the firm can reduce the expected process time for a particular process by fifty percent. The model can then be used to estimate the expected increase in the total number of orders that can be completely processed by the firm during a particular planning period to determine whether or not the firm is justified in purchasing the new piece of equipment.

A second example model that may serve to illustrate some of the basic elements of mathematical models is the simple macrodynamic "multiplier-accelerator" model developed by Paul A. Samuelson [39]. The components of this model include the household sector, the business sector, and the governmental sector of an economy. The purpose of this model is to relate total consumption (of households), total investment (in business), and total government expenditure for the economy to national income during a particular time period T. The model consists of the following variables, parameters, operating characteristics, and identities:

EXOGENOUS VARIABLES

U_T = a stochastic variate with a known probability distribution, expected value equal to zero, and a given standard deviation.   (1-21)

V_T = a stochastic variate with a known probability distribution, expected value equal to zero, and a given standard deviation.   (1-22)

G_T = government expenditure in period T.   (1-23)

ENDOGENOUS VARIABLES

C_T = consumption during period T.   (1-24)

I_T = investment during period T.   (1-25)

Y_T = national income during period T.   (1-26)

PARAMETERS

c = marginal propensity to consume.   (1-27)

b = accelerator coefficient.   (1-28)

OPERATING CHARACTERISTICS

$$C_T = cY_{T-1} + U_T.$$ (1-29)

$$I_T = b(Y_{T-1} - Y_{T-2}) + V_T.$$ (1-30)

IDENTITY

$$Y_T = C_T + I_T + G_T.$$ (1-31)

Having considered some of the basic elements of which most computer simulation models consist, we now turn our attention to a taxonomic system for classifying simulation models.

CLASSIFICATION OF SIMULATION MODELS

A number of different taxonomic systems have been suggested for classifying simulation models. For example, Moss [31] has suggested the possibility of classifying simulation models according to their degree of abstraction.

On the basis of the criteria (a) number of elements reproduced, (b) essentiality of elements, (c) faithfulness of reproduction, and (d) replicability, we can determine five degrees of abstraction:

0. The process, activity, or situation on which the model is based.
1. A replication of the initial process or situation; examples of this are controlled "runs" in industry, maneuvers in the area of military science, and (not to omit the arts) the drama, a model of a real or hypothetically real situation.
2. A controlled, laboratory-type model, capable of repetition; laboratory models of industrial processes, war games, and the cinema (as opposed to live drama) are examples of this.
3. A completely synthetic extraction of essential elements of the initial situation; computer models of industrial or military situations and (to maintain a labored analogy) the play-script.
4. A closed analytical model, usually merely nominally stochastic [31, p. 591].

However, since this book is concerned primarily with mathematical models, an alternative classificatory system appears to be more appropriate than the one proposed by Moss. Our system, which is admittedly completely arbitrary, will classify simulation models as deterministic, stochastic, static, and dynamic. Convenience is the sole virtue of this system, for in no sense are these model descriptions mutually exclusive.

Deterministic Models

In deterministic models neither the exogenous variables nor the endogenous variables are permitted to be random variables, and the operating characteristics are assumed to be exact relationships rather than probability density functions. Deterministic models are less demanding computationally than stochastic models and can frequently be solved analytically by such techniques as the calculus of maxima and minima. Most of the traditional models in microeconomic theory are deterministic models in which complete certainty is an implicit assumption. J. R. Hicks' model of the multifactor, multiproduct firm is a well-known deterministic model in economics [20]. Also certain types of sequencing and job-shop models are examples of deterministic models.

Although simulation, and in particular Monte Carlo analysis, can be used to obtain solutions to strictly deterministic models, we shall not concentrate on deterministic models in this book because in most cases analytical techniques are more efficient, computationally speaking, than simulation methods for solving deterministic models. (However, in Chapter 4 we will briefly consider the use of Monte Carlo analysis to compute areas under curves of non-probabilitistic functions.)

Stochastic Models

Those models in which at least one of the operating characteristics is given by a probability function are said to be stochastic models. Because stochastic models are considerably more complex than deterministic models, the adequacy of analytical techniques for obtaining solutions to these models is quite limited. For this reason simulation is much more attractive as a method for analyzing and solving stochastic models than deterministic models. Stochastic models are also of interest from the standpoint of generating random samples of data to be used in either the "observation" or "testing" stages of scientific inquiry. Hence, stochastic simulation models play a major role in this book. (Chapters 3, 4, and 5 are devoted entirely to stochastic simulation models.)

Static Models

Static models are those models which do not explicitly take the variable time into account. J. R. Hicks has proposed the following definition of static economic models:

I call Economic Statics those parts of economic theory where we do not trouble about dating; Economic Dynamics those parts where every quantity must be dated. For example, in economic statics we think of an entrepreneur employing such-and-such quantities of factors and producing by their aid such-and-such quantities of products; but we do not ask when the factors are employed and when the products come to be ready. In economic dynamics we do ask such questions; and we even pay special attention to the way changes in these dates affect the relations between factors and products [20, p. 115].

Most of the so-called equilibrium models in economic theory, such as Hicks' model of the firm [20, pp. 319–320] and the classical model of the economy as a whole [1, p. 157] are examples of static models. In operations research, with rare exceptions, most of the work in the area of linear programming, nonlinear programming, and game theory has been concerned with static models. However, there are two reasons for not emphasizing simulation as a method for analyzing static models in this book. First, most static models are completely deterministic, and solutions can usually be obtained by straightforward analytical techniques, such as optimality calculus and mathematical programming. Second, and even more important, our view of the role of static equilibrium models in economics and operations research coincides very closely with the views expressed by Joan Robinson in her book entitled *Economic Philosophy*.

> The concept of equilibrium, of course, is an indispensable tool of analysis. . . . But to use the equilibrium concept one has to keep it in its place, and its place is strictly in the preliminary stages of an analytical argument, not in the framing of hypotheses to be tested against the facts, for we know perfectly well that we shall not find facts in a state of equilibrium [36, p. 81].

Dynamic Models

Mathematical models that deal with time-varying interactions are said to be dynamic models. In relating dynamic models to economics, Baumol has defined a term that he calls *economic dynamics* as "the study of economic phenomena in relation to preceding and succeeding events" [4, p. 4]. Simulation has been rather widely used in the area of economic dynamics. Among the more well-known applications of simulation to economic dynamics are: (1) simulation of business cycle and macroeconomic growth models (2) simulation models of the firm, such as those developed by Bonini [5] Clarkson [9, 10], Cohen [11, 12], Cyert and March [13, 14], and Forrester [17]; and (3) queueing, scheduling, inventory, and job shop models.

Samuelson has proposed the following sixfold classification of dynamic systems [38, pp. 315–317].

1. Static and stationary.
2. Static and historical.
3. Dynamic and causal.
4. Dynamic and historical.
5. Stochastic and nonhistorical.
6. Stochastic and historical.

Samuelson's "static and stationary" systems correspond to what we have already called static equilibrium systems, in which time has been completely abstracted from the model. That is, no changes are taking place in the system, and the passage of time is not considered at all.

The second classification refers to those economic systems into which disturbances attributed entirely to exogenous or noneconomic causes have been injected. For example, national income in a particular period may depend in part on the birth rate in some preceding time period, and the birth rate, as we all know, may very well be attributed to noneconomic causes. Or the demand for air-conditioners in August may depend on the average temperature in June and July. Samuelson uses the word "historical" because the description of the economic system depends entirely on the time period being considered, and any particular analysis will be valid only for a particular time period [4, p. 7].

"Dynamic and causal" systems are economic systems in which, given a set of initial economic starting conditions, we can predict the behavior of the system in succeeding time periods. For example, in the Samuelson multiplier-accelerator model (assuming U_T and V_T are always equal to zero) if we are given the values of national income for two beginning time periods, then we can determine national income, investment, and consumption for any future time period by straightforward difference equation analysis. This type of dynamic system is characterized by the fact that all of the initial starting conditions are economic in nature. Hence, the future behavior of the system also depends entirely on economic variables.

The fourth classification is similar to the third except it admits the possibility of noneconomic disturbances in the system. That is, the behavior of the system in some future time period will depend not only on the economic starting conditions but also on noneconomic starting conditions and disturbances. For example, the output rate of a factory will depend not only on the type of equipment being used, the number of workers employed, and the amount of raw materials being consumed but also on the efficiency of the workers, which will in turn depend on such noneconomic variables as age, sex, temperament, health, etc.

If a stochastic element is introduced into either the third or fourth system, the resulting systems are said to be either "stochastic and nonhistorical" or "stochastic and historical," depending on whether the stochastic element is introduced into a closed economic system or an open system that is subject to noneconomic disturbances. Indeed, there appears to be considerable evidence supporting the thesis that most economic systems fall into Samuelson's sixth category. That is, most economic systems are dynamic and stochastic and are influenced by noneconomic variables. For this reason a significant portion of this book will be devoted to dynamic economic systems that are "stochastic and historical."

REFERENCES AND BIBLIOGRAPHY

1. Ackley, Gardner. *Macroeconomic Theory.* New York: The Macmillan Company, 1961.
2. Ackoff, R. E., (editor). *Progress in Operations Research* (Vol. I). New York: John Wiley and Sons, 1961.
3. Balderston, F. E., and Hoggatt, Austin C. *Simulation of Market Processes.* Berkeley: Institute of Business and Economic Research, 1962.
4. Baumol, William J. *Economic Dynamics.* New York: The Macmillan Co., 1959.
5. Bonini, Charles P. *Simulation of Information and Decision Systems in the Firm.* Englewood Cliffs: Prentice-Hall, 1963.
6. Chu, Kong, and Naylor, Thomas H. "A Dynamic Model of the Firm," *Management Science* (May 1965).
7. Churchman, C. West. "An Analysis of the Concept of Simulation," *Symposium on Simulation Models.* Edited by Austin C. Hoggatt and Frederick E. Balderston. Cincinnati: South-Western Publishing Co., 1963.
8. Clark, C. "A System of Equations Explaining the U.S. Trade Cycle 1921–41," *Econometrica,* XVII (April 1949), 93–124.
9. Clarkson, Geoffrey, P. E. *Portfolio Selection: A Simulation of Trust Investment.* Englewood Cliffs: Prentice-Hall, 1962.
10. Clarkson, G. P. E., and Simon, H. A. "Simulation of Individual and Group Behavior," *American Economic Review,* L No. 5 (Dec. 1960), 920–932.
11. Cohen, K. J. *Computer Models of the Shoe, Leather, Hide Sequence.* Englewood Cliffs: Prentice-Hall, 1960.
12. Cohen, Kalman, J., and Cyert, Richard M. "Computer Models in Dynamic Economics," *The Quarterly Journal of Economics,* LXXV (Feb. 1961), 112–127.
13. Cyert, Richard M., and March, James G. *A Behavioral Theory of the Firm.* Englewood Cliffs: Prentice-Hall, 1963.
14. Cyert, Richard M., and March, James G. "Research on Behavioral Theory of the Firm," *Contributions to Scientific Research in Management.* The Proceedings of the Scientific Program following the Dedication of the Western Data Processing Center, Graduate School of Business Admin., Univ. of Calif., Los Angeles, Jan. 29–30, 1959.
15. Duesenberry, James S., Eckstein, Otto, and Fromm, Gary, "A Simulation of the United States Economy in Recession," *Econometrica,* XXVIII (Oct. 1960), 749–809.
16. Duesenberry, James S., Fromm, Gary, Klein, Lawrence R., and Kuh, Edwin (editors). *The Brookings-SSRC Quarterly Econometric Model of the United States.* New York: Rand McNally & North-Holland Press, 1965.

17. Forrester, Jay W. *Industrial Dynamics*. New York: The M.I.T. Press and John Wiley and Sons, 1961.
18. Friend, Irwin, and Taubman, Paul, "A Short-Term Forecasting Model," *Review of Economics and Statistics*, XLVI (Aug., 1964), 229–236.
19. Hammersley, J. M., and Handscomb, D. C. *Monte Carlo Methods*. London: Methuen and Co., 1964.
20. Hicks, J. R. *Value and Capital*. Oxford: Clarendon Press, 1939.
21. Hoggatt, Austin C. "A Simulation Study of an Economic Model," *Contributions to Scientific Research in Management*. The Proceedings of the Scientific Program following the Dedication of the Western Data Processing Center, Graduate School of Business Administration, Univ. of Calif., Los Angeles, Jan. 29–30, 1959.
22. Hoggatt, Austin C. "Simulation of the Firm," I.B.M. Research Paper, RC-16, Aug., 1957.
23. Klein, L. *Economic Fluctuations in the United States, 1921–1941*. New York: John Wiley and Sons, 1950.
24. Klein, L. "The Use of Econometric Models as a Guide to Economic Policy," *Econometrica*, XV (April 1947), 111–151.
25. Klein, L., and Goldberger, A. S., *An Econometric Model of the United States, 1929–1952*. Amsterdam: North-Holland Publishing Co., 1955.
26. Liu, Ta-Chung, "An Exploratory Quarterly Econometric Model of Effective Demand in the Postwar U.S. Economy," *Econometrica*, XXXI (July 1963), 301–348.
27. McGlothlin, W. H. "The Simulation Laboratory as a Developmental Tool," The RAND Corporation, P-1454 (Aug. 7, 1958).
28. Marshall, A. W. "Experimentation by Simulation and Monte Carlo," The RAND Corporation, P-1174 (Jan. 28, 1958).
29. Mauer, William A., and Naylor, Thomas H. "Monopolistic-Monopsonistic Competition: The Multi-Product, Multi-Factor Firm," *The Southern Economic Journal*, XXXI (July 1964).
30. Morgenthaler, George W. "The Theory and Application of Simulation in Operations Research," *Progress in Operations Research*. Edited by Russell L. Ackoff. New York: John Wiley and Sons, 1961.
31. Moss, John H. "Commentary on Harling's Simulation Techniques in Operations Research," *Operations Research* VI (July–Aug. 1958), 591–593.
32. Orcutt, G. H. "Simulation of Economic Systems," *American Economic Review*, L, No. 5. (Dec. 1960), 897–907.
33. Orcutt, Guy H., Greenberger, Martin, Korbel, John, and Rivlin, Alice M. *Microanalysis of Socioeconomic Systems: A Simulation Study*. New York: Harper and Brothers, 1961.
34. *Proceedings of the Conference on Business Games*. Sponsored by the Ford Foundation and School of Business Administration, Tulane University, April 26–28, 1961.
35. Reichenbach, Hans. *The Rise of Scientific Philosophy*. Berkeley: University of California Press, 1951.
36. Robinson, Joan. *Economic Philosophy*. Chicago: Aldine Publishing Co., 1963.
37. Rosenblueth, Arturo, and Wiener, Norbert. "The Role of Models in Science," *Philosophy of Science* XII, No. 4 (Oct. 1945), 316–321.
38. Samuelson, Paul A. *Foundations of Economic Analysis*. Cambridge: Harvard Univ. Press, 1947.

39. Samuelson, Paul A. "Interactions between the Multiplier Analysis and the Principle of Acceleration," *Review of Economic Statistics,* **XII** (May 1938), 75–78.
40. Shubik, Martin. "Simulation and the Theory of the Firm." *Contributions to Scientific Research in Management.* The Proceedings of the Scientific Program following the Dedication of the Western Data Processing Center, Graduate School of Business Admin. Univ. of Calif., Los Angeles, Jan. 29–30, 1959.
41. Shubik, Martin. "Simulation of the Industry and the Firm," *American Economic Review,* L, No. 5 (Dec. 1960), 908–919.
42. Smithies, A. "Economic Fluctuations and Growth," *Econometrica,* **XXV** (Jan. 1957), 1–52.
43. Tinbergen, J. *Statistical Testing of Business Cycle Theories.* Geneva: League of Nations, 1939.
44. Tonge, Fred M. *A Heuristic Program for Assembly Line Balancing.* Englewood Cliffs: Prentice-Hall, 1961.

Chapter 2 | Planning Computer Simulation Experiments

Although we have outlined a number of different reasons why we might choose to use computer simulation, for the most part the emphasis of this book will be on the role of computer simulation as a device for conducting scientific experiments on business and economic systems. In fact, it may be argued that this is a book on planning and designing simulation experiments. In order to plan simulation experiments that are applicable to economic and industrial systems, we must necessarily draw very heavily on the tools of mathematical statistics, numerical analysis, econometrics, computer programming, and experimental design. Many of the problems and difficulties that we encounter with computer simulation are in reality classical problems in one or more of the aforementioned disciplines.

Experience suggests that planning simulation experiments involves a procedure consisting of the following nine elements:

1. Formulation of the problem.
2. Collection and processing of real world data.
3. Formulation of mathematical model.
4. Estimation of parameters of operating characteristics from real world data.
5. Evaluation of the model and parameter estimates.
6. Formulation of a computer program.
7. Validation.
8. Design of simulation experiments.
9. Analysis of simulation data.

Although the order in which these nine steps are implemented remains an open question, Figure 2-1 contains an ordering that has yielded reasonably good results in the past.

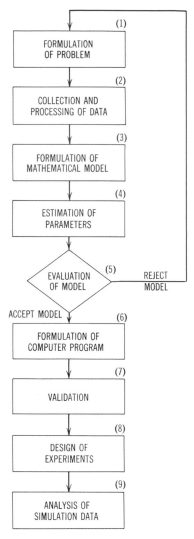

Figure 2-1. Flow chart for planning simulation experiments

To be sure, any procedure of this type is largely arbitrary in nature, and can only be judged on purely pragmatic grounds. We leave it to the reader to decide whether our procedure is a useful one to follow in planning simulation experiments. For our purpose, however, we have found that this arrangement provides a convenient outline of the subject matter of this book. In the remaining sections of this chapter we briefly describe each of the nine steps in the procedure outlined above. Although we shall cover a number of these topics in complete detail in the remaining chapters, in a volume of this type it is obviously impossible to treat all of them in depth, since full-length books have been written on such subjects as model building, estimation of parameters, computer programming, analysis of variance, and experimental designs. However, we shall attempt to place major emphasis on those steps in our simulation procedure that have not been previously spelled out in detail by any single source.

At best we can only hope to provide the reader with a checklist of some of the important factors to be taken into consideration in planning simulation experiments. This checklist may in turn serve to warn the reader of some of the many pitfalls that may arise while conducting a simulation experiment.

This book assumes that a decision has been made on the part of the investigator to use or at least experiment with computer simulation as a mode of analysis. To be sure, the decision whether or not to use simulation as a technique for solving a particular problem is by no means a simple task. In the final analysis such a decision rests on three major considerations—applicability, cost, and simplicity. Computer simulation should be utilized if and only if the answer to each of the following three questions is in the affirmative. First, are we reasonably certain that we can obtain either an exact solution or a satisfactory approximation to the solution of our problem by making use of computer simulation? Second, is computer simulation the lowest cost computational procedure for solving our problem? Third, does the particular simulation technique under consideration lend itself to relatively easy interpretation by those who are likely to use the results of the simulation study?

Unfortunately, it is seldom possibly to answer all three of these questions exactly before conducting a simulation experiment. Therefore, a certain amount of experimentation is necessary before we can decide whether or not to use computer simulation. For this reason, as well as the fact that computer simulation is still in the infant stages of development and does not lend itself to simple decision rules regarding when it should be used, we shall refrain from giving the reader a set of rules that tell him when to use computer simulation. Since computer simulation is merely one alternative method for problem solving, a decision whether to use this particular method is actually no different from a decision to use any other analytical tool such as   linear programming, queueing theory, or dynamic programming. If computer simulation is capable of yielding solutions to a

particular problem which are meaningful and relatively easy to intèr-
pret at a cost which is less than any other computational procedure,
then we should use it as a tool of analysis. If these conditions are
not fulfilled, computer simulation should be rejected in favor of some
other more attractive alternative.

We now turn to the problem of describing some of the major elements involved in planning simulation experiments.

1. FORMULATION OF THE PROBLEM

Not unlike other forms of scientific research, computer simulation
studies should begin with the formulation of a problem or an explicit
statement of the objectives of the experiment, since there is little
benefit to be derived from experiments that involve simulation for
the sake of simulation. In other words, we must first clearly define
the objectives of our research before we can begin to think about
planning a simulation experiment. To be sure, our initial statement
of the problem may very well differ considerably from our final version
of the problem because problem formulation is a sequential process
that usually calls for continuous and progressive reformulation and
refinement of the experimental objectives throughout the duration of the
experiment. Research objectives in business and economics, as well as
in most social sciences, usually take the form of (1) questions to be
answered, (2) hypotheses to be tested, and (3) effects to be estimated.

If the objective of our simulation study is to obtain answers to
one or more questions, then obviously we must attempt to specify
these questions with a high degree of detail at the outset of the experiment, even though we may attempt to refine our questions as the
experiment progresses. The following questions are typical of the kind
that we might want to raise about the behavior of an economic system
for which computer simulation may be capable of yielding answers.
How many workers should a firm hire in a particular month? Will
a policy of full employment and accelerated economic growth lead
to inflation? How many runways are required during peak hours at
Kennedy International Airport in New York? What is an optimum
production schedule for a job shop? Needless to say, it is not sufficient
just to specify the questions that are to be answered by a simulation
experiment, but we must also specify objective criteria for evaluating
possible answers to these questions. For example, we must define exactly what we mean by an "optimum" production schedule if we
expect to recognize such a schedule when we are confronted with

one. Unless we specify precisely what is meant by a "suitable" answer to a question that has been raised, then we cannot hope to achieve meaningful results from computer simulation.

On the other hand, the objective of our research efforts may be to test one or more hypotheses about the behavior of the system that we are studying. Is per capita income more sensitive to changes in governmental expenditures or to private investment? Do the starting conditions of a computer simulation experiment significantly affect the results? Will an increase in lead time significantly affect production cost? In each case, the hypotheses to be tested must be stated explicitly, as well as the criteria for "accepting" or "rejecting" them.

Finally, our objective may be to estimate the effects of certain changes in parameters, operating characteristics, or exogenous variables on the endogenous variables of the system. For example, we may want to experiment with different values of expected arrival time at a service station and estimate the expected waiting time and expected idle time at the station for each value of expected arrival time. Or we may wish to estimate total consumption for the economy when personal income taxes are reduced by 20%. However, before estimating the effects on any endogenous variable of a particular system of interest, we must specify in advance our requirements in terms of statistical precision.

Therefore, before we can begin work on any simulation experiment, two important decisions must be made. First, we must decide on the objectives of our research. Second, we must decide on a set of criteria for evaluating the degree to which our objectives are fulfilled by the experiment. It is indeed possible that after having made these two decisions, we may reject computer simulation entirely because of excessive cost, complexity, or inability to satisfy our experimental objectives.

2. COLLECTION AND PROCESSING OF REAL WORLD DATA

The reader may argue quite legitimately that a discussion of the data processing requirements of simulation experiments should have preceded our comments on problem formulation because it is simply impossible to formulate a problem or a set of experimental objectives without access to information (quantitative or otherwise) about the system being investigated. In other words, a certain amount of data must have been collected and processed before any problem can be defined. For our purposes it is completely irrelevant as to whether data processing precedes problem formulation or vice versa. The important factor is that both of these important functions must be carried out if we are going to conduct simulation experiments.

Although we have no intention whatsoever of going into a lengthy dissertation on data processing, we shall attempt to outline some of the important problems involved in collecting and reducing data to a suitable form for use in simulation experiments. There appear to be at least five reasons why efficient data processing is necessary in order to achieve "success" in carrying out computer simulation experiments.

First, as we have previously stated, descriptive and quantitative information (data) about the particular system to be investigated is a prerequisite for problem formulation. Second, data that have been reduced to a meaningful form may suggest tenable hypotheses which can be used in the formulation of mathematical models describing the behavior of a given system. Third, data may also suggest improvements or refinements of existing mathematical models of the system that is to be simulated. Fourth, data that have been reduced to a final form may be used to estimate parameters of the operating characteristics relating the system's endogenous, exogenous, and status variables. Fifth, without data it would be impossible to test the validity of a simulation model.

It is possible to identify six important functions of data processing that play an integral part in the procedure for implementing computer simulation experiments: collection, recording, conversion, transmission, manipulation, and output.

Data *collection* is the process of capturing the facts when they become available, which may be processed later, when needed. In reality, data collection and data *recording* take place simultaneously, since the collection of data implies that data are being or have been recorded. The sources of data for simulating business and economic systems are manyfold and might include questionnaires, field surveys, samples, physical experiments, and primary and secondary source documents. Among the primary and secondary source documents that might be required are governmental agencies (state, local, and federal), international organizations (United Nations), accounting and engineering records of business firms, and private research organizations. The collection and recording of data frequently prove to be expensive and time-consuming tasks consisting of identification, auditing, editing, assigning codes, transcribing, and verification.

Frequently the medium on which data are recorded during the first stage of processing is not the most efficient medium to use in later stages of processing. Therefore, the *conversion* of the data from one medium to another may play a crucial role in determining data processing efficiency. For example, certain information may be recorded most efficiently in the form of handwritten documents. However, if this information is to be used as input data for a computer it will have to first be punched on cards and then converted to magnetic tape. In addition to the problem of converting data from one form to another, under certain circumstances, there may also be problems involving data *transmission,* that is, moving information from one location to the place where it will be processed.

Once the data have been collected, recorded, converted into an efficient medium, and transmitted to the final processing area, then data *manipulation* operations and final *output* preparations can begin. The manipulation stage calls for the performance of such operations as sorting, collating, merging, information retrieval, as well as arithmetic and logical operations. These operations can be carried out either with or without the use of a computer depending on the amount of data to be manipulated and the nature of the final use that is to be made of the data.

3. FORMULATION OF MATHEMATICAL MODELS

As we indicated in Chapter 1 the formulation of mathematical models consists of three steps:

1. Specification of components.
2. Specification of variables and parameters.
3. Specification of functional relationships.

One difficulty in formulating mathematical models of economic and industrial systems seems to be that model building is an art and not a science. Although the tools used by a builder of mathematical models differ somewhat from those of the sculptor, the painter, and the woodcarver, this factor does not completely disqualify him from consideration as an artist. Even after arming oneself with such tools as econometrics, mathematical statistics, probability theory, matrix algebra, difference equations, and mathematical programming, the job of constructing a mathematical model of a particular system is still analogous to the work of an artist. The process of observing some economic system in the real world, formulating one or more hypotheses about how the system "works," and reducing these hypotheses to a level of abstraction that permits the formulation of mathematical models describing the behavior of the system is by no means a straightforward process. Although a complete knowledge of the system which is being analyzed as well as proficiency in mathematics are necessary conditions for the construction of valid mathematical models, in no sense can they be considered sufficient conditions, since successful mathematical model building depends in part on (1) the analyst's experience, (2) trial-and-error procedures, and (3) a considerable amount of luck. It goes without saying, that we cannot provide the reader with any of these three attributes, but we can (1) suggest some desirable characteristics of mathematical models used in computer simulation experiments, (2) outline some of the major difficulties in model building, and (3) specify some of the basic elements of which mathematical models are composed.

One of the first considerations that enters into the formulation of a mathematical model is the question of how many variables to include in the model. As a general rule we encounter very little difficulty with regard to the endogenous or output variables of our model because these variables are usually determined at the outset of the experiment when we formulate the objectives of the study. (Obviously there is an upper limit on the number of endogenous variables that can be investigated in a single simulation experiment because of the limitations imposed by the size of the computer available to the investigator.) However, the real difficulty arises in the choice of the exogenous variables (some of which may be stochastic) affecting the endogenous variables. Too few exogenous variables may lead to invalid models whereas too many exogenous variables may render computer simulation impossible because of insufficient computer memory capacity or make computational programs unnecessarily complicated.

A second major consideration in the formulation of mathematical models is the complexity of the model. On the one hand it can be argued that economic systems are indeed quite complicated and that mathematical models which claim to describe the behavior of economic systems must also necessarily be complicated. To a certain extent this is true but, on the other hand, we would not want to go to the extreme of constructing such complex models, regardless of how realistic they may be, that they require unreasonable computation time. In general we are interested in formulating mathematical models that yield reasonably accurate descriptions or predictions about the behavior of a given system while minimizing computational and programming time. The complete interdependence of these characteristics of mathematical models cannot be over emphasized. For example, the number of variables in a model and its complexity are directly related to programming time, computation time, and validity. By altering any one of the characteristics of a model we in turn alter all of the other characteristics.

A third area of consideration in the formulation of mathematical models for computer simulation purposes is computational efficiency. By computational efficiency we mean the amount of computer time required to achieve some specific experimental objective. As a general rule, we are usually interested in one of the following two objectives with regard to the efficiency of simulation experiments. In the first case we may want to minimize the amount of computer time required to generate values of our endogenous variables over some specific time period, such as six months or twenty years. That is, we might want to minimize the computer time required to simulate the behavior of the economy of a state over a ten-year period. In the second case, we may be interested in minimizing the amount of computer time required to achieve some predetermined level of statistical precision in estimating the values of certain statistical parameters generated by our computer simulation model. For example, we might want to minimize the computational time of obtaining an estimate of expected waiting time from a simulation run for a waiting line problem that is significant at the .05 level. This second case leads us into the area of statistics, which is concerned with variance reduction techniques. In Chapter 9 we shall mention a number of techniques that have been designed to minimize the amount of computation time (or sample size) of obtaining estimates of parameters (based on simulated data) with given levels of statistical precision. Among the important variance-reducing techniques are included importance sampling, Russian roulette and splitting, use of expected values, correlation and regression, systematic sampling, and stratified sampling.

Computer programming time represents a fourth area of consideration in formulating mathematical models for computer simulation. The amount of time required to write a computer program for generating the time paths for the endogenous variables of a particular set of mathematical models depends in part on the number of variables used in the models and the complexity of the models. If some of the variables utilized in the model are stochastic in nature, then both programming time and computation time are likely to be increased significantly. The amount of effort one expends in attempting to reduce programming time must, of course, be balanced against the questions of validity and computational speed. If the costs in terms of realism are not too great, it may even pay the analyst to formulate his models in such a manner that they satisfy the requirements of one of the simulation languages such as SIMSCRIPT [14], GPSS [3], DYNAMO [17], and GASP [13]. The gains made in terms of reduced programming time may completely offset the loss in validity which may result from such a modification.

The fifth area of interest in model building is the validity of the model or the amount of "realism" built into it. That is, does the model adequately describe the system of interest, and does it give reasonably good predictions of the behavior of the system in future time periods? Unless the answer to one or both of these questions is "yes," then the value of our models is reduced considerably, and our simulation experiment becomes merely an exercise in deductive logic. We need not restate the role in which the other characteristics of mathematical models (number of variables, complexity, etc.) play in determining the validity of a model.

The sixth and final consideration in formulating computer simulation models is their compatibility with the type of experiments that are going to be carried out with them. Since our primary objective in formulating mathematical models is to enable us to conduct simulation experiments, some thought must be given to the particular type of experimental design features that must be built into our models.

In the preceding paragraphs we have attempted to outline what we think are a set of desirable properties of mathematical models, or at least a set of factors the model builder may want to bear in mind. Unfortunately, these properties represent highly idealized goals that are seldom fulfilled in dealing with problems in the real world. For this reason, it seems appropriate that we list several potential difficulties that the model builder is likely to encounter in his efforts to describe the behavior of business and economic systems by means of mathematical models. First, it may simply be impossible to quantify or measure certain types of variables that affect the behavior of the system. Second, the number of variables that must be considered in describing a particular system may exceed the capacity of the computer hardware available to us. Third, some of the significant exogenous variables affecting the output of the system may not be known to us. Fourth, some of the relationships between the exogenous and endogenous variables of our system may not be known to us and may be impossible to obtain. Fifth, in many cases the relationships between the variables affecting the behavior of the system may be so complex that they cannot be expressed in the form of one or more mathematical equations.

Two basic designs have emerged from formulating mathematical models for use in computer simulation: (1) *generalized designs* and (2) *modular* or *building-block* designs. Generalized models represent an attempt to describe the behavior of an entire system, such as a business firm or the economy of a nation. Although this approach has been widely used in microeconomics, macroeconomics, and econometrics, in general it cannot claim a record of overwhelming success in either describing or predicting the future behavior of economic systems. The principal reason for this lack of success on the part of generalized models is that the human mind has great difficulty in comprehending the vast complexities of most economic systems when they are viewed as a whole rather than in terms of their major components. Although generalized models may be quite useful in formulating initial hypotheses about the behavior of certain economic systems, they simply do not stand up when subjected to rigorous statistical testing procedures. Therefore, the philosophy of this book is biased very heavily toward the modular approach to model building described in Chapter 5. By synthesizing a generalized model of an economic system from a set of models describing the major components of the system, we would expect to achieve gains in terms of the realism of the total model and computational efficiency. If we are fortunate enough to be able to utilize block recursive models in our simulation study, then we can reduce the magnitude of the problem of estimating parameters for our models considerably, as well as the computational time required to generate the time paths of our endogenous variables.

Whether or not a real economy can be adequately represented by a block-recursive model depends upon the choice of blocks and how short time lags can be without being represented as zero time lags. Given flexibility in choice of blocks and the use of very short time lags where appropriate, it is difficult to see how the requirement of block-recursiveness places any serious limitations on the model builder. The advantage of working with models which are block-recursive is that digital computers now available all perform their operations in a sequential fashion. This doesn't prevent solving sets of reasonably small numbers of linear simultaneous equations. It does make extremely difficult or impossible the handling of large numbers of nonlinear simultaneous equations. Use of block-recursive models does limit any given set of simultaneous equations to those needed in generating the output of a single block and thus greatly facilitates computer simulation with computing equipment that is or will be available within the next few years [16, p. 902].

4. ESTIMATION OF PARAMETERS OF OPERATING CHARACTERISTICS FROM REAL WORLD DATA

Once we have collected the appropriate data from the system and have formulated a number of mathematical models describing the behavior of this system, we must then estimate the values of the parameters of these models and test the statistical significance of these estimates. The estimation of the parameters of economic models properly falls within the domain of the discipline known as "econometrics."

Econometrics may be defined as the social science in which the tools of economic theory, mathematics, and statistical inference are applied to the analysis of economic phenomena. Its main objective is to give empirical content to economic theory; econometrics in fact encompasses a wide range of activities aimed at accomplishing this objective. First, there is continuing work on the mathematical formulation of economic theory—this is the field known as mathematical economics. Second, there is work on the development of appropriate techniques of statistical inference—this is the field we are calling econometric theory. And third, there is actual statistical inference from economic data—this is the field which may be termed empirical econometrics [4, p. 1].

At a very minimum, one should possess a thorough knowledge of ordinary least-squares estimating techniques and classical testing procedures before attempting to estimate the parameters of the operating characteristics of an economic system. However, if one is to adequately handle such difficult (and in some cases unresolved) problems as errors in variables, lagged variables, multicollinearity, heteroscedasticity, autocorrelation, identification, and simultaneous equations, then he should possess more than a cursory knowledge of the methodology of econometrics. "A comprehensive program of training in econometrics involves the study of economic theory, mathematics, mathematical statistics, social accounting and survey methods, and empirical analysis" [4, p. 1].

Since a treatise on econometrics is obviously beyond the scope of this book, the reader who is not acquainted with econometric theory may find the two textbooks by Goldberger [4] and Johnston [10] quite useful. Goldberger asserts that econometric theory consists of three basic components:

. . . a specification of the process by which certain observed "independent variables" are generated, a specification of the process by which unobserved "disturbances" are generated, and a specification of the relationship connecting these two observed "dependent variables." Taken together these components provide a model for the generation of economic observations, and implicitly, at least, they define a statistical population. A given body of economic observations may then be viewed as a sample from the population.

Once we have a specification of a parent population we may rely on the rules and criteria of statistical inference in order to develop a rational method of measuring a relationship of economic theory from a given sample of observations. In many cases we may rely also on previous theoretical or empirical knowledge about the value of parameters of the population. Such a priori information is a characteristic feature of econometric theory. In any event, it should be clear that the quantification of economic theory is not a mechanical task. In particular, it is not simply a matter of fitting curves to data, of "measurement without theory." . . . rational methods of measuring economic relationships must be grounded in a specification of the probabilistic mechanisms that link economic observations to economic theory [4, p. 4].

Among the important econometric estimating methods described by Goldberger [4] and Johnston [10] and compared on the basis of their statistical and computational properties are included:

1. Single-equation methods
   a. Ordinary least squares
   b. Indirect least squares
   c. Limited information single equation
   d. Two-stage least squares
2. Simultaneous-equation methods
   a. Full information maximum likelihood
   b. Three-stage least squares

5. EVALUATION OF THE MODEL AND PARAMETER ESTIMATES

Once we have formulated a set of mathematical models describing the behavior of our economic system and have estimated the parameters of the operating characteristics on the basis of observations taken from the real world, we must then make an initial value judgment concerning the adequacy of our model. That is, we must test the model. Clearly, there is very little to be gained by using an inadequate model to carry out simulation experiments on a computer because we would merely be "simulating our own ignorance."

This step of the simulation procedure merely represents the first stage of testing a simulation model prior to actual computer runs. At this point we are primarily interested in testing the assumptions or inputs that will be programmed into the computer. In step 7 of our simulation procedure our concern will be with the validity of the output data generated by a computer simulation model. In that case we will be interested in comparing simulated data with historical data to determine the predictive capabilities of the model.

In the case of operating characteristics that take the form of probability distributions we want to apply "goodness of fit" tests to determine how well a given hypothetical probability distribution fits the real world data from which it was derived. We shall also want to test the statistical significance of our estimates of the expected values, variances, and other parameters of these probability distributions. These tests might include [1, 7, 15]:

1. Tests concerning means
    a. One-sample tests concerning means
    b. Differences between means
2. Tests concerning variances
    a. Chi-square tests
    b. F-tests
3. Tests based on count data
    a. Test concerning proportions
    b. Differences among k proportions
    c. Contingency tables
    d. Tests of goodness of fit
4. Nonparametric tests
    a. The sign test
    b. Tests based on rank sums
    c. The median test
    d. The U-test
    e. Tests of runs
    f. Serial correlation tests

In the case of operating characteristics that take the form of econometric models we want to test the statistical significance of each of the parameter estimates of these models using standard t-tests and F-tests. We also want to apply tests that will enable us to detect any violations in the assumptions underlying our econometric models. These might include tests for [4, 10]:

1. Errors in variables
2. Multicollinearity
3. Heteroscedasticity
4. Autocorrelation
5. Identification

Among the questions that we may wish to raise at this point in our procedure are the following ones.

1. Have we included any variables which are not pertinent in the sense that they contribute little to our ability to predict the behavior of the endogenous variables of our system?

2. Have we failed to include one or more exogenous variables that are likely to affect the behavior of the endogenous variables in our system?

3. Have we inaccurately formulated one or more of the functional relationships between our system's endogenous and exogenous variables?

4. Have the estimates of the parameters of the system's operating characteristics been estimated properly?

5. Are the estimates of the parameters in our model statistically significant?

6. On the basis of hand calculations (since we have not yet formulated a computer program) how do the theoretical values of the endogenous variables of our system compare with historical or actual values of the endogenous variables?

If, and only if, we can answer all six of these questions satisfactorily should we proceed to step 6 and the formulation of a computer program. Otherwise, we should repeat steps 1 through 5 until such time that we can achieve satisfactory answers to the aforementioned questions.

6. FORMULATION OF A COMPUTER PROGRAM

The formulation of a computer program for the purpose of conducting computer simulation experiments with our models of the system under study requires that special consideration be given to six activities.

1. Flow chart
2. Computer code
   a. General purpose compilers
   b. Special purpose simulation languages
3. Error checking
4. Data input and starting conditions
5. Data generation
6. Output reports

The first step in writing a computer simulation program involves formulating a flow chart outlining the logical sequence of events to be carried out by the computer in generating the time paths of the endogenous variables of our model. The importance of flow charting in writing computer programs cannot be overemphasized. Throughout Chapters 4 through 6 we shall formulate a multiplicity of flow charts for simulating a wide variety of different kinds of systems beginning with stochastic variates in Chapter 4 and followed by scheduling systems and economic systems in Chapters 5 and 6, respectively.

Upon completion of a flow chart of the logic of our given experiment, we must then consider the matter of writing the actual computer code that will be used to run our experiments on a computer. In general there are two alternatives available to us. We can either write our program in a general purpose language such as FORTRAN, ALGOL, COBOL, or PL/I, or we can use one of the new special purpose simulation languages such as GPSS [3], SIMSCRIPT [14] GASP [13], SIMPAC [18], DYNAMO [17], or PROGRAM SIMULATE [8]. The principal advantage of using a special purpose simulation language rather than a general purpose compiler is that it requires less programming time. These languages have been written to facilitate the programming of certain types of systems. For example, PROGRAM SIMULATE was designed primarily for simulating large-scale economic systems that have been formulated as econometric models consisting of large sets of equations (up to 200). On the other hand, GPSS, SIMSCRIPT, and GASP are particularly well suited for scheduling and waiting line problems. (Chapter 7 contains a detailed description of the leading simulation languages.) Although we can reduce programming time by using a simulation language, we must usually pay a price for this benefit in terms of reduced flexibility in models and increased computer running times. Another important advantage of special purpose simulation languages is that they usually provide error checking techniques that are far superior to those provided by FORTRAN, ALGOL, etc.

Another aspect of the computer programming phase of the development of simulation experiments is the matter of input data and starting conditions for the simulation experiments. Since simulation experiments are by their very nature dynamic experiments, a question arises as to what values should be assigned to the model's variables and parameters at the point in time when we begin simulating the system. That is, we must break into the system at some particular point in time. When we do so, what assumptions should we make about the equilibrium conditions or starting conditions of the system? Needless to say, this question is not easily answered for most systems, and the investigator usually must resort to trial-and-error methods for determining a set of initial values for the system that will not lead to distorted results in later time periods.

A problem directly related to the one of writing computer simulation programs is the development of numerical techniques (which can be programmed on a computer) for data generation. Data used in computer simulation experiments can either be read into the computer from external sources, such as punched cards and magnetic tapes, or it may be generated internally by special subroutines. Of particular interest to us in this book are subroutines for generating pseudorandom numbers and stochastic variates.

If one or more of the exogenous variables included in our mathematical models is assumed to be a stochastic variate with a known probability distribution, then we are confronted with the problem of devising a process of random selection from the given probability distribution so that the results of the repetition of this process on a digital computer will give rise to a probability distribution of sampled values that corresponds to the probability distribution of the variable of interest. "The problem of sampling from any distribution is that of transforming a random number representing the uniform random variable in the range 0-1 by means of the inverse cumulative distribution function" [20, p. 13].

Chapter 3 contains an extended treatment of alternative methods for generating pseudorandom numbers [9, 19, 20] on a digital computer, and Chapter 4 outlines procedures and FORTRAN programs for generating samples taken from most of the well-known theoretical probability distributions as well as any empirical distribution [2, 5, 19, 20]. In the final analysis, a decision concerning which method should be used to simulate a particular probability distribution rests on such grounds as programming time, computational time, amount of computer memory capacity required, and the statistical precision of the results.

One final consideration in the development of a computer program for our simulation experiment is what kind of output reports are needed to give the required information about the behavior of our simulated system. If we use a general purpose computer language such as FORTRAN, then there will be a minimum number of restrictions imposed on the format of our output reports. However, if we use a special purpose simulation language such as SIMSCRIPT, then we must adhere to the output format requirements of the language.

7. VALIDATION

The problem of validating computer simulation models is indeed a difficult one because it involves a host of practical, theoretical, statistical, and even philosophical complexities. Validation of simulation experiments is merely part of a more general problem, namely the validation of any kind of model or hypothesis. The basic questions are, "What does it mean to validate a hypothesis?" and "What criteria should be used to establish the validity of a hypothesis?"

Since the scientific philosophers do not agree about the answers to these two questions, the reader will not be surprised to find that they remain unanswered in this book. In Chapter 8, however, we do outline some of the major methodological and philosophical positions concerning the validation of scientific hypotheses with special emphasis placed on the problem of verifying economic theories.

In general, however, two tests seem appropriate for validating simulation models. First, how well do the simulated values of the endogenous variables compare with known historical data, if historical data are available? Second, how accurate are the simulation model's predictions of the behavior of the real system in future time periods? Associated with each of these two tests is a variety of classical and more recent vintage statistical tests outlined in Chapter 8.

8. DESIGN OF SIMULATION EXPERIMENTS

Once we are reasonably satisfied with the validity of our computer model, we are then ready to consider using our model to conduct actual simulation experiments. Having already defined our experimental problem, endogenous variables, and factors (exogenous variables and parameters), we must now turn our attention to questions of experimental design.

In this phase we can identify two important goals. First, we must select factor levels and combinations of levels and the order of experimentation [6]. Second, having selected our factor combinations, we must endeavor to ensure that our results will be reasonably free from random error.

Much has been written in the experimental design literature about the first of the aforementioned objectives, a great part of which is relevant to the design of simulation experiments. Much has also been written in the literature about the second objective, but because of some special features of computer simulation experiments as distinguished from real world experiments, much less of the existing material is relevant to the second objective for computer simulation experiments. Some material relevant to the second objective is contained in the literature on Monte Carlo techniques.

Chapter 9 contains a more detailed treatment of this subject. It should be emphasized, however, that the application of experimental design techniques to the design of computer simulation experiments remains an area of research where there is still a great deal of work to be done.

9. ANALYSIS OF SIMULATED DATA

The final step in the procedure calls for the analysis of the data generated by the computer from the model of the system being simulated. The analysis of simulated data consists of the following three steps:

1. Collection and processing simulated data.
2. Computation of test statistics.
3. Interpretation of results.

Although the analysis of simulated data is indeed similar to the analysis of real world data (see steps 2 through 4 of Figure 2-1), there are some important differences. By comparing computer simulation with the statistical technique known as distribution sampling, which has been used in the field of statistics for many years, Teichroew has pointed out that the analysis of computer simulation data is considerably more difficult than the analysis of real world data.

In distribution sampling, the way in which randomness enters is well understood and can be explicitly stated. In simulation experiments randomness enters in a very complicated form, and usually the relationship cannot be stated explicitly other than in the algorithm by which the numerical values are computed.

Another major complication is the fact that, while distribution sampling usually dealt with static models, simulation by its very nature deals with dynamic models. The output is a set of related time series. The analysis of these is much more difficult than the analysis of a set of numbers which may be regarded as a sample from a given distribution. Techniques for analysis of multiple, non-independent, non-stationary time series are not yet well developed.

Another factor is the large number of parameters which enter in to the simulation studies. Distribution sampling usually dealt with, at most, a few parameters; simulation experiments frequently have thousands. These are not all equally significant, but unfortunately their relative significance is not known. In any particular case, it is almost impossible to determine a small enough set of important parameters for which designed experiments can be run [19].

REFERENCES AND BIBLIOGRAPHY

1. Freund, John E. *Mathematical Statistics,* Englewood Cliffs, N.J.: Prentice-Hall, 1962.
2. Galliher, Herbert P. "Simulation of Random Processes," *Notes on Operations Research 1959.* Cambridge: The Technology Press, M.I.T., 1959.
3. *General Purpose Simulation II,* Program Library, Reference 7090-CS-13x, International Business Machines Corporation.
4. Goldberger, A. S. *Econometric Theory.* New York: John Wiley and Sons, 1964.
5. Hammersley, J. M., and Handscomb, D. C. *Monte Carlo Methods.* New York: John Wiley and Sons, 1964.
6. Hicks, Charles R. *Fundamental Concepts in the Design of Experiments.* New York: Holt, Rinehart and Winston, 1964.
7. Hoel, Paul G. *Introduction to Mathematical Statistics.* New York: John Wiley and Sons, 1954.
8. Holt, Charles C.; Shirey, Robert W.; Steward, Donald V.; Midler, Joseph L., and Stroud, Arthur. "Program SIMULATE, a User's and Programmer's Manual," Social Systems Research Institute, University of Wisconsin, May 1964 (Mimeographed).
9. Hull, T. E., and Dobell, A. R. "Random Number Generators," *SIAM Review* IV, No. 3 (July 1962), 230–254.
10. Johnston, J. *Econometric Methods.* New York: McGraw-Hill Book Co. 1963.
11. Kahn, Herman. "Use of Different Monte Carlo Sampling Techniques," The RAND Corporation P-766 (Nov. 30, 1955).
12. Kahn, Herman, and Mann, Irwin. "Monte Carlo," The RAND Corporation, P-1165 (July 30, 1957).
13. Kiviat, Philip J. "GASP—A General Activity Simulation Program," Project No. 90. 17-019 (2), Applied Research Laboratory, United States Steel, Monroeville, Pennsylvania, July 8, 1963.
14. Markowitz, H. M., Hausner, Bernard, and Karr, H. W. *SIMSCRIPT: A Simulation Programming Language,* The RAND Corporation RM-3310 (Nov. 1962).
15. Mood, A. M. *Introduction to the Theory of Statistics.* New York: McGraw-Hill Book Co., 1950.
16. Orcutt, Guy H. "Simulation of Economic Systems," *American Economic Review,* L, No. 5 (December, 1960), 897–907.
17. Pugh, Alexander L. *DYNAMO User's Manual.* Cambridge, Mass.: The M.I.T. Press, 1963.
18. *SIMPAC User's Manual,* TM 602/000/00, Systems Development Corporation, Santa Monica, California, April 15, 1962.
19. Teichroew, Daniel. "A History of Distribution Sampling Prior to the Era of the Computer and Its Relevance to Simulation," *American Statistical Association Journal* (March 1965), 27–49.
20. Tocher, K. D. *The Art of Simulation.* Princeton, N.J.: D. Van Nostrand, 1963.

Chapter 3 | Techniques for
Generating Random Numbers

INTRODUCTION

The importance of random numbers or pseudorandom numbers in Monte Carlo sampling experiments was discussed in Chapter **2**. In this chapter we are concerned primarily with methods of generating random numbers with digital computers, leaving the matter of applications of random numbers to Chapter **4**.

In discussing the concept of generating random numbers the following terminology will be useful. The term *random variable* is used to mean a real-valued function defined over a sample space associated with the outcome of a conceptual chance experiment. A particular outcome of an experiment, i.e., a numerical or sample value of a random variable, is called a *random variate*. We will use capital letters to denote random variables and lower case letters for random variates. For example, $F(x)$, the cumulative distribution function for a random variable X, denotes the probability that X is less than or equal to the particular variate x. In a similar manner $f(x)$ represents the value of the probability density function of the random variable X when $X = x$.

One convenient way of classifying random variables is according to their probability density functions. We shall concentrate here exclusively on random variables with *uniform probability density functions*. The cumulative distribution function for the standardized uniform distribution is defined as

$$F(x) = \begin{cases} 0, & x \leq 0 \\ x, & 0 < x < 1 \\ 1, & x \geq 1 \end{cases} \qquad (3\text{-}1)$$

The values of x on the unit interval will be called *uniform random variates*. The random variates considered here will be represented by numbers that, at least, appear to be drawn at random, as sample values from a uniformly distributed population. Random variate is used as a collective term, meaning random numbers in the form of digits, integers, or rational numbers with a well-defined interval and number system. Since the main emphasis in the following paragraphs will be placed on the properties of *numbers* corresponding to uniform random variates, the term *uniform random number* or simply *random number* will be used instead of the collective term.

In practice, a *sequence of random numbers* is usually required. Consequently all of the methods discussed here embody some quasi-random physical process that generates sequences of random numbers of any desired length. One of the principal requirements of these sequences, as in any other random sampling procedures, is statistical independence [7, p. 47].

Four alternative methods have been used by practitioners to generate sequences of random numbers:

1. Manual methods.
2. Library tables.
3. Analog computer methods.
4. Digital computer methods.

Manual methods are the simplest and also the least practicable of the methods for generating random numbers. These methods are too slow for general use but have widespread appeal as a pedagogical device in the classroom because they include such colorful techniques as coin flipping, dice rolling, card shuffling, and roulette wheels. Although it has been said that only mechanical and electronic devices yield "truly" random numbers, these methods suffer from the additional disadvantage that it is impossible to reproduce a sequence of random numbers generated by such devices.

A number of *library tables* of random numbers (for example, the Rand Corporation's *A Million Random Digits*) have been published [22]. Of course, these numbers must first be generated by one of the aforementioned methods before recording them in table form. The one advantage offered by this method is reproducibility. However, it suffers from a lack of speed and the fact that some problems require more random numbers than have been published. Also, one might object to using the same "random" data for every problem.

Analog computers have also been used to generate random numbers. For example, the Rand Corporation's random numbers were generated by an analog computer. Since analog computer methods depend on some random physical process (for example, the behavior of an electric current), they are deemed to yield "truly" random numbers. These methods are much faster than either manual methods or library tables, but they share a common handicap with manual methods—nonreproducible sequences of random numbers.

Three modes of providing random numbers for use on *digital computers* have been suggested by Tocher [26]: external provision, internal generation by a random physical process, and internal generation of sequences of digits by a recurrence relation.

External Provision

One alternative is to record random number tables such as the *Rand Tables* on magnetic tape for input into a digital computer and then treat these random numbers as data for the problem of interest. "Since input to these machines is invariably the slowest process, this seriously slows the rate of progress of the machine and constitutes the major objection to this method" [26, p. 40]. For example, it may take ten times as long to read one character of information from magnetic tape into a computer as it does to perform an arithmetic operation on a single character. Random rearrangements of existing random number tables, using part of these to determine those rearrangements, cannot be considered as an adequate alternative since the extended tables of digits are not completely random [26, p. 40.]

Internal Generation by a Random Physical Process

The second alternative involves the use of a special adjunct to a digital computer that can record the results of some random process and can reduce these to a sequence of digits [26, p. 41]. Among the random processes used to generate digits by this method include the decay of radioactive material and the thermal noise in an electronic valve circuit. The major shortcoming of this method is that results are not reproducible so that calculations cannot be checked. Another objection is that the random process producing the digits may go out of control and a check on its production of digits is required [26, p. 41]. Such a check can only be made with large sets of data, and this may severely limit the memory capacity of a particular computer.

Internal Generation by a Recurrence Relation

The third alternative involves the generation of "pseudorandom numbers" by the "indefinitely continued transformation of a group of arbitrarily chosen numbers" [26, p. 41]. The term "pseudorandom number" has been defined by Lehmer [18] as "a vague notion embodying the idea of a sequence in which each term is unpredictable to the uninitiated and whose digits pass a certain number of tests, traditional with statisticians and depending somewhat on the use to which the sequence is to be put." This method overcomes two of the objections to the preceding methods since there is no problem of input or computer memory capacity and the whole process, depending only on arithmetical steps, is reproducible. Tocher has stated [26, p. 41] that, "the principal objection to this solution is on the rather philosophical grounds that a sequence of digits generated by a purely deterministic rule is the direct antithesis of a random sequence." However, this objection can at least partially be overcome by taking the pragmatic view that a sequence may be considered random if it satisfies some predetermined set of statistical tests of randomness. From this point of view the method of generating a sequence is totally irrelevant.

Historically, the first arithmetic method of generating pseudorandom numbers on a digital computer was the *mid-square* method, in which each number in a sequence is obtained by using the middle digits of the square of the preceding number in the sequence. This method was first proposed by von Neumann and Metropolis in 1946. However, the mid-square method was later abandoned in favor of congruential methods because the mid-square method was found to be difficult to analyze, relatively slow, and statistically unsatisfactory [6]. At the present time nearly all computer codes for generating random numbers use some variation of the congruential methods developed by Lehmer [18].

After examining several methods for generating random numbers it would appear that an "acceptable" method for generating random numbers must yield sequences of numbers which are (1) uniformly distributed, (2) statistically independent, (3) reproducible, and (4) nonrepeating for any desired length. Furthermore, such a method must also be capable of (5) generating random numbers at high rates of speed, yet (6) requiring a minimum amount of computer memory capacity. (It should be obvious to the reader that these criteria have been established on purely a priori grounds.) The congruential methods to be discussed in this chapter were designed specifically to fulfill as many of the aforementioned requirements as possible.

Tocher has even gone one step further and defined a four-stage "optimum" procedure for generating random numbers consisting of [26, p. 41]:

a. A process (physical or mathematical) that produces "roughly random" numbers.

b. A process applied to sequences of numbers that will improve the randomness of the sequence.

c. A set of tests of the digits for randomness.

d. Use of a method of storage that enables large quantities of these random numbers to be read into a digital computer at a rate commensurate with its operating speed.

Although steps (*a*) through (*c*) of Tocher's idealized method can be achieved to a rather high degree of perfection today, step (*d*) is still beyond the technical capabilities of present day computers.

We now turn to a detailed description and evaluation of the so-called congruential methods for generating random numbers on a digital computer, to be followed by a discussion of statistical tests of randomness for numbers generated by these methods. However, since a minimal knowledge of number theory is necessary to understand the rationale behind these methods, an appendix on the elements of number theory (Appendix A) has been included.

CONGRUENTIAL METHODS FOR GENERATING PSEUDORANDOM NUMBERS

As we have previously indicated, congruential methods for generating random numbers are completely deterministic because the arithmetic processes involved in the calculations uniquely determine each term in a sequence of numbers. In fact, formulas are available for calculating in advance the exact value of the ith number in a sequence of numbers $\{n_0, n_1, n_2, \ldots, n_i, \ldots\}$ before the sequence is actually generated [24]. Although these processes are not random processes at all, pragmatic grounds dictate that we treat them as though they were, if the sequences that result consistently pass a certain number of statistical tests designed to test various properties of random variates. For example, if it can be shown that the numbers in a sequence appear to be uniformly distributed and statistically independent, then the process can be assumed to be random even though it is deterministic. (It can be shown that congruential methods satisfy both of these requirements reasonably well.) Properties (3) and (6) of the aforementioned requirements of random number generators are automatically satisfied by the application of congruential methods because the sequences generated by these methods are completely reproducible and require only a minimum amount of memory capacity on a computer. Properties (4) and (5) are the only requirements whose degree of satisfaction depends entirely on the properties of the methods applied. These properties will be thoroughly analyzed in the following pages.

Congruential methods are based on a fundamental congruence relationship (See Definition 7, Appendix A), which may be expressed as the following recursive formula

$$n_{i+1} \equiv an_i + c \ (\text{mod} \ m), \tag{3-2}$$

where n_i, a, c, and m are all nonnegative integers. Expanding Eq. 3-2 for $i = 0,1,2, \ . \ . \ .$ we obtain

$$n_1 \equiv an_0 + c \ (\text{mod} \ m)$$

$$n_2 \equiv an_1 + c = a^2 n_0 + (a + 1)c \ (\text{mod} \ m)$$

$$n_3 \equiv a^3 n_0 + (a^2 + a + 1)c = a^3 n_0 + \frac{c(a^3 - 1)}{(a - 1)} \ (\text{mod} \ m) \tag{3-3}$$

. . . .

$$n_i \equiv a^i n_0 + \frac{c(a^i - 1)}{(a - 1)} \ (\text{mod} \ m) \cdot$$

Given an initial *starting value* n_0, a *constant multiplier* a, and an *additive constant* c, then Eq. 3-3 yields a congruence relationship (modulo m) for any value of i over the sequence $\{n_1, n_2, \ . \ . \ . \ , n_i, \ . \ . \ .\}$. The subsequent terms of $\{n_i\}$ as determined by Eq. 3-3 are all integers forming a sequence of residues modulo m. (See Definition 8, Appendix A). This, in turn, implies that $n_i < m$ for all n_i. From the integers in the sequence $\{n_i\}$, rational numbers in the unit interval $(0,1)$ can be obtained by forming the sequence $\{r_i\} = \{n_i/m\}$.

We now turn to the question of whether there exists a smallest positive value of $i, i = h$, such that $n_h = n_0$ where h is the *period* of the sequence $\{n_i\}$. If such an h does exist, what conditions can be imposed on n_0, a, c, and m so that the period of $\{n_i\}$ is as large as possible? (See Definition 14, Appendix A.) Our interest in this problem stems from the fact that if $n_i = n_0$ for some $i = h$, then $n_{h+1} = n_1, n_{h+2} = n_2$, etc. That is, the sequence of pseudorandom numbers will repeat itself after a period equal to h.

Theorems are available (Theorems 5 and 10, Appendix A) to show that such an h always exists and that its maximum value depends on m. This is equivalent to saying that it is impossible to obtain non-repeating sequences by congruential methods. In practice, however, the period of a sequence can be set satisfactorily high by choosing a sufficiently large modulus or by other techniques [19].

Three basic congruential methods have been developed for generating pseudorandom numbers by using different versions of the formula given by Eq. 3-2. The objective of each method is the generation of sequences with a maximum period in a minimum amount of time. These methods are the additive congruential method, the multiplicative congruential method, and the mixed congruential method. Each of these methods is known to be in operation on a variety of computers.

The *additive congruential method* [4] assumes k starting values, where k is a positive integer and computes a sequence of numbers by means of the following congruence relation

$$n_{i+1} \equiv n_i + n_{i-k} \ (\text{mod } m). \tag{3-4}$$

If $k = 1$, Eq. 3-4 generates the well-known Fibonacci sequence, which behaves like sequences obtainable by the multiplicative congruential method with the unfavorably low multiplier, $a = (1 + \sqrt{5})/2$. The statistical properties of the sequence tend to improve as k increases. This is the only method that produces periods larger than m [11].

The *multiplicative congruential method* computes a sequence $\{n_i\}$ of nonnegative integers each less than m by means of the congruence relation.

$$n_{i+1} \equiv a n_i \ (\text{mod } m). \tag{3-5}$$

This method is a special case of congruence relation (Eq. 3-2), where $c = 0$. The multiplicative method has been found to behave quite well statistically [16, pp. 240–241]. That is, frequency tests and serial tests, as well as other tests for randomness, when applied to sequences generated by this method indicate that the random numbers are uncorrelated and uniformly distributed [15, 19]. Furthermore, it is possible to impose conditions on both the multiplier a and the starting value N_0 so as to insure a maximum period for sequences generated by this method. The multiplicative method also offers relative advantages in terms of computational speeds.

Numbers obtained by means of congruence relation (Eq. 3-2) in its original form (with a and c both greater than zero) are said to be generated by the *mixed congruential method* [16, 23]. The mixed congruential method has been found to offer some small advantages over the multiplicative method in terms of increased computational speeds and a lack of periodicity of the last digits. The principal advantage of the mixed method lies in its full period [16, p. 238. Although its statistical behavior is generally good, in a few cases it is completely unacceptable.

Recently signs have appeared in the literature indicating dissatisfaction with the statistical properties of pseudorandom numbers generated by congruential methods [14, 19]. More frequent and more complex usage of random numbers has necessitated the use of more elaborate statistical tests and has revealed a number of surprising shortcomings in the randomness of pseudorandom numbers generated by some methods [14]. Aside from arguments suggesting the use of a table of random numbers stored on magnetic tape when calculation time exceeds the access time necessary to obtain the next random number in case of demands not exceeding one million random numbers, several new versions of the congruential methods have been suggested in the literature.

Lach [14] has developed a procedure using five multipliers that are alternated by use of a multiplicative random switch. McLaren and Marsaglia [19] have suggested a *combination method* in which a mixed congruential generator computes indices that determine which random number from p previously stored numbers should be next in the sequence. The p numbers $n_1, n_2, \ldots , n_i, \ldots , n_p$ are generated by the multiplicative congruential method in such a manner that the ith number is replaced by a new n_i value if i is the index generated by the mixed method. McLaren and Marsaglia used $p = 128$ locations in testing their method. The combination method passed all the statistical tests which were applied, while the other congruential methods failed to pass some of the tests.

The general discussion of congruential methods would be incomplete without reference to some theoretical relations developed by Coveyou [3] and Greenberger [13]. Although previous theoretical studies have been concerned with number theoretical properties, especially the period, and simplicity of calculation of sequences of pseudorandom numbers, Greenberger's formula presents theoretical conditions on the optimum values of a, c, and m in Eq. 3-2 from the point of view of an a priori determination of the serial correlation between the numbers. The magnitude of the serial correlation coefficient $\rho(n_i, n_{i+1})$ lies between the values

$$\frac{1}{a} - \left(\frac{6c}{am}\right)\left(1 - \frac{c}{m}\right) \pm \frac{a}{m}, \qquad (3\text{-}6)$$

In general, $a = m^{1/2}$ will yield the smallest values for ρ regardless of the value of c. This result provides a necessary condition for minimizing first-order serial correlation for a sequence but it is by no means a sufficient condition.

A further interesting conclusion from Eq. 3-6 is that sampling only every kth number from the sequence will have the equivalent effect of choosing a^k as the multiplier and $c_k = (a^k - 1)c/(a - 1)$ as the additive constant in Eq. 3-2.

The Multiplicative Congruential Method

Most computerized versions of the multiplicative congruential method employ a modulus $m = p^e$, representing the word size of the computer, where p denotes the number of numerals in the number system utilized by the computer and e denotes the number of digits in a word. For binary computers $p = 2$, and for decimal computers $p = 10$. On variable word length computers the value of e is left to the programmer's discretion, whereas on fixed word length computers e is a constant. The symbols b and d will be used in place of e to denote binary and decimal digits, respectively.

There are two reasons for choosing $m = p^e$. First, reduction modulo m is accomplished by truncating and retaining only the low order e digits; and second, conversion to the unit interval (to obtain uniformly distributed variates) involves only moving the binary or decimal point to the left of the number. By the proper choice of m these divisions can be circumvented [17, p. 5].

Since most computers utilize either a binary or a decimal number system, we will consider the multiplicative method for each of these two number systems. In both cases we will be concerned with generating sequences of non-negative integers (less than p^e) by means of the congruence relation.

$$n_{i+1} \equiv an_i \;(\text{mod } p^e), \tag{3-7}$$

which is the formula for generating power residues. (See Definition 13 and Theorem 5, Appendix A.) We shall discuss for both cases conditions that may be imposed on the constant multiplier a and the starting value n_0 to assure maximal periods for sequences generated by this method.

Binary Computers

For a binary computer we choose $m = 2^b$, where b is the number of binary digits (bits) in a word. According to Theorem 8 (Appendix A) for $b > 2$, the maximum attainable period is $h = 2^{b-2}$. The next problem is to find constant multipliers that have order $h = 2^{b-2}$. From Definition 14 and Theorem 5 (Appendix A), it follows that a must be relatively prime to m. Furthermore, if a is relatively prime to $m = 2^b$, it must be an odd number. It can be shown that those values of a which satisfy these requirements reside in a residue class represented by the congruence relation [17]

$$a \equiv \pm 3 \;(\text{mod } 8). \tag{3-8}$$

This relation can also be expressed as

$$a = 8t \pm 3, \tag{3-9}$$

where t is any positive integer. (See Definitions 1, 2, and 7, Appendix A.)

According to Greenberger's formula, values of a that are close to $2^{b/2}$ will minimize first-order serial correlation between the pseudo-random numbers. Since small serial correlation is a highly desirable characteristic of random number generators, this rule will be applied in determining the "best" constant multipliers for both the binary and decimal cases.

Having selected a constant multiplier, we must now consider a method for choosing a starting value. According to Theorem 5, n_0 must be relatively prime to 2^b. This requirement can be satisfied by selecting any positive odd number for a starting value.

The multiplicative procedure for generating random numbers on a binary machine may be summarized as follows:

1. Choose any odd number as a starting value n_0.
2. Choose an integer $a = 8t \pm 3$, where t is any positive integer for a constant multiplier. A value of a close to $2^{b/2}$ will satisfy the Cove-you-Greenberger condition. (If $b = 35, a = 2^{17} + 3$ is a good selection.)
3. Compute an_0 using fixed point integer arithmetic. This product will consist of $2b$ bits, from which the high-order b bits are discarded, and the low-order b bits represent n_1. (The integer multiplication instruction in FORTRAN automatically discards the high-order b bits.)
4. Calculate $r_1 = n_1/2^b$ to obtain a uniformly distributed variate defined on the unit interval.
5. Each successive random number n_{i+1} is obtained from the low-order bits of the product an_i.

Consider the following illustrative example in which b is assumed to be equal to 4. The multiplicative procedure will produce 4 random numbers ($h = 2^{4-2} = 4$) before repeating.

1. Choose $n_0 = 7$. This is equivalent to $n_0 = 0111$ in binary form.
2. Choose an a which is close to $2^{b/2} = 4$. For $t = 1$ from Eq. 3-9 a is either equal to 11 or 5. Hence, we choose $a = 5$ or $a = 0101$ in binary form.
3. $an_0 = (0101)(0111) = 00100011$. Therefore, $n_1 = 0011$ and $r_1 = 3/16 = 0.1875$.
4. $an_1 = (0101)(0011) = 00001111$. Therefore, $n_2 = 1111$ and $r_2 = 15/16 = 0.9375$.

5. $an_2 = (0101)(1111) = 01001011$. Therefore, $n_3 = 1011$ and $r_3 = 11/16 = 0.6875$.

6. $an_3 = (0101)(1011) = 00110111$. Therefore, $n_4 = 0111 = n_0$ and $r_4 = 7/16 = 0.4375$.

Decimal Computers*

For a decimal computer we choose $m = 10^d = 2^d 5^d$, where d is the number of decimal digits in a word. According to Theorems 8 and 9 (Appendix A), a must be relatively prime to 10, and since 10 is a composite number, the order h of a (mod 10^d) is at most

$$h = \text{l.c.m.}[2^{d-2}, 4 \times 5^{d-1}] = 5 \times 10^{d-2} \qquad (3\text{-}10)$$

for $d > 3$. The numbers with this maximum period must be of the form $a \equiv \pm 3$ (mod 8) so as to assure maximum order mod 2^d and must simultaneously have order 5^{d-1} or $2 \times 5^{d-1}$ or $4 \times 5^{d-1}$ (mod 5^d). The constant multipliers with period $5 \times 10^{d-2}$ reside in 32 different residue classes modulo 200, denoted by

$$a \equiv \pm(3, 11, 13, 19, 21, 27, 29, 37, 53, 59, 61, 67, 69, 77, 83, 91)$$
$$\text{(mod 200)}.\dagger \qquad (3\text{-}11)$$

Consequently, a can also be expressed as

$$a = 200t \pm p, \qquad (3\text{-}12)$$

where t is any positive integer and p is one of the 32 numbers in Eq. 3-11. According to Theorem 5 (Appendix A) n_0 must be relatively prime to 10^d, which implies that any *odd* number not divisible by 5 can be selected for a starting value.

The multiplicative procedure for generating random numbers on a decimal machine can be summarized as:

1. Choose any odd integer not divisible by 5 as a starting value n_0.

2. Choose an integer $a = 200t \pm p$ for a constant multiplier, where t is any integer and p is any of the values 3, 11, 13, 19, 21, 27, 29, 37, 53, 59, 61, 67, 69, 77, 83, 91. A value of a close to $10^{d/2}$ will satisfy the Coveyou-Greenberger condition. (If $d = 10$, $a = 100,000 \pm 3$ is a good selection.)

---

* This discussion was taken almost verbatim from [17, p. 6].

† "Although the calculations are omitted here, it can be seen that all of these numbers are congruent to ±3 (mod 8), and their order mod 5^d can be checked by applying the binomial theorem. Similarly, it can be verified that any number not included above has a smaller order mod 10^d" [17, p. 6].

3. Compute an_0 using fixed point integer arithmetic. This product will consist of $2d$ digits, from which the high-order d digits are discarded, and the low-order digits are the value of n_1. Integer multiplication instructions automatically discard the high-order d digits.

4. The decimal point must be shifted d digits to the left to convert the random number (which is an integer) into a uniformly distributed variate fefined over the unit interval $(r_1 = n_1/10^d)$.

5. Each successive random number n_{i+1} is obtained from the low-order digits of the product an_i.

Consider the following illustrative example in which d is assumed to be equal to 4. The multiplicative procedure will produce 500 random numbers ($h = 5 \times 10^{4-2} = 500$) before repeating.

1. Choose $n_0 = 5379$.

2. Choose an a close to $10^{d/2} = 100$. Either $a = (200)(0) + 91 = 91$ or $a = (200)(1) - 91 = 109$ are both good choices for a value of a. The value 91 will be selected for this example.

3. $an_0 = (91)(5379) = 00489489$. Therefore, $n_1 = 9489$ and $r_1 = 0.9489$.

4. $an_1 = (91)(9489) = 00863499$. Therefore, $n_2 = 3499$ and $r_2 = 0.3499$.

5. $an_2 = (91)(3499) = 00318409$. Therefore, $n_3 = 8409$ and $r_3 = 0.8409$.

6. $an_3 = (91)(8409) = 00765219$. Therefore, $n_4 = 5219$ and $r_4 = 0.5219$.

The example shows that the low order digits are far from random. With multiplicative generators only the highest order digit position has full period, and the period decreases for the lower order digits. Therefore if a random number smaller than word size is required, the higher order digits should be used.

Since the multiplicative congruential method is the easiest to program and is very fast on most computers, a warning is in order. Recent investigations [14, 19] reveal serious shortcomings in serial correlations and in simple functions of multiples. For instance, the multiplier $a = 2^{18} + 3$ (mod 2^{35}) adopted by many program libraries and publications turns out to be aberrant in the second-order correlations. It can be shown that if $n_{i+1} = (2^{18} + 3)n_i$ (mod 2^{35}), then $n_{i+2} = 6n_{i+1} - 9n_i$ (mod 2^{35}). Other recommended multipliers do not pass the serial test for triples. The circumvention of these difficulties gave rise to the combination method discussed in [19].

The Mixed Congruential Method

The mixed congruential method of generating a sequence of pseudo-random numbers is a relatively new development, which offers a few advantages but introduces problems of statistical acceptability in use. The method is based on the recursive formula presented in Eq. 3-2, and with properly selected multiplier and additive constant $c \neq 0$, the period covers the full set of m different numbers, if m is the modulus.

The conditions imposed on a as well as c in order to achieve a full period for m may be summarized as follows:

$$c \text{ is relatively prime to } m. \tag{3-13}$$

$$a \equiv 1 \pmod{p} \text{ if } p \text{ is a prime factor of } m. \tag{3-14}$$

$$a \equiv 1 \pmod 4 \text{ if } 4 \text{ is a factor of } m. \tag{3-15}$$

The modulus m is expressed as $m = 2^b$ for binary computers and $m = 10^d$ on decimal computers. The practical interpretation of these rules follows below.

Binary Computers

With binary computers $m = 2^b$, where b is the number of binary bits in a word. From Theorem 10 (Appendix A) we know that a sequence of pseudo-random numbers may have a full period with length equal to 2^b. The rules to achieve this require that in Eq. 3-2 the parameter c must be an odd number and that

$$a \equiv 1 \pmod 4, \tag{3-16}$$

which can be achieved by setting

$$a = 2^s + 1 \tag{3-17}$$

for $s \geq 2$. Any positive number can be selected for n_0. However, the aforementioned conditions are not sufficient for assuming that sequences generated by the mixed congruential method will be statistically satisfactory. For example, the selection of a constant multiplier which satisfies the Coveyou-Greenberger condition

$$a = 2^{b/2} + 1 \tag{3-18}$$

is not a sufficient condition for minimizing first-order serial correlation for sequences generated by this method. Only by empirical testing can we have confidence in the statistical properties of sequences genrated by the mixed congruential method. Systematic testing of mixed generators on binary computers has been described in [15, 19] and indicates valid results only for $m = 2^{35}$. These tests reveal that n_0 plays a minor role in determining the statistical properties of sequences generated by the mixed congruential method, although certain values of c tend to improve the statistical properties of sequences. A good choice of a multiplier is $a = 2^7 + 1$ when $c = 1$.

Decimal Computers

With decimal computers $m = 10^d$, where d is the number of decimal digits in a word. In order to generate a sequence of pseudorandom numbers with full period, the constant c must be a positive odd number not divisible by 5, and the multiplier a must satisfy the condition

$$a \equiv 1 \ (\mathrm{mod} \ 20) \tag{3-19}$$

or alternatively,

$$a = 10^s + 1 \tag{3-20}$$

for $s > 1$. These rules can be supplemented by the Coveyou-Greenberger condition that

$$a = 10^{d/2} + 1. \tag{3-21}$$

Again these conditions are not sufficient to guarantee acceptable statistical properties for sequences of pseudorandom numbers generated by the mixed congruential method. Limited experience with statistical tests has suggested some criteria for selecting values of a and c on an empirical basis.

As was the case before, certain numbers for c yield better statistical results than others, and n_0 has little or no effect on the statistical properties of sequences. Satisfactory results have been achieved [1] using $a = 101$, $c = 1$, and $d \geq 8$.

Each digit in the random numbers generated by this method (including the last digit in a word) has a full period. This property makes small word sizes and higher speeds possible when the length of the period is not a significant requirement.

The Additive Congruential Method

The simple additive process of generating random numbers according to formula 3-4 has been programmed on several computers with modifications discussed and tested by Green [11, 12]. The basic formula used in this investigation was

$$n_j \equiv (n_{j-1} + n_{j-k}) \;(\mathrm{mod}\; 2^b), \tag{3-22}$$

where b is the number of bits carried by a binary computer. With this additive generator k random numbers should be provided in an original storage. The pseudorandom numbers generated this way have a period equal to $p_k \cdot 2^{b-1}$, where p_k is a constant that depends on k and b. For $b = 35$ several p_k values have been tabulated in [11] out of which only $p_6 = 63$ and $p_{16} = 255$ are given here. Statistical tests indicate that $k = 16$ is the smallest value for acceptable pseudorandom numbers. This selection gives a period equal to 255×2^{34}. Discarding every second number from the sequence produces acceptable random numbers with $k = 6$ and with a period of 63×2^{34}. Comparative tests on the advantages of the additive method over the multiplicative methods are not reported in the literature. The speed characteristics of additive generators depend on the programming codes and computers used, and the statistical properties of the random numbers require empirical tests as with any other method.

STATISTICAL TESTS OF PSEUDORANDOM NUMBERS

The statistical properties of pseudorandom numbers generated by the methods outlined in the previous section should coincide with the statistical properties of numbers generated by an idealized chance device that selects numbers from the unit interval (0,1) independently and with all numbers equally likely. Clearly, the pseudorandom numbers produced by computer programs are not random in this sense, since they are completely determined by the starting data and have limited precision. But so long as our pseudorandom numbers can pass the set of statistical tests implied by the aforementioned idealized chance device, these pseudorandom numbers can be treated as "truly" random numbers even though they are not. The following statistical tests are among the more important tests for randomness cited in the literature [17].

The Frequency Test

The frequency test is used to check the uniformity of a sequence of M consecutive sets of N pseudorandom numbers. For each set of N pseudorandom numbers $r_1, r_2, \ldots, r_N$ we divide the (0,1) unit interval into x equal subintervals. The expected number of random numbers in each subinterval is N/x. Next let f_j, where $j = 1, 2, \ldots, x$, denote the actual number of pseudorandom numbers r_i $(i = 1, 2, \ldots, N)$ in the subinterval $(j - 1)/x \leq r_i < j/x$. The statistic

$$\chi_1{}^2 = \left(\frac{x}{N}\right) \sum_{j=1}^{x} \left(f_j - \frac{N}{x}\right)^2 \tag{3-23}$$

has approximately a chi-square distribution with $x - 1$ degrees of freedom for a sequence of "truly" random numbers. This statistic is then computed for all M consecutive sets of N pseudorandom numbers. Next we let F_j denote the number of the resulting M values of $\chi_1{}^2$, which lie between the $(j - 1)$th and the jth quantile of a chi-square distribution with $x - 1$ degrees of freedom $(j = 1, 2, \ldots, u)$. Compute the statistic

$$\chi_F{}^2 = \frac{u}{M} \sum_{j=1}^{u} \left(F_j - \frac{M}{u}\right)^2. \tag{3-24}$$

The hypothesis that the pseudorandom numbers in the sequence consisting of M sets of pseudorandom numbers are "truly" random numbers is rejected if $\chi_F{}^2$ with $u - 1$ degrees of freedom exceeds the critical value set by the desired level of significance. A popular set of values for this test consists of the following values: $x = u = 10$, $M = 100$, and $N = 1000$. The expected values N/x and M/u should always be greater than 5 [1, 16, 19].

Serial Tests [9, 10]

Serial tests are used to check the degree of randomness between successive numbers in a sequence. A serial test is usually applied to pairs of numbers where the pseudorandom numbers are taken as the coordinates of a point in a unit square divided into x^2 cells [19]. The idea can be extended to triplets of pseudorandom numbers representing random points in a unit cube. The serial test we will describe is also based on the chi-square test and consists of the following steps.

We begin by generating a sequence of M consecutive sets of N pseudorandom numbers and compute the $\chi_1{}^2$ statistic for each of the M sets of pseudorandom numbers according to Eq. 3-23. Then for each set of N pseudorandom numbers we let f_{jk} denote the number of pseudorandom numbers r_i $(i = 1, 2, \ldots, N - 1)$, which satisfies $(j - 1)/x \leq r_i < j/x$ and $(k - 1)/x \leq r_{i+1} < k/x$, where $j, k = 1, 2, \ldots, x$.

Next we compute the statistic

$$\chi_2{}^2 = \frac{x^2}{N-1} \sum_{j=1}^{x} \sum_{k=1}^{x} \left(f_{jk} - \frac{N-1}{x^2} \right)^2 \qquad (3\text{-}25)$$

for each set of N pseudorandom numbers. However, Good [9, 10] has shown that $\chi_2{}^2 - \chi_1{}^2$ has approximately a chi-square distribution with $x^2 - x$ degrees of freedom for a "truly" random sequence of numbers.

Next we calculate $\chi_2{}^2 - \chi_1{}^2$ for each of the M sets of N pseudorandom numbers and let s_j denote the number of the resulting M values of $\chi_2{}^2 - \chi_1{}^2$ that lie between the $(j-1)$th and the jth quantile $(j = 1, 2, \ldots, u)$ of a chi-square distribution with $x^2 - x$ degrees of freedom. Finally we compute

$$\chi_s{}^2 = \frac{u}{M} \sum_{j=1}^{u} \left(s_j - \frac{M}{u} \right)^2, \qquad (3\text{-}26)$$

which has $u - 1$ degrees of freedom. The serial randomness of a sequence of pseudorandom numbers is acceptable at a given level of significance if the values of $\chi_F{}^2$ and $\chi_s{}^2$ are not inconsistent with the hypothesis that they were drawn at random from chi-square distributions with the appropriate degrees of freedom. Similar tests can also be devised for randon triplets.

The Lagged Product Test

Another measure of the independence of pseudorandom numbers is provided by a lagged product coefficient. If k is the length of lag, the lagged product coefficient C_k for sequence r_i $(i = 1, 2, \ldots, N)$ is defined as

$$C_k = \frac{1}{N-k} \sum_{i=1}^{N-k} r_i r_{i+k}. \qquad (3\text{-}27)$$

It can be shown* that if there is no correlation between r_i and r_{i+k}, the values of C_k will be approximately normally distributed with expected value equal to 0.25 and standard deviation equal to

---

* If $N \gg k$, the normality follows by the Central Limit Theorem. The formula for the standard deviation of C_k follows from the fact that the variance of a sum is equal to the sum of the variances plus twice the sum of the co-variances. Each $r_i r_{i+k}$ has variance 7/144, and there are $N - k$ such terms. The only nonzero covariances are those of form cov $(r_{i-k} r_i, r_i r_{i+k}) = 3/144$, and there are $N - 2k$ such covariances.

$\sqrt{13N - 19k}/12(N - k)$ for $k > 0$. The chi-square goodness of fit test can be applied to test for normality.

Tests of Runs [17]

The random oscillatory nature of sequences of pseudorandom numbers can be tested by "tests of runs." Two different types of tests will be described here—tests for runs "up and down" and "above and below the mean."

Runs Up and Down

For a sequence of N pseudorandom numbers $r_1, r_2, \ldots, r_N$ we define an $N - 1$ bit binary sequence S whose ith term is equal to *zero* if $r_i < r_{i+1}$ and is equal to *one* if $r_i > r_{i+1}$. A subsequence of k zeroes, bracketed by ones at each end, forms a run of zeroes of length k, and similarly for runs of ones. The test involves counting the actual number of occurrences of runs of different lengths and comparing these counts with their corresponding expected theoretical values. The expected values based on a "truly" random sample are

$$\frac{(2N - 1)}{3} \text{ for total runs,}$$

$$\frac{(5N + 1)}{12} \text{ for runs of length 1,}$$

$$(11N - 14)/60 \text{ for runs of length 2,}$$

$$\cdots\cdots\cdots\cdots\cdots\cdots\cdots\cdots,$$

$$\frac{2[(k^2 + 3k + 1)N - (k^3 + 3k^2 - k - 4)]}{(k + 3)!}$$

$$\text{for runs of length } k \text{ for } k < N - 1,$$

$$\frac{2}{N!} \text{ for runs of length } N - 1.$$

Again the chi-square goodness of fit test may be used to check whether a pseudorandom number generator is acceptable at a given level of significance. A common characteristic of nonrandom sequences of numbers is an excess of long runs.

Runs Above and Below the Means

For a sequence of N pseudorandom numbers $r_1, r_2, \ldots, r_N$ we define an N bit binary sequence S whose ith term is equal to zero if

$r_i < 1/2$ and is equal to one if $r_i > 1/2$. Again the runs in S are counted; the expected number of runs of length k is $(N - k + 3)2^{-k-1}$, and the expected total number of runs is $(N + 1)/2$. A chi-square test may be used to check whether a given pseudorandom number generator is acceptable.

The Gap Test

Although the preceding tests have been concerned with the randomness of sequences of numbers where each number consisted of some fixed number of digits, for example, 10 digits, the gap test is concerned with the randomness of the digits in a sequence of numbers. For any given digit d, we are interested in the lengths of gaps of non-d digits between any two of the given digits. A gap of length k occurs when k non-d digits occur between two d's. Two consecutive d's produce a gap of length $k = 0$. For a "truly" random sequence of digits the probability of obtaining a gap of length k is given by

$$P(k) = (0.9)^k(0.1). \qquad (3\text{-}28)$$

For a given sequence of digits, tallies are made of the number of gaps occurring for each length. A chi-square goodness of fit test can be used to compare the expected and actual number of gaps of length k, and the chi-square values for several samples can be treated in a manner similar to Eqs. 3-23 and 3-26 to test the hypothesis that the gaps are random.

The Maximum Test

For a set of N independent uniform random numbers on the (0,1) unit interval, we can define a random variable $R = \max(r_1, r_2, \ldots, r_N)$, which has a probability distribution defined by order statistics such that R^N is uniformly distributed over (0,1) [19]. The test of the observed values for R^N is a simple frequency test that can be repeated with several sets of N random numbers. The maximum test of N uniform random numbers is also called the test of N-tuples $(r_1, r_2, \ldots, r_N)$ and is considered to be a more stringent test than the basic frequency test.

The Poker Test

The poker test is a special frequency test for combinations of five or more digits in a random number. Counts of "busts," "pairs," "two pairs," "threes," "full house," etc. are tested against the expected frequencies of these occurrences.

Conclusions

The selection of the appropriate statistical tests for pseudorandom numbers is always limited by a set of desiderata for a given generator and by a particular application. There is empirical evidence that the multiplicative and especially the combined congruential methods produce acceptable pseudorandom numbers that pass all of the aforementioned tests. It is advisable, however, for the user to design his own statistical tests if certain functions or properties of the random numbers not covered here are going to be crucial in the evaluation or validation of results.

Appendix A | Elements of
Number Theory

In order to fully understand and appreciate the methods of generating pseudorandom numbers discussed in Chapter 3, a basic knowledge of the elements of number theory is a prerequisite. Appendix A has been included to provide those readers who have not had a formal course in number theory with the rudiments. Appendix A contains a basic set of definitions, examples, and theorems of number theory that are pertinent to the understanding of the rationale behind the methods discussed in Chapter 3. (All references cited in this appendix are found at the end of Chapter 3.)

DEFINITIONS

Definition 1. For two integers a and b, with $b \neq 0$, there exists a unique pair of integers, t and n, so that

$$a = bt + n \qquad 0 \leq n < |b|,$$

where t is the *quotient* and n is the *remainder*.

Definition 2. An integer a is divisible by an integer b if there exists an integer t such that $a = bt$.

Definition 3. An integer p is a *prime number* if it is neither 0 nor ± 1 and if its only divisors are ± 1 and $\pm p$. Example: the first few positive primes are 2, 3, 5, 7, 11, 13, 17, 19, 23, 29, 31, 37.

Definition 4. An integer g is the *greatest common divisor* (g.c.d.) of two integers a and b if g is a common divisor of a and b and is a multiple of every other common divisor of a and b. Notation: g.c.d. $(a,b) = g$, or simply $(a,b) = g$.

Definition 5. An integer d is the *least common multiple* (l.c.m.) of two integers a and b if d is a divisor of every common multiple of a and b, and it is a common multiple. Notation: l.c.m. $[a,b] = d$ or $[a,b] = d$.

Definition 6. The integers a and b are said to be *relatively prime* if $(a,b) = 1$.

Definition 7. Two integers a and b are *congruent modulo m* if their difference is an integral multiple of m. The congruence relation is expressed by the notation $a \equiv b \pmod{m}$, which reads "a is congruent to b modulo m"; this also means that (1) $(a - b)$ is divisible by m and (2) a and b leave identical remainders when divided by $|m|$. Example: $5590 \equiv 6 \equiv -2 \pmod{8}$ and $2327 \equiv 27 \pmod{10^2}$.

Definition 8. For a given a the smallest positive integer n such that $a \equiv n \pmod{m}$ is said to be a *residue* modulo m. There are m distinct residues $\pmod{m}$; $0,1,2, \ldots , m - 1$.

Definition 9. A class of integers that are mutually congruent for a given modulus form a *residue class*. There are m distinct residue classes $\pmod{m}$. Example: if $m = 2$, the two distinct residue classes are the collection of all odd numbers and even numbers, respectively.

Definition 10. For a given modulus m, the set of m integers congruent in some order to the residues $0,1,2, \ldots , m - 1$ form a *complete residue system*.

Definition 11. A subset of a complete residue system containing all integers that are relatively prime to m is a *reduced residue system*.

Definition 12. The number of positive integers which are less than m and relatively prime to m is known as *Euler's phi-function* and is denoted by $\varphi(m)$. A reduced residue system contains $\varphi(m)$ integers. If $m = p$ is a prime, $\varphi(p) = p - 1$.

Definition 13. Power residues are the residues of the successive powers of an integer a modulo m. If the residue of the ith power of $a \pmod{m}$ is denoted by n_i, then all power residues satisfy the congruence relation $n_i \equiv a^i \pmod{m}$ $(i = 1,2,3 \ldots .)$.
Examples of power residues:

(1) $a = 5$, $m = 31$, $\varphi(m) = 30$

i	a^i	$n_i \equiv a^i \pmod{m}$
1	5	5
2	25	25
3	125	1*
4	625	5

. . . .

(2) $a = 3$, $m = 31$, $\varphi(m) = 30$

i	a^i	n_i	i	n_i	i	n_i
1	3	3	11	13	21	15
2	9	9	12	8	22	14
3	27	27	13	24	23	11
4	81	19	14	10	24	2
5	243	26	15	30	25	6
6	729	16	16	28	26	18
7	2187	17	17	22	27	23
8	6561	20	18	4	28	7
9	19683	29	19	12	29	21
10	59049	25	20	5	30	1*

* The sequence of the power residues repeats for higher powers.

Definition 14. If $(a,m) = 1$, the least positive exponent $i = h$, such that $a^h \equiv 1$ (mod m), is said to be the *order of a* (*mod m*). The least positive exponent h is also called the *indicator of m* when a is said to belong to m. In this case h is denoted by $h = \lambda(m)$. The order h of a (mod m) is equal to the total number of distinct numbers, that is, the length of a nonrepeating sequence of power residues of a, called the *period* of the sequence $\{n_i\}$, $i = 1,2, \ldots$, h (mod m).

Definition 15. An integer a with order $h = \varphi$ (m) (mod m) is the *primitive root of m*. Example: $h = 3 \neq \varphi$ (31) for $a = 5$ in Example 1 of Definition 13, but $h = 30 = \varphi$ (31) for $a = 3$ in Example 2; consequently 3 is the primitive root of 31.

THEOREMS

Theorem 1. If $a \equiv b$ (mod m) and $x \equiv y$ (mod m), then $a \pm x \equiv b \pm y$ (mod m) and $ax \equiv by$ (mod m).

Theorem 2. If $(d,m) = g$, then $dx \equiv dy$ (mod m) implies that $x \equiv y$ (mod m/g).

Theorem 3. If $a \equiv b$ (mod m) and d is a divisor of m, then $a \equiv b$ (mod d). The proofs of Theorems 1,2, and 3 follow from the definitions [2, p. 24].

Theorem 4. Any integer m (other than 0 or ± 1) can be factored uniquely into primes, that is, $m = \Pi p_i{}^{e_i}$, ($i = 1,2,3, \ldots$), where e_i is a constant and Π denotes the product $p_1{}^{e_1} \times p_2{}^{e_2} \times p_3{}^{e_3} \ldots$. The proof is due to Euclid [2, p. 21].

Theorem 5. If $(a,m) = 1$, then $a^{\varphi(m)} \equiv 1$ (mod m), from which it follows that:

(1) The largest possible order of a is $h = \varphi(m)$, when a is a primitive root of m.

(2) For $n < m$ such that $(n,m) = 1$, $na^h \equiv n \pmod{m}$, where $h = \varphi(m)$. The proof is attributed to Euler [21, p. 273] and follows from Theorems 2 and 3.

Theorem 6. Primitive roots exist for all powers of a prime number $p > 2$, i.e., a number exists such that $(a,p^e) \equiv 1$ and $a^{\varphi(p^e)} \equiv 1$ $\pmod{p^e}$, where $h = \varphi(p^e)$. (See [21, p. 285].)

Theorem 7. If $m = \Pi p_i^{e_i}$, then $\varphi(m) = \Pi(p_i - 1)p_i^{e_i-1}$. The proof is due to Euler [21, p. 113].

Theorem 8. If $m = p^e$ and p is an odd prime, then $h = \lambda\ (m) = (p-1)p^{e-1} = \varphi(m)$ for values of a that are primitive roots of m. Corollary: if $p = 2$, i.e., $h = \lambda(m) = 2^{e-2}$ for $e > 2$, then $\lambda(m) \neq \varphi(m)$. The proof is due to Euler [21, pp. 283–290].

Theorem 9. If $m = \Pi p_i^{e_i}$ for $i = 1, 2, \ldots s$, then:

(1) $\lambda(m) = \text{l.c.m.}[\lambda(p_1^{e_1}), \lambda(p_2^{e_2}), \ldots, \lambda(p_s^{e_s})]$.

(2) there exist values of a that have order equal to (i.e., belong simultaneously to) each $\lambda(p_i^{e_i})$. The proof is in [21, p. 293] and follows from the Chinese Remainder Theorem due to Sun-Tse [21, p. 246]. Corollary: if $p_1 = 2$, then $\lambda(m) = \text{l.c.m.}\ [\lambda(2^{e_1}), \varphi(p_2^{e_2}), \varphi(p_3^{e_3}), \ldots]$.

Theorem 10. The smallest positive integer h such that $(a^h - 1)/(a - 1) \equiv 0 \pmod{m}$ is $h = m$, if (1) $a \equiv 1 \pmod{p}$ if p is a prime factor of m, and (2) $a \equiv 1 \pmod 4$ if 4 is a factor of m. The proof is due to Hull and Dobell [16, pp. 233–235].

REFERENCES AND BIBLIOGRAPHY

1. Allard, J. L., Dobell, A. R., and Hull, T. E. "Mixed Congruential Random Number Generators for Decimal Machines," *Journal of the Association for Computing Machinery*, X, No. 2 (1963), 131–141.
2. Birkhoff, G., and MacLane, S. *A Survey of Modern Algebra*. New York: The Macmillan Company, 1953.
3. Coveyou, R. R., "Serial Correlation in the Generation of Pseudo-Random Numbers," *Journal of the Association for Computing Machinery*, VII (1960), 72–74.
4. Duparc, H. J. A., Lekkerkerker, C. G., and Peremans, W. "Reduced Sequences of Integers and Pseudo-Random Numbers," Mathematische Centrum Report ZW 1953-002, Amsterdam (1953).
5. Fisher, R. A., and Yates, F. *Statistical Tables for Biological Agricultural and Medical Research*. London: Oliver and Boyd, 1953.
6. Forsythe, G. E. "Generation and Testing of Random Digits at the National Bureau of Standards, Los Angeles," in *Monte Carlo Method*. National Bureau of Standards Applied Mathematics Series No. 12. Washington, D.C., 1951.

7. Freund, J. E. *Mathematical Statistics*. Englewood Cliffs: Prentice-Hall, 1962.
8. Golenko, D. K. and Smiriagin, V. O. "A Source of Random Numbers Which Are Equidistributed in [0,1]," *Publications Math. Inst.* Hungarian Acad. Sci. 5, Series A. Fasc. 3, in Russian, with English abstract (1960), 241–253.
9. Good, I. J. "The Serial Test for Sampling Numbers and Other Tests of Randomness" *Proc. Camb. Phil. Soc.*, XLIX (1953), 276–284.
10. Good, I. J. "On the Serial Test for Random Sequences," *Annals of Mathematical Statistics* XXVIII (1957), 262–264.
11. Green, B. F., *Digital Computers in Research*. New York: McGraw-Hill Book Co., 1963.
12. Green, B. F., Smith, J., and Klem, L. "Empirical Tests of an Additive Random Number Generator," *Journal of the Association for Computing Machinery*, VI, No. 4 (1959), 527–537.
13. Greenberger, M. "An a Priori Determination of Serial Correlation in Computer Generated Random Numbers," *Mathematics of Computations*, XV (1961), 383–389.
14. Greenberger, M., "Method in Randomness," *Communications of the ACM*, VIII, No. 3 (1965), 177–179.
15. Hull, T. E. and Dobell, A. R. "Mixed Congruential Random Number Generators for Binary Machines," *Journal of the Association for Computing Machinery*, XI, No. 1 (1964), 31–40.
16. Hull, T. E. and Dobell, A. R. "Random Number Generators," *SIAM Review*, IV, No. 3 (July 1962) 230–254.
17. International Business Machines Corporation, "Random Number Generation and Testing," Reference Manual (C20-8011), New York, 1959.
18. Lehmer, D. H. "Mathematical Methods in Large-Scale Computing Units," *Annals Computer Laboratory Harvard University*, XXVI (1951), 141–146.
19. MacLaren, M. D. and Marsaglia, G. "Uniform Random Number Generators," *Journal of the Association for Computing Machinery*, XII, No. 1 (1965), 83–89.
20. National Bureau of Standards. *Monte Carlo Method*. Applied Mathematics Series No. 12. Washington, D.C., 1951.
21. Ore, O. *Number Theory and Its History*. New York: McGraw-Hill Book Co., 1948.
22. RAND Corporation. *A Million Random Digits with 100,000 Normal Deviates*. Glencoe, Ill.: The Free Press, 1955.
23. Rotenberg, A. "A New Pseudo-Random Number Generator," *Journal of the Association for Computing Machinery*, VII, (1960), 75–77.
24. Stockmal, F. "Calculations with Pseudo-Random Numbers," *Journal of the Association for Computing Machinery*, XI, No. 1 (Jan., 1964), 41–52.
25. Taussky, O., and Todd, J. "Generation and Testing of Pseudo-Random Numbers" in *Symposium on Monte Carlo Methods*, ed. Herbert A. Meyer. New York: John Wiley and Sons, Inc., 1956.
26. Tocher, K. D. "The Application of Automatic Computers to Sampling Experiments," *Journal of the Royal Statistical Society*, B16 (1954), 39–61.
27. Uspensky, James V., and Heaslet, M. A. *Elementary Number Theory*. New York: McGraw-Hill Book Co., 1939.
28. Wold, H. "Random Normal Deviates," *Tracts for Computers*, No. XXV. London: Cambridge University Press, 1955.

Chapter 4 | Generation of Stochastic
Variates for Simulation

INTRODUCTION

Two somewhat divergent types of problems provide the rationale underlying the use of existing methods of generating stochastic variates with a digital computer. These two different problem types can be conveniently classified as deterministic (nonprobabilistic) or stochastic. The term "Monte Carlo" has recently become a popularized synonym for "simulation of stochastic processes." However, in the past the term applied only to the use of stochastic simulation methods for solving strictly deterministic problems.

Stochastic simulation methods were first applied by mathematicians and physical scientists to the solution of certain deterministic problems that could be expressed in the form of mathematical equations for which solutions were not easily obtainable by standard numerical or analytical methods. For a number of important mathematical problems it is possible to find a stochastic process with probability distributions or parameters that satisfy the required mathematical properties of the equations of the problem. Furthermore, it may actually be more efficient computationally speaking to construct such a process and generate the statistics on a computer rather than attempt to use standard methods. Among the deterministic mathematical problems for which stochastic simulation has been found to be useful in obtaining solutions are included the evaluation of multiple integrals, solutions to high-order difference equations, complex queueing problems, and job-shop scheduling problems. Although analytical methods exist for solving each of these problems, simulation methods have been shown to be more effective in obtaining solutions to these problems than other more orthodox methods. However, it should be pointed out that solutions obtained by simulation afford no special advantages that standard analytical solutions of the same problem do not. Simulation is merely a technique of numerical analysis and is to be preferred only if its relative efficiency in yielding numerical solutions is superior to that of other techniques.

The second type of problem that lends itself to solution by stochastic simulation methods arises in situations where some method of statistical sampling is indicated but where the actual taking of a sample is either impossible or economically nonfeasible. Such might be the case with data on machine breakdowns in a factory where no accurate records are available on the history of a particular machine (or machines) or with demand data for some date in the future for a firm's product. In both of these cases statistical data are impossible to obtain, but some knowledge may be available about the statistical population from which the data would originate if they were possible to obtain. For example, it may have been observed that the time between breakdowns for a particular machine can be approximated by a negative exponential probability distribution. The characteristic which differentiates this type of simulation from a mere sampling experiment in the classical sense is that of the stochastic model. A stochastic simulation entails the construction of a probabilistic model of the process to be studied whereas a classical sampling experiment in statistics is usually performed directly on raw data.

The generation of simulated statistics (random variates) is entirely numerical in nature and is carried out by supplying pseudorandom numbers (perhaps generated by the methods of Chapter 3) into the process or system under study (where the system is represented by a probabilistic model) and obtaining numbers (random variates) from it as answers. As a rule, stochastic simulation involves replacing an actual statistical universe of elements by its theoretical counterpart, a universe described by some assumed probability distribution (for example, the normal distribution) and then sampling from this theoretical population by means of some type of random number generator. However, in some cases it may not be possible to find a standard theoretical distribution that describes a particular stochastic process or some component of such a process. In these cases the stochastic process can be reproduced (or simulated) only by sampling from empirical distributions rather than some well-known theoretical distribution. (This, of course, assumes the existence of empirical data.) It is advisable to consider the use of standard theoretical distributions first. If none of the standard distributions adequately describe the behavior of the process, then we must necessarily resort to empirical distributions.

The primary aim of this chapter is to provide the reader with a set of specific techniques for generating (on a computer) random variates from some of the better known probability distributions as well as some general methods for generating variates from any empirical distributions that may arise in attempting to solve stochastic problems.

In considering stochastic processes involving either continuous or discrete random variables, we define a function $F(x)$ called the *cumulative distribution function* of x, which denotes the probability that a random variable X takes on the value of x or less. If the random variable is discrete, then x takes on specific values, and $F(x)$ is a step function. If $F(x)$ is continuous over the domain of x, it is possible to differentiate this function and define $f(x) = dF(x)/dx$. The derivative $f(x)$ is called a probability density function. The cumulative distribution function can be stated mathematically as

$$F(x) = P(X \leq x) = \int_{-\infty}^{x} f(t) \, dt, \qquad (4\text{-}1)$$

where $F(x)$ is defined over the range $0 \leq F(x) \leq 1$, and $f(t)$ represents the value of the probability density function of the random variable X when $X = t$.

In Chapter 3 we discussed several methods of generating pseudorandom numbers or uniformly distributed random variates on the interval $(0,1)$. Uniformly distributed random variates play a major role in the generation of random variates drawn from other probability distributions. Hence, we will denote the uniform random variates by r, when $0 \leq r \leq 1$, and $F(r) = r$.

There are three basic methods for generating variates from probability distributions—the "inverse transformation method," the "rejection method," and the "composition method." These methods or some variation of them provide the basis for simulating most of the distributions discussed in this chapter.

The Inverse Transformation Method

If we wish to generate random variates x_i's from some particular statistical population whose density function is given by $f(x)$, we first obtain the cumulative distribution function $F(x)$. (See Figure 4-1.) Since $F(x)$ is defined over the range 0 to 1 we can generate uniformly distributed random numbers and set $F(x) = r$. It is clear that x is uniquely determined by $r = F(x)$. It follows, therefore, that for any particular value of r, say r_0, which we generate, it is possible to find

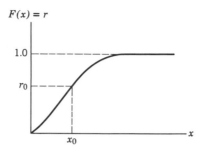

$F(x) = r$

1.0

r_0

x_0

x

Figure 4-1. A cumulative distribution function.

the value of x, in this case x_0, corresponding to r_0 by the inverse function of F if it is known. That is,

$$x_0 = F^{-1}(r_0), \qquad (4\text{-}2)$$

where $F^{-1}(r)$ is the inverse transformation (or mapping) of r on the unit interval into the domain of x. We can summarize this method mathematically by saying that if we generate uniform random numbers corresponding to a given $F(x)$,

$$r = F(x) = \int_{-\infty}^{x} f(t)\, dt \qquad (4\text{-}3)$$

then

$$P(X \leq x) = F(x) = P[r \leq F(x)] = P[F^{-1}(r) \leq x], \qquad (4\text{-}4)$$

and consequently $F^{-1}(r)$ is a variable that has $f(x)$ as its probability density function. This is equivalent to solving Eq. 4-3 for x in terms of r. This procedure is illustrated by two examples.

Example 1. Generate random variates x with density function $f(x) = 2x,\ 0 \leq x \leq 1$. From Eq. 4-3 it follows that

$$r = F(x) = \int_{0}^{x} 2t\, dt \qquad 0 \leq x \leq 1 \qquad (4\text{-}5)$$

$$= x^2.$$

Then taking the inverse transformation $F^{-1}(r)$, that is, solving Eq. 4-5 for x, we obtain

$$x = F^{-1}(r) = \sqrt{r}, \qquad 0 \leq r \leq 1. \qquad (4\text{-}6)$$

Therefore, values of x with density function $f(x) = 2x$ can be generated by taking the square root of random numbers r.

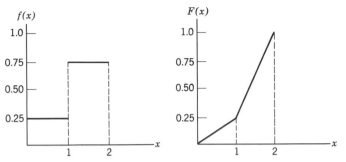

Figure 4-2. Density function and cumulative distribution function for Example 2.

Example 2. Generate random variates x with density function

$$f(x) = \frac{1}{4} \quad 0 \leq x < 1 \quad (4\text{-}7)$$

$$= \frac{3}{4} \quad 1 \leq x \leq 2$$

(The density function and cumulative distribution function are illustrated graphically in Figure 4-2.) From Eq. 4-3 it follows that,

$$r = F(x) = \int_0^x \frac{1}{4} \, dt \quad 0 \leq x < 1 \quad (4\text{-}8)$$

$$= \frac{x}{4}$$

$$r = F(x) = \frac{1}{4} + \int_1^x \frac{3}{4} \, dt \quad 1 \leq x \leq 2 \quad (4\text{-}9)$$

$$= \frac{3}{4} x - \frac{1}{2}.$$

Taking the inverse transformation $F^{-1}(r)$, that is, solving Eqs. 4-8 and 4-9 for x, we obtain,

$$x = 4r \quad 0 \leq r < \frac{1}{4} \quad (4\text{-}10)$$

$$x = \frac{4}{3} r + \frac{2}{3} \quad \frac{1}{4} \leq r \leq 1. \quad (4\text{-}11)$$

To generate a value of x we first generate an r. If r is less than 1/4, then x is determined by Eq. 4-10. If r is greater than or equal to 1/4, then x is determined by Eq. 4-11. This procedure can easily be generalized for multiple intervals on the r-scale to generate random variates that follow some empirical distribution.

Unfortunately, for many probability distributions it is either impossible or extremely difficult to express x in terms of the inverse transformation F^{-1} (r). In these cases we must either obtain a numerical approximation to the inverse function F^{-1} or resort to one of the following two methods.

The Rejection Method

If $f(x)$ is bounded and x has a finite range, say $a \leq x \leq b$, the rejection technique [29] can be used to generate random variates. The application of this technique requires the following steps:

1. Normalize the range of f by a scale factor c, such that

$$c \cdot f(x) \leq 1 \qquad a \leq x \leq b. \qquad (4\text{-}12)$$

2. Define x as a linear function of r,

$$x = a + (b - a)r. \qquad (4\text{-}13)$$

3. Generate pairs of random numbers (r_1, r_2).
4. Whenever we encounter a pair of random numbers that satisfies the relationship

$$r_2 \leq c \cdot f[a + (b - a)r_1]. \qquad (4\text{-}14)$$

then "accept" the pair and use $x = a + (b - a)$ r_1 as the random variate generated.

The theory behind this method is based on the realization that the probability of r being less than or equal to $c \cdot f(x)$ is

$$P[r \leq c \cdot f(x)] = c \cdot f(x). \qquad (4\text{-}15)$$

Consequently, if x is chosen at random from the range (a,b) according to Eq. 4-13 and then rejected if $r > c \cdot f(x)$, the probability density function of the accepted x's will be exactly $f(x)$. Tocher [28, p. 25] has shown that the expected number of trials before a successful pair is found is equal to $1/c$. This implies that the method may be quite inefficient for certain probability density functions. This method will be used in several of the generating techniques described in this chapter. Two examples are included to clarify the method.

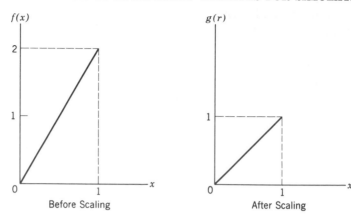

Figure 4-3. An example of scaling.

Example 1. Use the rejection method to generate random variates x with density function $f(x) = 2x$, where $0 \leq x \leq 1$.

Since x was defined over the unit interval, $x = r$. But $f(r) = 2r$ is defined over the interval $0 \leq f(r) \leq 2$. Scaling will transform $f(r)$ to the unit interval if we let $g(r) = 1/2 \, f(r)$, in which case $g(r) = r$. Figure 4-3 shows the density function $f(x) = 2x$ before and after scaling.

The rejection method consists of four steps for Example 1.

1. Generate r_1 and calculate $g(r_1)$.

2. Generate r_2 and compare it with $g(r_1)$.

3. If $r_2 \leq g(r_1)$, accept r_1 as x from $f(x)$. If $r_2 > g(r_1)$, then reject r_1 and repeat step 1.

4. Repeat this procedure until n values of x have been generated. The rejection method can also be used as a Monte Carlo technique to evaluate a definite integral.

Example 2. Use the rejection method to compute the area of the first quadrant of a unit circle with coordinate axes r_1 and r_2, respectively (Figure 4-4). This numerical integration problem will serve to illustrate the use of the Monte Carlo method in solving a completely deterministic problem. Any pair of uniform random numbers (r_1, r_2) defined over the unit interval corresponds to a point within the unit square of Figure 4-4, and the points satisfying the equation $r_1^2 + r_2^2 = 1$ lie on the circle. Let $g(r_1) = \sqrt{1 - r_1^2}$. If $g(r_1^0) \geq r_2^0$ for the generated random numbers (r_1^0, r_2^0), then (r_1^0, r_2^0) is a random point under the curve. If $g(r_1^0) < r_2^0$, then (r_1^0, r_2^0) lies above the curve. "Accepting" and counting the first type of random occurrences and dividing this count by the total number of pairs generated we obtain a ratio corresponding to the proportion of the area of the unit square lying under the curve. This ratio will approach $\pi/4$ as the number of random pairs increases. The same technique can be applied to the solution of multiple integrals of functions with more than one independent variable.

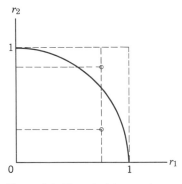

Figure 4-4. Numerical integration.

The Composition Method

Another method of generating stochastic variates on a computer is the "composition method" or "method of mixtures" [7, 13, 18, 19, 28]. In this method $f(x)$ is expressed as a probability mixture of properly selected density functions $g_n(x)$. In mathematical terms we have

$$f(x) = \Sigma g_n(x)p_n. \qquad (4\text{-}16)$$

The selection of $g_n(x)$ is guided by considerations of "best fit" and by the objective of minimizing $\Sigma T_n p_n$, where T_n is expected computation time for generating variates from $g_n(x)$.

In the subsequent parts of this chapter the reader will be provided with a set of (relatively simple) specific techniques for simulating random variates from some of the better known probability distributions. For some distributions more than one alternative method will be considered. We intend to move from specific probability distributions to stochastic models in general in our discussion of simulation techniques. For a review of the elements of probability theory the reader is referred to the following textbooks [1, 8, 10, 23, 31].

At the outset continuous and discrete probability distributions will be separately covered. Six of the most common continuous distributions, the uniform, exponential, gamma, normal, multivariate normal, and log-normal distributions will be treated first. For each distribution the following information will be provided: (1) a brief statement concerning the nature and use of the distribution; (2) formulas for the density function, cumulative distribution function (if it exists in explicit form), expected value and variance of the distribution; (3) the parameters of the distribution expressed in terms of the moments of the distribution; (4) an explanation or derivation of the simplest techniques for generating variates from the distribution; (5) a flow chart and a FORTRAN computer program for generating the random variates on a digital computer; (6) alternative techniques for generating the same variates; (7) a listing of useful related or derived variates (if any). A similar format will be observed in the treatment of five basic discrete probability distributions—geometric, Pascal, binomial, hypergeometric, and Poisson. Special sections will be devoted to empirical distributions, Markov processes, and autocorrelated variates.

Although this chapter is oriented towards the use of digital computers in simulating probability distributions, a computer is by no means a prerequisite for using the techniques to be found in this chapter. To be sure, hand calculation techniques can be used on any of the methods discussed here. However, if the number of probability distributions to be simulated is large or if the amount of data to be simulated is sizeable, then a computer may very well be considered a necessity.

The FORTRAN computer programming system was selected for use in this book because it is a widely used computer language that closely resembles the language of mathematics and was designed primarily for scientific and engineering computation. One of the principal advantages of FORTRAN is that it provides the analyst with an efficient means of writing computer programs requiring a relatively short period of instruction and no detailed knowledge of the computer itself. Furthermore, FORTRAN compilers are now available for nearly all of the computers used most often by industry, government, and colleges and universities. The FORTRAN language found in this book is not designed for any particular computer, but with very minor modifications it can be adapted to the FORTRAN language of any computer having a FORTRAN compiler. For this reason the FORTRAN statements appearing in this book have deliberately been kept quite simple and do not require the use of input-output media. The reader who is not familiar with FORTRAN may wish to consult a FORTRAN manual published by one of the computer manufacturers or one of the following textbooks on FORTRAN [15, 22].

Throughout this chapter FORTRAN statements will be arranged in SUBROUTINE's with the assumption that there is a main simulation program called MAIN, which calls for the appropriate subroutine by stating its name in a CALL statement. Each subroutine generates and returns to the main program a single random variate from the probability distribution for which it was programmed. The main program must contain instructions on how to read in the required parameter values, how many random variates are to be generated, and how to handle the output statistics.

In order to avoid notational complications in writing FORTRAN subroutines that contain other subroutines, it will be assumed that pseudorandom numbers used in a given subroutine will be generated by a preprogrammed library or compiler function. This function, denoted by RND, is assumed to be programmed in machine language according to one of the methods described in Chapter 3. Other library functions assumed by the subroutines are the logarithmic (base e) function denoted by LOG and the exponential (base e) function denoted by EXP.

We now turn our attention to the task of developing the aforementioned methods of generating random variates from probability distributions.

CONTINUOUS PROBABILITY DISTRIBUTIONS

The Uniform Distribution

Perhaps the simplest continuous probability density function is the one that is constant over the interval (a,b) and is zero otherwise. This density function defines what is known as the uniform or rectangular distribution. The uniform distribution may arise in the study of rounding errors when measurements are recorded to a certain accuracy. For example, if measurements of weights are recorded to the nearest gram, one might assume that the difference in grams between the actual weight and the recorded weight is some number between —0.5 and +0.5 and that the error is uniformly distributed throughout this interval. The principal value of the uniform distribution for simulation techniques lies in its simplicity and in the fact that it can be used to simulate random variables from almost any kind of probability distribution.

Mathematically the uniform density function is defined as follows,

$$f(x) = \begin{cases} \dfrac{1}{b-a} & a < x < b \\ 0 & \text{otherwise} \end{cases} \qquad (4\text{-}17)$$

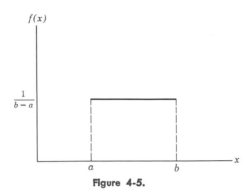

Figure 4-5.

Here X is a random variable defined over the interval (a,b). The graph of the uniform distribution is illustrated by Figure 4-5.

The cumulative distribution function $F(x)$ for a uniformly distributed random variable X is

$$F(x) = \int_a^x \frac{1}{b-a}\, dt = \frac{x-a}{b-a} \qquad 0 \le F(x) \le 1. \tag{4-18}$$

The expected value and variance of a uniformly distributed random variable are given by,*

$$EX = \int_a^b \frac{1}{b-a}\, x\, dx = \frac{b+a}{2} \tag{4-19}$$

$$VX = \int_a^b \frac{(x-EX)^2}{b-a}\, dx = \frac{(b-a)^2}{12}. \tag{4-20}$$

In actual applications the parameters of the uniform density function 4-17, (i.e., the numerical values of a and b) may not necessarily be known directly. Typically, although not for uniform distributions, we know only the expected value and variance of the statistics to be generated. In this case the values of the parameters must be derived by solving the equation system consisting of Eqs. 4-19 and 4-20 for a and b, since EX and VX are assumed to be known. This procedure—similar to an estimation technique known in the statistical literature as "the method of moments"—provides the following two

---

* In order to avoid confusion with FORTRAN subscripted variables we use the symbols EX and VX to denote respectively the expected value and variance of X rather than the customary $E(X)$ and $V(X)$.

expressions:

$$a = EX - \sqrt{3VX} \qquad (4\text{-}21)$$

$$b = 2EX - a. \qquad (4\text{-}22)$$

To simulate a uniform distribution over some given domain (a,b) we must first obtain the inverse transformation for Eq. 4-18, according to Eq. 4-2.

$$x = a + (b - a)r \qquad 0 \le r \le 1. \qquad (4\text{-}23)$$

We then generate a set of random numbers corresponding to the range of cumulative probabilities, i.e., uniform random variates defined over the range 0 to 1. Each random number r determines uniquely a uniformly distributed variate x.

A graphical explanation will perhaps serve to clarify the issues here. Figure 4-6 illustrates that each generated value of r is associated with one and only one value of x. For example, the specific value of the cumulative distribution function at r_0 fixes the value of x at x_0. Obviously, this procedure can be repeated as many times as desired, each time generating a new value of x. Generating random variates through the use of cumulative probabilities will also be followed in simulating several other distributions in this chapter. Furthermore this technique serves as the basis for developing the more general Monte Carlo methods, discussed later in the chapter.

Figure 4-7 contains a flow chart of the logic that must be utilized in simulating a uniform distribution for a given range (a,b), if it is to be programmed for use on a computer. The flow chart has been formulated in such a manner that it is compatible with the FORTRAN subroutine, which follows in Figure 4-8.

The first statement of our FORTRAN flow chart for generating uniform variates is a CALL statement, which includes the name of the

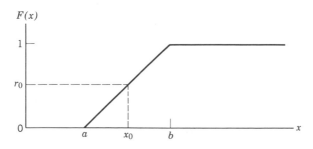

Figure 4-6.

subroutine and the variables of the subroutine. Subroutine names are usually limited to six characters. Therefore, the name UNIFRM has been given to this particular subroutine. The symbols A, B, and X appearing in the parentheses represent respectively the parameters a and b and the uniform variate x, which is generated by the subroutine and returned to the main program by the subroutine. It should be noted that the CALL statement is actually a part of the main program and is, therefore, not included in the FORTRAN statements in Figure 4-8.

The first statement in the subroutine itself (Figure 4-8) is an initialization statement that identifies the particular subroutine as the one called by the main program. Each of the subroutines described in this chapter will begin with a similar initialization or identification statement.

The second statement in the subroutine (Figure 4-8) is a library function that causes the variable R to be set equal to a pseudorandom number generated by the function RND. Each time the subroutine is called a new value of R will be generated. The variable R is the FORTRAN symbol for r used in Eq. 4-23.

The third statement in our FORTRAN subroutine (Figure 4-8) transforms R from the $(0,1)$ interval to the (a,b) interval by use of FORTRAN arithmetic and Eq. 4-23.

The fourth statement in Figure 4-8 returns the generated value of X and the program control back to the main program.

Similar subroutines will be developed throughout this chapter.

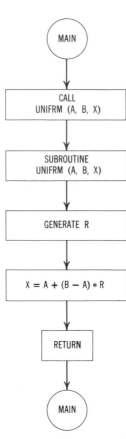

Figure 4-7. Generation of uniform variates, flow chart.

1. SUBROUTINE UNIFRM (A, B, X)
2. R = RND (R)
3. X = A + (B − A) * R
4. RETURN

Figure 4-8. Generation of uniform variates, FORTRAN subroutine.

The Exponential Distribution

Throughout our daily life we observe time intervals between the occurrences of distinct random events. We receive information about numerous events that take place in our environment such as births, deaths, accidents, and world conflicts on the basis of a completely independent time schedule. If the probability that an event will occur in a small time interval is very small, and if the occurrence of this event is statistically independent of the occurrence of other events, then the time interval between the occurrence of events of this type is exponentially distributed. Whether a stochastic process in the real world actually yields exponential variates or not is an empirical question, whose answer depends on the degree to which the assumptions underlying the exponential distribution are satisfied. Specifically, the following assumptions must be satisfied by exponential variates.

1. The probability that an event occurs during the time interval $[t,(t + \Delta t)]$ is $\alpha \Delta t$.
2. α is a constant and independent of t and other factors.
3. The probability that more than one event will occur during the time interval $[t, (t + \Delta t)]$ approaches 0 as $\Delta t \rightarrow 0$ and is of a smaller order of magnitude than $\alpha \Delta t$.

Curiously enough, the behavior of a number of time dependent processes has been found to satisfy these rather strong assumptions. For example, the time interval between accidents in a factory, the arrival of orders at a firm, the arrival of patients in a hospital, and the arrival of aircraft at airports have been found to follow the exponential distribution.

A random variable X is said to have an exponential distribution if its density function is defined as,

$$f(x) = \alpha e^{-\alpha x} \qquad (4\text{-}24)$$

for $\alpha > 0$ and $x \geq 0$.

The cumulative distribution function of X is

$$F(x) = \int_0^x \alpha e^{-\alpha t}\, dt = 1 - e^{-\alpha x}, \qquad (4\text{-}25)$$

and the expected value and variance of X are given by the following formulas

$$EX = \int_0^\infty x\alpha e^{-\alpha x}\, dx = \frac{1}{\alpha} \qquad (4\text{-}26)$$

$$VX = \int_0^\infty \left(x - \frac{1}{\alpha}\right)^2 \alpha e^{-\alpha x}\, dx = \frac{1}{\alpha^2} = (EX)^2 \qquad (4\text{-}27)$$

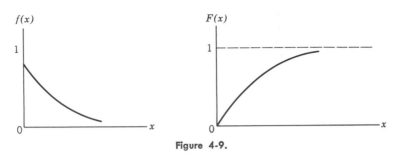

Figure 4-9.

Graphically the exponential distribution appears as in Figure 4-9.

Since the exponential distribution has only one parameter α it is possible to express α as,

$$\alpha = \frac{1}{EX}. \tag{4-28}$$

The generation of exponential random variates can be accomplished in a number of different ways. Since $F(x)$ exists in explicit form, the inverse transformation technique provides a straightforward method. Because of the symmetry of the uniform distribution, $F(x)$ and 1-$F(x)$ are interchangeable. Therefore,

$$r = e^{-\alpha x} \tag{4-29}$$

and consequently,

$$x = -\left(\frac{1}{\alpha}\right) \log r = -EX \log r. \tag{4-30}$$

Thus for each value of the pseudorandom number r, a unique value of x is determined, which will take only non-negative values (since $\log r \leq 0$ for $0 \leq r \leq 1$) and will follow the exponential density function (4-24) with expected value EX. Although this technique seems very simple, the reader is reminded that the computation of the natural logarithm on digital computers includes a power series expansion (or some equivalent approximation technique) for each uniform variate generated.

Figure 4-10 contains a flow chart for generating exponential variates, and Figure 4-11 contains the corresponding FORTRAN subroutine. The name of the subroutine is EXPENT.

The inverse transformation technique is not the only method for generating exponential variates internally. Two additional methods are outlined here, one because of its historical significance and the other because of its speed potential.

Von Neumann's [29] method for generating exponential variates is an ingenious example of the rejection technique. It is a sad fact of life that it is slightly quicker to use the logarithmic transformation for the same purpose. Since this method is often quoted in the literature, a short description is offered here.

Generate uniform random numbers r_1, r_{11}, $r_{12}, \cdots, r_{1j}, r_2, r_{21} \cdots$ and form the sequence of sums:

$$1 - r_1 + \sum_{i=1}^{j} r_{1i},$$

$$1 - r_2 + \sum_{i=1}^{j} r_{2i},$$

$$\cdots \cdots \cdots \cdots$$

$$1 - r_t + \sum_{i=1}^{j} r_{ti}.$$

The individual sums are terminated for that value of j for which $1 - r_t + \sum_{i=1}^{j} r_{ti} \geq 1$ for the first time. The sequence is terminated on the first value of t that involves an odd value of j. The quantity

$$x = (t - 1) + r_t \qquad (4\text{-}31)$$

is an exponential variate with $EX = 1$. A proof of the method and a flow chart of the program are given in [7, p. 262] and [5, p. 166], respectively.

The second method outlined here, which is due to G. Marsaglia [18], also generates exponential variates with unit mean and variance without the benefit of logarithmic transformation. This method is faster than the inverse transformation technique if the program is written in a language similar to that of the subroutine calculating the logarithms. It provides an excellent example of the composition method.

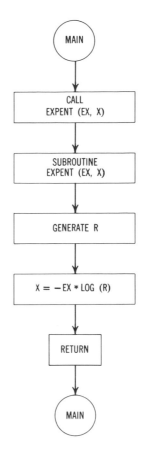

Figure 4-10. Generation of exponential variates, flow chart.

1. SUBROUTINE EXPENT (EX, X)
2. R = RND (R)
3. X = −EX * LOG (R)
4. RETURN

Figure 4-11. Generation of exponential variates, FORTRAN subroutine.

The exponentially distributed variate x is given as

$$x = m + \min_i (r_1, r_2, \ldots, r_i, \ldots, r_n), \qquad (4\text{-}32)$$

where the r_i's are uniformly distributed pseudorandom numbers and the values of m and n for any particular x are determined by the following discrete cumulative probability distributions,

$$P(M \leq m) = \sum_{k=0}^{m} \frac{1}{c e^{k+1}} \qquad \text{for } m = 0, 1, 2, \ldots \qquad (4\text{-}33)$$

$$P(N \leq n) = \sum_{k=1}^{n} \frac{c}{k!} \qquad \text{for } n = 1, 2, 3, \ldots \qquad (4\text{-}34)$$

where $c = 1/(e\text{-}1)$. The variates m and n are calculated by generating two random numbers and finding their corresponding values through the inverse transformation of Eqs. 4-33 and 4-34. The probability is 0.58 that only three random numbers must be generated, and the probability is 0.97 that no more than five random numbers must be generated in order to obtain one exponential variate. To generate variates with $EX \neq 1$ multiply the value of x determined by Eq. 4-32 by EX.

The exponential distribution is based on the assumption of a constant parameter α. That is, all events are assumed to have been generated by a single random process. This condition is frequently violated in the real world when we deal with indistinguishable events that are the products of different but intermixed, random processes. It is possible, indeed likely, that a sample may be taken from two or more exponential distributions each having a different value of α. Many queueing problems fall into this category. For example, arrivals may occur at rates α_i with probabilities p_i, where α_i is the parameter of the ith population ($i = 1, 2, \ldots, s$) such that $\alpha_i \neq \alpha_j$ and $\sum_{i=1}^{s} p_i = 1$. Such a mixture of exponential variates is said to follow a hyperexponential ($s = 2$) or generalized exponential ($s > 2$) distribution. To generate a given mixture of s exponential variates we merely introduce a probability switch before the CALL statement in Figure 4-10 to decide which one of the s previously stored $1/\alpha_i$'s should be applied in the inverse transformation. The real problem lies in the fact that it is seldom known exactly what kind of mixture exists or should be generated. Sometimes, however, simplifying assumptions can be made. Two such instances are described below:

1. Arrivals originate in two populations only, with probabilities p and $(1 - p)$ and parameters $p2\alpha$ and $(1 - p)2\alpha$, respectively. This process generates hyperexponential variates [20] with mean $1/\alpha$ and density function:

$$f(x) = 2p^2\alpha \exp(-2p\alpha x) + 2(1 - p)^2\alpha \exp[2(1 - p)\alpha x] \quad (4\text{-}35)$$

The variance of x is

$$VX = \frac{1}{\alpha^2}\left[\frac{1}{2p(1 - p)} - 1\right], \quad (4\text{-}36)$$

which indicates that hyperexponential variates always have a higher variance than $1/\alpha^2$ unless $p = 1/2$. If the desired value of overdispersion, i.e., $VX/(EX)^2$ is known for a given value of $EX = 1/\alpha$, p can be determined from

$$p = \frac{1}{2} - \frac{1}{2}\left[1 - \frac{2}{VX/(EX)^2 + 1}\right]^{1/2} \quad (4\text{-}37)$$

and used in the program as indicated previously.

2. Arrivals originate in an infinite number of different populations with a corresponding number of different α's. Since α is always positive and not restricted to integers, we can assume that the probability of any value of α follows a gamma distribution. When we compound exponentially distributed variates with a gamma distribution, we have a *generalized exponential* (or Pearson XI type) distribution [16]. Its density function is

$$f(x) = ka^k(a + x)^{-(k+1)}, \quad (4\text{-}38)$$

and its cumulative distribution function is given by

$$F(x) = 1 - \left(\frac{a}{a + x}\right)^k, \quad (4\text{-}39)$$

where k and a are the parameters of the gamma distributed random variable α. Taking the inverse transformation of Eq. 4-39 using $r = 1 - F(x)$, it follows that

$$x = a\left[\left(\frac{1}{r}\right)^{1/k} - 1\right] \quad (4\text{-}40)$$

is a random variable with density function 4-38. To obtain generalized exponential variates with expected value EX and variance VX, $[VX > (EX)^2]$, the following formulas can be derived:

$$k = \frac{2VX}{[VX - (EX)^2]} \tag{4-41}$$

$$a = (k - 1)EX. \tag{4-42}$$

The formulas are valid only for $k > 2$.

The exponential distribution can be easily generalized for positive variables such that $x \geq a$, where a is larger than 0. The substitution of $(x - a)$ for x yields the so-called noncentral or two-parameter exponential distribution, which can be simulated without any difficulty using any of the methods discussed previously.

A further extension of the exponential distribution is known as the Weibull distribution [30]. The density function and cumulative distribution are as follows:

$$f(x) = \frac{c}{b}\left(\frac{x - a}{b}\right)^{c-1} \exp\left[-\left(\frac{x - a}{b}\right)^c\right] \tag{4-43}$$

$$F(x) = 1 - \exp\left[-\left(\frac{x - a}{b}\right)^c\right] \tag{4-44}$$

for $x \geq a$, $a \geq 0$, $b > 0$, and $c > 0$.

In the present description, a, the location parameter, will be assumed to be equal to zero. This leaves only b, the scale parameter, and c, the shape parameter, to consider. The role of $1/b$ is similar to that of α in the exponential distribution. If $c = 1$, expression 4-43 becomes identical to Eq. 4-24. If $c > 1$, the distribution is bell-shaped, otherwise it is J-shaped like the exponential. The distribution has been found to be useful in treating problems concerned with life testing, breaking strength, and reliability data.

The expected value of Eq. 4-43 is

$$EX = b\Gamma\left(\frac{1}{c} + 1\right), \tag{4-45}$$

and the variance is

$$VX = b^2\Gamma\left(\frac{2}{c} + 1\right) - (EX)^2. \tag{4-46}$$

The inverse transformation of Eq. 4-44 using $r = 1 - F(x)$, leads to the generation of Weibull variates by the following expression

$$x = b(-\log r)^{1/c}. \tag{4-47}$$

The Gamma Distribution

If a process consists of k successive events and if the total elapsed time of this process can be regarded as the sum of k independent exponential variates each with parameter α, the probability distribution of this sum will be a gamma distribution with parameters α and k. The sum of k (where k is a positive integer) exponential variates each having the same parameter α is also called an Erlang distribution [4]. Mathematically, the Erlang distribution is a convolution of k exponential distributions, i.e., the distribution of the sum of k exponential variables. Furthermore, the sum of k exponential variates with identical α is also gamma distributed if k follows the negative binomial or geometric distribution [6]. The most general form of the gamma distribution arises when k is positive but not restricted to integral values. A form of the gamma distribution may be fitted to many positively skewed distributions of statistical data.

The gamma distribution is described by the following density function

$$f(x) = \frac{\alpha^k x^{(k-1)} e^{-\alpha x}}{(k-1)!} \tag{4-48}$$

where $\alpha > 0$, $k > 0$, and x are nonnegative. Although the cumulative distribution function does not exist in explicit form for the gamma distribution, the values of the so-called incomplete gamma function have been tabulated by Pearson [31]. The expected value and variance are given by

$$EX = \frac{k}{\alpha} \tag{4-49}$$

$$VX = \frac{k}{\alpha^2}. \tag{4-50}$$

If $k = 1$, the gamma distribution is identical to the exponential distribution. If k is a positive integer, the gamma distribution is identical to the Erlang distribution. As k increases, the gamma distribution approaches a normal distribution asymptotically.

To generate variates from a gamma distribution with a given expected value and variance, the following formulas can be used to determine the parameters of $f(x)$ in Eq. 4-48

$$\alpha = \frac{EX}{VX} \tag{4-51}$$

$$k = \frac{(EX)^2}{VX}. \tag{4-52}$$

Since the cumulative distribution function for a gamma distribution cannot be formulated explicitly, we must consider an alternative method of generating gamma variates. Erlang variates may be generated by simply reproducing the random process on which the Erlang distribution is based. This can be accomplished by taking the sum of k exponential variates, $x_1, x_2, \ldots, x_k$, with identical expected value $1/\alpha$. Therefore, the Erlang variate x can be expressed as

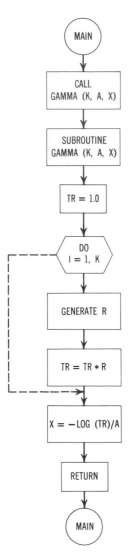

$$x = \sum_{i=1}^{k} x_i = -\frac{1}{\alpha} \sum_{i=1}^{k} \log r_i. \quad (4\text{-}53)$$

A flow chart and FORTRAN subroutine for generating an Erlang gamma distribution (k is an integer) appear in Figures 4-12 and 4-13. The reader should note that Eq. 4-53 is not used in the FORTRAN code. Instead, it has been replaced by the equivalent, but faster, computational form.

$$x = -\frac{1}{\alpha}\left(\log \prod_{i=1}^{k} r_i\right), \quad (4\text{-}54)$$

where A and K denote α and k, respectively.

The problem of generating gamma variates when k is not an integer is indeed an unsettled one. There is no stochastic model for this case, and therefore, simulation may not be fully justified. However, one approach is briefly outlined. If k is a rational number, it can be expressed as the sum of an integer and a fraction, such that $k = k_1 + q$, where $0 < q < 1$. Furthermore if $k_2 = k_1 + 1$, then $k_2 - k = 1 - q$. (We consider only the case in which $k > 1$.) Since the expected value, variance, and third central moment of gamma variates are all linear functions of k [23], a mixture of gamma variates choosing k_2 with probability q and k_1 with probability $1 - q$ will approximate a gamma distribution with parameter k. This approximation yields better results with higher values of k. If we utilize

Figure 4-12. Generation of gamma variates, flow chart.

1. SUBROUTINE GAMMA (K, A, X)
2. TR = 1.0
3. DO 5 I = 1, K
4. R = RND (R)
5. TR = TR * R
6. X = $-$ LOG (TR)/A
7. RETURN

Figure 4-13. Generation of gamma variates, FORTRAN subroutine.

this technique in the FORTRAN program, a probability switch defining k_1 must be inserted before the DO statement in Figure 4-13.

There are several probability distributions that are related to gamma variables. Two of the more important ones are the chi-square and beta distributions.

The chi-square distribution is a gamma distribution with $\alpha = 1/2$. Consequently, chi-square variables have $EX = 2k$, which is called the degrees of freedom and $VX = 4k$. If EX is an even number, then k is an integer, and the generation technique in Eq. 4-54 applies. If EX is an odd number, then $k = EX/2 - 1/2$, and

$$x = - \frac{1}{\alpha} \log \left(\prod_{i=1}^{k} r_i \right) + z^2, \tag{4-55}$$

where z^2 is the square of a normal variate with zero mean and unit variance. The generation of normal variates is described in the next section.

The beta distribution is the distribution of the ratio of two gamma variables x_1 and $(x_1 + x_2)$, where x_1 and x_2 are both independent gamma variables with identical values of α and parameters k_1 and k_2 respectively, such that $k = k_1 + k_2$ is the parameter of $(x_1 + x_2)$. The beta variable is given by

$$x = \frac{x_1}{x_1 + x_2} \qquad 0 < x < 1. \tag{4-56}$$

Therefore to generate a beta variate x, the ratio of two gamma variates, one with parameter k_1 the other with parameter k, must be obtained.

The density function of the beta distribution is

$$f(x) = \frac{\Gamma(a + b) \, x^{a-1}(1 - x)^{b-1}}{\Gamma(a) \, \Gamma(b)} \tag{4-57}$$

with expected value and variance

$$EX = a/(a + b) \tag{4-58}$$

$$VX = \frac{(EX)(b)}{(a + b + 1)(a + b)}, \tag{4-59}$$

where a and b correspond to k_1 and k_2 parameters of the gamma variates in Eq. 4-56. The beta distribution is widely used in critical path scheduling techniques such as PERT [9]. A generalized version of the beta distribution called the Dirichlet distribution can be generated on the same principles if more than two nonconstant ratios should be considered in the model. This case might arise in simulating rows or fixed vectors of stochastic matrices with variable probability elements and also in modeling random compositions of some physical unit that is subdivided into randomly distributed parts.

The Normal Distribution

The normal distribution is the best known and most frequently used probability distribution. There are at least two explanations that seem to support its popularity. "Mathematical proof tells us that, under *certain qualifying conditions*, we are justified in expecting a normal distribution, while statistical experience shows that, in fact, distributions are often approximately normal" [8, p. 232].

The normal distribution derives its usefulness from the Central Limit Theorem. The Central Limit Theorem states that the probability distribution of the sum of N independently and identically distributed random variates x_i with respective means μ_i and variances σ_i^2, as N becomes very large, approaches the normal distribution asymptotically with mean and variance:

$$\mu = \sum_{i=1}^{N} \mu_i \tag{4-60}$$

$$\sigma^2 = \sum_{i=1}^{N} \sigma_i^2. \tag{4-61}$$

Hence, the Central Limit Theorem permits the use of a normal distribution to represent overall measurements on effects of independently distributed additive causes (errors) regardless of the probability distribution of the measurements of individual causes [25, p. 262]. The role played by this form of the Central Limit Theorem is of particular importance. It provides the mathematical justification for the empirical evidence of the frequent appearance of approximately normally distributed data in many research problems.

Another practical value of the normal distribution is its usefulness in approximating Poisson and binomial distributions as well as many other distributions. Furthermore, there are several other probability distributions that play very important roles in modern statistics which are directly derived from the normal distribution. These are the chi-square, the t (Student), and F distributions, all of which find their origin in the probability distribution of the sum of the squares of a specific number of standard normal variates [8, p. 233].

If a random variable X has a density function $f(x)$ given as follows:

$$f(x) = \frac{1}{\sigma_x \sqrt{2\pi}} e^{-1/2\left(\frac{x-\mu_x}{\sigma_x}\right)^2}, \qquad -\infty < x < \infty, \qquad (4\text{-}62)$$

where σ_x is positive, then X is said to have a normal or Gaussian distribution with parameters μ_x and σ_x. The familiar bell-shaped graph of the normal density function is well known to all. (See Figure 4-14.)

If the parameters of the normal distribution have values of $\mu_x = 0$ and $\sigma_x = 1$, the distribution function is known as the *standard normal distribution* with density function denoted by

$$f(z) = \frac{1}{\sqrt{2\pi}} e^{-\frac{1}{2}z^2} \qquad -\infty < z < \infty. \qquad (4\text{-}63)$$

Any normal distribution can be converted into the standard form by the substitution

$$z = \frac{x - \mu_x}{\sigma_x}. \qquad (4\text{-}64)$$

The cumulative distribution function $F(x)$ or $F(z)$ does not exist in explicit form, although the latter is tabulated in almost any book

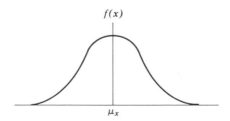

$f(x)$

μ_x

Figure 4-14. A normal distribution.

on statistics. The expected value and variance of the nonstandard normal distribution are given by

$$EX = \mu_x \tag{4-65}$$

$$VX = \sigma_x^2. \tag{4-66}$$

There are several ways to generate normally distributed random variates on a computer. For the purpose of exposition and because of its popularity, only the so-called Central Limit approach will be discussed and demonstrated here in detail. A short outline of other approaches will also be included.

In order to simulate a normal distribution with a given expected value μ_x and a given standard deviation σ_x, the following mathematical interpretation of the Central Limit Theorem may be given. If r_1, r_2, . . . , r_N are independent random variables each having the same probability distribution with $E(r_i) = \theta$ and Var $(r_i) = \sigma^2$, then

$$\lim_{N \to \infty} P\left[a < \frac{\sum_{i=1}^{N} r_i - N\theta}{\sqrt{N}\,\sigma} < b \right] = \frac{1}{\sqrt{2\pi}} \int_a^b e^{-\frac{1}{2}z^2}\, dz, \tag{4-67}$$

where

$$E\left(\sum_{i=1}^{N} r_i\right) = N\theta, \tag{4-68}$$

$$\text{Var}\left(\sum_{i=1}^{N} r_i\right) = N\sigma^2, \tag{4-69}$$

$$z = \frac{\sum_{i=1}^{N} r_i - N\theta}{\sigma\sqrt{N}}. \tag{4-70}$$

It follows from the definition of the standard normal distribution and from Eq. 4-64 that z is a standard normal variate.

The procedure for simulating normal variates on a computer involves taking the sum of K uniformly distributed random variates r_1, r_2, . . . , r_K, where r_i is defined over the interval $0 \le r_i \le 1$. Then applying the notation of the mathematical statement of the Central Limit Theorem and our previous knowledge of the uniform distribution, we find that

$$\theta = \frac{a + b}{2} = \frac{0 + 1}{2} = \frac{1}{2}, \tag{4-71}$$

$$\sigma = \frac{b - a}{\sqrt{12}} = \frac{1}{\sqrt{12}}, \qquad (4\text{-}72)$$

$$z = \frac{\sum\limits_{i=1}^{K} r_i - K/2}{\sqrt{K/12}}. \qquad (4\text{-}73)$$

But by definition, z is a standard normal variate and can be written in the form of Eq. 4-64, where x is a normally distributed random variate to be simulated with mean μ_x and standard deviation σ_x. By equating Eqs. 4-73 and 4-64 we obtain,

$$\frac{x - \mu_x}{\sigma_x} = \frac{\sum\limits_{i=1}^{K} r_i - K/2}{\sqrt{K/12}}, \qquad (4\text{-}74)$$

and solving for x we get

$$x = \sigma_x \left(\frac{12}{K}\right)^{1/2} \left(\sum\limits_{i=1}^{K} r_i - \frac{K}{2}\right) + \mu_x. \qquad (4\text{-}75)$$

Equation 4-75 now provides us with a simple formula for generating normally distributed random variates with mean equal to μ_x and variance equal to $\sigma_x{}^2$. To generate a single value of x (a normally distributed random variate) merely sum K random numbers that are defined over the interval 0 to 1. Substituting the value of this summation into Eq. 4-75 as well as the values of μ_x and σ_x for the desired distribution, we find that a particular value of x is determined. This procedure can of course be repeated as many times as there are normally distributed variates required.

The value of K that should be applied to the formulas is usually determined by balancing computational efficiency against accuracy. Considering the asymptotic convergence implied in the Central Limit approach, a large number for K would be desirable. Considering the time involved in generating K uniform variates for each normal variate, a small value of K is desired. The smallest value of K recommended for use in simulation is $K = 10$. There is some computational advantage, however, to choosing $K = 12$, since in Eq. 4-75 a constant multiplication can be avoided this way. Although this value of K truncates the distribution at the $\pm 6\sigma$ limits and has been found to be unreliable for values of x larger than three standard deviations, it does lead to reasonably fast programs [21, p. 381]. In order to attain higher accuracy, larger values of K up to $K = 24$ or Teichroew's approximation technique may be considered [27], but in these cases the efficiency of the Central Limit approach is significantly less than that of other approaches.

The Teichroew approximation improves the accuracy of tail probalities obtained by the Central Limit approach. With $K = 12$ one must compute,

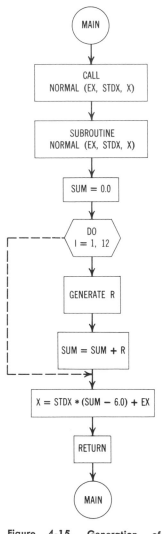

$$y = \frac{(\sum_{i=1}^{12} r_i - 6)}{4}, \qquad (4\text{-}76)$$

and the following polynomial yields the value of a standard normal variate z

$$z = a_1 y + a_3 y^3 + a_5 y^5 + a_7 y^7 + a_9 y^9, \qquad (4\text{-}77)$$

where

$$a_1 = 3.949846138$$
$$a_3 = 0.252408784$$
$$a_5 = 0.076542912$$
$$a_7 = 0.008355968$$
$$a_9 = 0.029899776.$$

Although the Teichroew approximation method can easily be programmed in FORTRAN, our flow chart (Figure 4-15) and FORTRAN subroutine (Figure 4-16) for generating normally distributed variates with a given expected value and standard deviation follow the Central Limit procedure. The following notation has been used in the subroutine:

Figure 4-15. Generation of normal variates, flow chart.

$$EX = \mu_x \qquad (4\text{-}78)$$

$$STDX = \sigma_x \qquad (4\text{-}79)$$

$$SUM = \Sigma R. \qquad (4\text{-}80)$$

A short outline of two other approaches for generating normally distributed random variates is included here.

1. SUBROUTINE NORMAL (EX, STDX, X)
2. SUM = 0.0
3. DO 5 I = 1, 12
4. R = RND (R)
5. SUM = SUM + R
6. X = STDX * (SUM − 6.0) + EX
7. RETURN

Figure 4-16. Generation of normal variates, FORTRAN subroutine.

The Direct Approach [3]

Let r_1 and r_2 be two uniformly distributed independent random variates defined on the (0,1) interval, then

$$x_1 = (-2 \log_e r_1)^{1/2} \cos 2\pi r_2 \qquad (4\text{-}81)$$

$$x_2 = (-2 \log_e r_1)^{1/2} \sin 2\pi r_2 \qquad (4\text{-}82)$$

are two random variates from a standard normal distribution. This method produces exact results and the speed of calculations compares fairly well with the Central Limit approach subject to the efficiency of the special function subroutines [21, p. 382].

Fast Procedure [19]

This technique is alleged to be the fastest but requires several hundred storage locations for specified constants. The random normal deviates are calculated from the mixture of three densities:

$$f(x) = 0.9578g_1(x) + 0.0395g_2(x) + 0.0027g_3(x). \qquad (4\text{-}83)$$

The rationale behind this mixture is that 96 to 97 percent of the time only $g_1(x)$ is used, which provides an immediate normal variable with a table of minimal length. The other two functions are considerably more complicated. Further details and the constants involved in this approach are found in the reference given.

Other methods such as the "rejection method" (von Neumann) and "Hastings' method" can also be used for generating normal variates, but neither of these methods offers more in terms of simplicity, accuracy, or speed than the methods discussed previously.

The following distributions are derived from the normal distribution and hence can be simulated indirectly by certain functions of normal variates.

The chi-square distribution is the distribution of the sum of the squares of independent standard normal variates. The chi-square variable is denoted by

$$x = \chi_m{}^2 = \sum_{i=1}^{m} z_i{}^2, \tag{4-84}$$

where z_i is a standard normal variable and m denotes the "degrees of freedom." The density function of $\chi_m{}^2$ or x is a gamma density (See Eq. 4-48) with $k = m/2$ and $\alpha = 1/2$. Consequently,

$$f(x) = \frac{x^{\frac{m}{2}-1} e^{-\frac{x}{2}}}{2^{\frac{m}{2}} \left(\dfrac{m}{2} - 1\right)!}, \tag{4-85}$$

and $EX = m$ and $VX = 2m$.

The degrees of freedom completely describe this distribution, and it can be easily simulated by Eq. 4-54 if m is even. For odd degrees of freedom and $m < 30$, formulas 4-55 or 4-84 can be used whereas for $m > 30$ the normal approximation for chi-square variates, based on the following well-known formula, can be used:

$$z = \sqrt{2\chi_m{}^2} - \sqrt{2m - 1}. \tag{4-86}$$

Solving for $\chi_m{}^2$, the chi-square variate, we obtain

$$x = \chi_m{}^2 = \frac{(z + \sqrt{2m - 1})^2}{2}. \tag{4-87}$$

The t distribution describes a random variable such that

$$t = \frac{z}{\sqrt{\chi_m{}^2/m}} \tag{4-88}$$

with density function

$$f(t) = \frac{\Gamma\left(\dfrac{m+1}{2}\right)}{\Gamma\left(\dfrac{m}{2}\right)\left[\pi m \left(1 + \dfrac{t^2}{m}\right)^{m+1}\right]^{1/2}}. \tag{4-89}$$

The cumulative distribution for the t distribution is available only in tabulated form. $EX = 0$ and $VX = m/(m - 2)$. For simulation purposes formula 4-88, i.e., the ratio of standard normal and chi-square variates, can be used, or alternatively a standard normal variate with variance $m/(m-2)$ can be used. For $m > 30$ the straight forward normal approximation will usually suffice.

The F distribution is the probability distribution of the ratio of the sum of the squares of random normal variates. The F variable can be denoted by

$$F_{m,n} = \frac{\chi_m^2/m}{\chi_n^2/n},$$
(4-90)

where m and n are degrees of freedom of the corresponding independent sums as well as the chi-square variates. Both the density and cumulative distribution of the F variables are too complicated to include here, but the moments are relatively simple [31, p. 187]

$$EX = \frac{n}{n-2}, \quad n > 2$$
(4-91)

$$VX = \frac{2n^2(m+n-2)}{m(n-2)^2(n-4)}, \quad n > 4.$$
(4-92)

F variates can be generated by using Eqs. 4-90 and 4-84 or Eq. 4-54.

The Multivariate Normal Distribution

The multivariate normal distribution is defined for a vector of random variables where each component of the random vector is a random normal variable with given mean and variance. If the components of this random normal vector are independent, the generation of random normal vectors follows directly from the techniques of the previous section. If the components of the random normal vector are not independent, then the covariances between the component variables are not zero and a variance-covariance matrix is necessary for the generation of random normal vectors.

We shall denote the m dimensional random normal vector by $\mathbf{x}$ with $E(\mathbf{x}) = \boldsymbol{\mu}$, where $\boldsymbol{\mu}$ is the mean vector. We shall assume that $\mathbf{x}$ has a variance-covariance matrix $\mathbf{V}$, where

$$\mathbf{V} = E[(\mathbf{x} - \boldsymbol{\mu}) \cdot (\mathbf{x} - \boldsymbol{\mu})'] = \begin{bmatrix} \sigma_{11} & \cdots & \sigma_{1m} \\ \cdots & \cdots & \cdots \\ \sigma_{m1} & \cdots & \sigma_{mm} \end{bmatrix}.$$
(4-93)

In the expression of $\mathbf{V}$, by convention σ_{ii} denotes the variance of the ith component, and σ_{ij} denotes the covariance between the ith and jth components of the random vector. Statistical theory asserts that $\mathbf{V}$ is always symmetric and the inverse $\mathbf{V}^{-1}$ exists [2].

The probability density function of $\mathbf{x}$ is given by

$$f(\mathbf{x}) = |2\pi\mathbf{V}|^{-1/2} \exp\left[-1/2(\mathbf{x} - \boldsymbol{\mu})'\mathbf{V}^{-1}(\mathbf{x} - \boldsymbol{\mu})\right], \qquad (4\text{-}94)$$

where $|2\pi\mathbf{V}|$ is the determinant of the $2\pi\mathbf{V}$ matrix.

The integral of Eq. 4-94 is quite complicated, and we are not aware of the existence of tables of probability areas for random normal vectors with more than three components [12]. This is one of the reasons why we might want to simulate random normal vectors. The other reason is the frequency with which dependence among normal variables occurs in interdependent systems.

The generation of random normal vectors with given mean vector and variance-covariance matrix utilizes a theorem [2, p. 19], which states that if $\mathbf{z}$ is a standard normal vector, i.e., it contains independent normal variable components with zero mean and unit variance, there exists a unique lower triangular matrix $\mathbf{C}$ such that

$$\mathbf{x} = \mathbf{C}\mathbf{z} + \boldsymbol{\mu}. \qquad (4\text{-}95)$$

In this case $(\mathbf{x} - \boldsymbol{\mu})$ has the variance-covariance matrix

$$\mathbf{V} = \mathbf{C} \cdot \mathbf{C}'. \qquad (4\text{-}96)$$

In order to obtain $\mathbf{C}$ from $\mathbf{V}$ the so-called "square root method" can be used which provides a set of recursive formulas for the computation of the elements of $\mathbf{C}$ [26].

$$c_{i1} = \frac{\sigma_{i1}}{\sigma_{11}^{1/2}}, \qquad 1 \leq i \leq m$$

$$c_{ii} = \left(\sigma_{ii} - \sum_{k=1}^{i-1} c_{ik}^2\right)^{1/2} \qquad 1 < i \leq m$$

$$c_{ij} = \frac{\left(\sigma_{ij} - \sum_{k=1}^{j-1} c_{ik}c_{jk}\right)}{c_{jj}} \qquad 1 < j < i \leq m.$$

$$(4\text{-}97)$$

Since $\mathbf{C}$ is lower triangular, $c_{ij} = 0$ for all $j > i$. After obtaining the elements of $\mathbf{C}$, all components of $\mathbf{x}$ can be determined from $\mathbf{z}$ as weighted sums:

$$x_i = \Sigma c_{ij}z_i + \mu_i. \qquad (4\text{-}98)$$

The generation of a random vector x with mean μ and variance-covariance matrix V can be programmed in the following steps:

1. Obtain the triangular matrix C from V according to Eq. 4-97.
2. Generate m independent standard normal variates with zero mean and unit variance according to Figure 4-16 or by some other equivalent method.
3. Perform the matrix-vector multiplication and vector addition as expressions 4-95 or 4-98 indicate. The result is a normal random vector from the multivariate distribution defined by μ, V, and Eq. 4-94.

The techniques for generating vectors from multivariate normal distributions can be utilized in problems where normal variates with prescribed correlation are to be generated. The solution is demonstrated in the case of two correlated random normal variables x_1 and x_2, where $E(x_1) = \mu_1$, $E(x_2) = \mu_2$, Var $(x_1) = \sigma_1^2$, Var $(x_2) = \sigma_2^2$, Cov $(x_1, x_2) = \rho\sigma_1\sigma_2$. Consequently,

$$V = \begin{bmatrix} \sigma_1^2 & \rho\sigma_1\sigma_2 \\ \rho\sigma_1\sigma_2 & \sigma_2^2 \end{bmatrix}, \tag{4-99}$$

$$C = \begin{bmatrix} \sigma_1 & 0 \\ \rho\sigma_2 & \sigma_2\sqrt{1-\rho^2} \end{bmatrix}, \tag{4-100}$$

and

$$x = \begin{bmatrix} x_1 \\ x_2 \end{bmatrix} = Cz + \mu = \begin{bmatrix} \sigma_1 z_1 \\ \sigma_2(\rho z_1 + \sqrt{1-\rho^2} \cdot z_2) \end{bmatrix} + \begin{bmatrix} \mu_1 \\ \mu_2 \end{bmatrix}. \tag{4-101}$$

This means that x_1 and x_2 are generated as correlated normal variates with coefficient of correlation being equal to ρ. The example shows that two correlated random normal variates can be generated from two independent standard normal variates by the transformation process described in Eq. 4-95.

The Lognormal Distribution

If the logarithm of a random variable has a normal distribution, the random variable has a positively skewed continuous distribution known as the lognormal distribution. The lognormal distribution is frequently used to describe random processes that represent the product of several small independent events [5]. This property of the lognormal distribution is known as the "law of proportionate effects" and provides the basis on which we can decide to assume that a lognormal distribution describes a particular random variable.

Most of the important applications of the lognormal distribution are in the fields of probit analysis, sales analysis, and theory of breakage. The latter theory provides the basis for identifying the distribution of certain particle sizes (including sizes of firms or oil reservoirs) and the distribution of income as lognormal [1,8]. For example, instead of using a normal distribution to graduate a set of numerical data such as income (or sales) we might use the normal distribution function to graduate the logarithms of the numerical values. Near the greater end of a logarithm scale given differences in arguments (income) are associated with small differences in logarithms, whereas at the smaller end the same differences in arguments (income) are associated with larger differences in logarithms. The logarithmic scale thus has the effect of compressing the distribution of income at higher levels and stretching the distribution at lower levels. This type of transformation would be likely to change any positively skewed distribution into an approximately symmetrical distribution.

If the logarithm (to the base e) of a random variable X has a density function $f(y)$ given as follows

$$f(y) = \frac{1}{\sigma_y \sqrt{2\pi}} \exp\left[\left(-\frac{1}{2}\right)\left(\frac{y - \mu_y}{\sigma_y}\right)^2\right] \quad -\infty < y < \infty, \quad (4\text{-}102)$$

where $\log x = y$ and only positive values of x are considered, then X is said to have a lognormal distribution. The parameters μ and σ_y^2 correspond to the mean and variance of y.

The expected value and the variance of the lognormally distributed variate x are given by the following formulas:

$$EX = \exp\left(\mu_y + \frac{\sigma_y^2}{2}\right) \qquad (4\text{-}103)$$

$$VX = [\exp(2\mu_y + \sigma_y^2)][\exp(\sigma_y^2) - 1]$$

$$= (EX)^2[\exp(\sigma_y^2) - 1]. \qquad (4\text{-}104)$$

Simulation of lognormal variates with given mean and variance requires expressing μ_y and σ_y^2 in terms of EX and VX. This can be accomplished by first solving Eq. 4-104 for $\exp(\sigma_y^2)$.

$$\frac{VX}{(EX)^2} = \exp(\sigma_y^2) - 1 \qquad (4\text{-}105)$$

$$\exp(\sigma_y^2) = \frac{VX}{(EX)^2} + 1. \qquad (4\text{-}106)$$

Then taking the logarithm of both sides of Eq. 4-106, we obtain

$$\sigma_y{}^2 = \log\left[\frac{VX}{(EX)^2} + 1\right]. \tag{4-107}$$

Next we take the logarithm of both sides of Eq. 4-103

$$\log(EX) = \mu_y + \frac{\sigma_y{}^2}{2} \tag{4-108}$$

and solve for μ_y

$$\mu_y = \log(EX) - \frac{1}{2}\log\left[\frac{VX}{(EX)^2} + 1\right]. \tag{4-109}$$

Now that μ_y and $\sigma_y{}^2$ have been expressed in terms of the mean and variance of x, the lognormal variate to be generated, the standard normal variate z, can be defined as

$$z = \frac{\log x - \mu_y}{\sigma_y}. \tag{4-110}$$

Solving Eq. 4-110 for $\log x$ and taking the anti-log of both sides we obtain

$$\log x = \mu_y + \sigma_y z \tag{4-111}$$

$$x = \exp(\mu_y + \sigma_y z). \tag{4-112}$$

Substituting the value of z in Eq. 4-73 into Eq. 4-112 we get,

$$x = \exp\left[\mu_y + \sigma_y\left(\frac{K}{12}\right)^{-1/2}\left(\sum_{i=1}^{K} r_i - \frac{K}{2}\right)\right] \tag{4-113}$$

or for FORTRAN purposes (when $K = 12$)

$$X = EXP\ (EY + STDY * (SUMR - 6.0)). \tag{4-114}$$

In order to generate lognormal variates $x_1, x_2, \ldots x_n$ with EX and VX given, we must first determine μ_y and σ_y from Eqs. 4-107 and 4-109 and substitute these values into Eq. 4-113 or 4-114. Once EY and STDY are defined, the procedure for simulating lognormal variates differs from the procedure for simulating normal variates in only one minor sense. Equation 4-114 replaces statement 6 of the FORTRAN subroutine in Figure 4-16.

DISCRETE PROBABILITY DISTRIBUTIONS

A significant number of probability distributions are defined on random variables that take only discrete, non-negative integer values. The cumulative probability distribution for a discrete random variable X is defined in a manner similar to Eq. 4-1.

$$F(x) = P(X \leq x) = \sum_{X=0}^{x} f(x), \qquad (4\text{-}115)$$

where $f(x)$ is the frequency or probability function of X defined for integer x values such that

$$f(x) = P(X = x) \qquad (4\text{-}116)$$

for $x = 0, 1, 2, \ldots$.

Discrete probability distributions serve as stochastic models for certain *counting* processes over either finite or infinite samples, where the presence or absence of a binary attribute is governed by chance. Empirically, discrete distributions may also occur as a result of rounding continuous measurements on a discrete scale. Strictly speaking, however, discrete probability distributions are appropriate models of random phenomena only if the values of the random variates are measurable by counting.

The following sections contain descriptions of techniques for generating stochastic variates from most of the well-known discrete probability distributions. The format used in outlining these methods is similar to the format used with continuous distributions.

The Geometric Distribution

Among the earliest and perhaps simplest mathematical formulations of stochastic processes were the so-called Bernoulli trials. These trials are independent chance-experiments in which the outcome of each trial is expressed as either a success or failure. The probability of a success is usually denoted by p, $(0 \leq p \leq 1)$, where p is assumed to be constant for a particular sequence of trials. The probability of a failure is denoted by q, where

$$q = 1 - p. \qquad (4\text{-}117)$$

A sequence of Bernoulli trials combined with certain counting processes forms the conceptual basis for a large family of discrete probability distributions including the geometric, negative binomial, Poisson, and binomial distributions. The variates generated by counting the number of failures in a sequence of trials (events) before the first success occurs are variates from a geometric probability distribution. The geometric distribution has been found to be quite useful in the area of statistical quality control and for lag-distributions in econometric models.

The geometric distribution is described by the following probability function:

$$f(x) = pq^x \qquad x = 0, 1, 2, \ldots \qquad (4\text{-}118)$$

The cumulative distribution function is defined as

$$F(x) = \sum_{X=0}^{x} pq^x \qquad X = 0, 1, 2, \ldots, x. \qquad (4\text{-}119)$$

Since $F(x) = P(X \leq x)$ by definition and $P(X = 0) = F(0) = p$, the range of $F(x)$ is $p \leq F(x) \leq 1$. On the other hand, $P(X > x) = 1 - F(x)$, which implies that $P(X > 0) = q$ and that

$$1 - F(x) = q^{x+1}. \qquad (4\text{-}120)$$

The expected value and variance of the geometric variable are given by

$$EX = \frac{q}{p} \qquad (4\text{-}121)$$

$$VX = \frac{q}{p^2} = \frac{EX}{p}. \qquad (4\text{-}122)$$

The latter expression implies that the variance differs from the mean by a factor of $1/p$. From Eq. 4-118 it is clear that the distribution is always J-shaped with a mode at $x = 0$ [23].

The geometric distribution has only one parameter p, which can be expressed as a function of EX

$$p = \frac{1}{1 + EX}. \qquad (4\text{-}123)$$

The generation of geometric variates on a computer utilizes the inverse transformation technique and formula 4-120 [11]. Noting that $[1 - F(x)]/q$ has unit range we can write

$$r = q^x, \qquad (4\text{-}124)$$

and consequently

$$x = \frac{\log r}{\log q},\qquad(4\text{-}125)$$

where x is rounded to the next smallest integer. This can be easily accomplished by retaining the numbers before the decimal point only, or converting floating-point numbers into fixed-point mode [15]. Equation 4-125 shows that only one uniform random number is required to generate a geometric variate by this technique.

For a given probability of a failure q and for the number of successes k equal to one, Figures 4-17 and 4-18 in the next section describe a flow chart and FORTRAN subroutine that can be used in generating geometric variates.

An alternative method that utilizes the rejection technique to generate geometric variates reproduces Bernoulli trials on a computer. This method is usually preferred to the previous alternative if more accuracy is needed for large values of p. First, we define a variable x, which is to be used as a counter and set it equal to zero. Then we generate a sequence of uniform variates $r_1, r_2, \ldots, r_i, \ldots$, terminating the sequence when we reach a value of r_i less than or equal to p. For each value of r_i (in the sequence) greater than p, we increment x by one. That is, we count the number of failures or r_i's greater than p. When we reach the first value of r_i less than or equal to p, the sequence is terminated, and the value of x corresponds to the value of a geometric variate. After resetting x to zero, a second sequence is generated yielding a second value of x.

In the preceding discussion x was defined as the number of failures occurring before the first success. However, x can also be defined to include the number of failures plus the first success. Although the procedure for generating geometric variates is similar to the previous procedure, Eqs. 4-118 and 4-121 become

$$f(x) = pq^{x-1}\qquad x = 1, 2, \ldots\qquad(4\text{-}126)$$

$$EX = \frac{1}{p}.\qquad(4\text{-}127)$$

The Negative Binomial Distribution

When Bernoulli trials, such as those described in the preceding section, are repeated until k successes occur $(k > 1)$, then the random variable denoting the number of failures will have a negative binomial distribution. Negative binomial variates are, therefore, essentially the sum of k geometric variates. In this case k is an integer, and the distribution is called a Pascal distribution. This implies that the geometric distribution is a special case of the Pascal distribution in which k is equal to one.

The probability distribution function for the negative binomial distribution is

$$f(x) = \binom{k + x - 1}{x} p^k q^x \qquad x = 0, 1, 2, \ldots, \qquad (4\text{-}128)$$

where k is the total number of successes out of $k + x$ trials and x is the number of failures that occur before k successes occur. The expected value and variance of X are given by

$$EX = \frac{kq}{p} \qquad (4\text{-}129)$$

$$VX = \frac{kq}{p^2}. \qquad (4\text{-}130)$$

It should be noted that both the geometric and negative binomial distributions are characterized by overdispersion, that is, $VX > EX$.

For a given mean and variance the parameters k and p can be determined by

$$p = \frac{EX}{VX} \qquad (4\text{-}131)$$

$$k = \frac{(EX)^2}{VX - EX}. \qquad (4\text{-}132)$$

However, if the computed value of k in Eq. 4-132 is not an integer, the simulation procedure is complicated considerably.

When k is an integer, Pascal variates can be generated by taking the sum of k geometric variates. Consequently,

$$x = \frac{\left(\sum_{i=1}^{k} \log r_i \right)}{\log q} = \frac{\log \left(\prod_{i=1}^{k} r_i \right)}{\log q} \qquad (4\text{-}133)$$

is a Pascal variate after it is rounded to the next smallest integer.

Figures 4-17 and 4-18 contain a flow chart and FORTRAN subroutine for generating Pascal variates by the aforementioned technique. X is a FORTRAN integer variable which corresponds to x. Rounding takes place automatically in statement 7 by FORTRAN integer arithmetic.

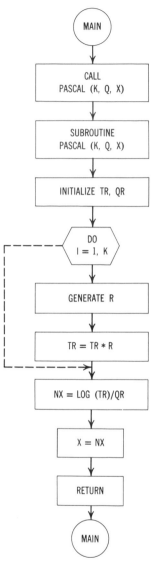

Figure 4-17. Generation of Pascal variates, flow chart.

If k is not an integer, we must rely on approximation methods for generating negative binomial variates. One method involves generating a mixture of variates with two different integral values of k. For example, if k is equal to 3.60, we might generate a mixture of Pascal variates with k equal to 3 and k equal to 4 but with the expected value of k equal to 3.60. Another alternative involves generating Poisson variates whose single parameter has a gamma distribution with parameters k and α [10]. Negative binomial variates generated by the latter method have parameters k and p, where

$$p = \frac{\alpha}{1 + \alpha}. \qquad (4\text{-}134)$$

Pascal variates can also be defined as the total number of trials such that x failures occur before k successes occur. In this case the Pascal variate becomes $k + x$, [6]. The expected value of Pascal variates defined accordingly is

$$E(k + x) = \frac{kq}{p} + k = \frac{k}{p}. \qquad (4\text{-}135)$$

The Binomial Distribution

Random variables defined by the number of successful events in a sequence of n independent Bernoulli trials, where the probability of a success is p for each trial, follow the binomial distribution. This stochastic model also applies for the process of random sampling with replacement, where the sampled elements have only two kinds of attributes (for example, "yes" or "no" responses or "defective" and "acceptable" items). A randomly drawn sample of n elements is an analog of n independent Bernoulli trials, where x is a binomial variate

```
1. SUBROUTINE PASCAL (K, Q, X)
2. TR = 1.0
3. QR = LOG (Q)
4. DO 6 I = 1, K
5. R = RND(R)
6. TR = TR * R
7. NX = LOG (TR)/QR
8. X = NX
9. RETURN
```

Figure 4-18. Generation of Pascal variates, FORTRAN subroutine.

denoting the number of elements in the sample of size n with identical attributes. This analogy makes the binomial distribution one of the most important models in the areas of statistical sampling and quality control.

The binomial distribution gives the probability that an event or a "success" occurs x times out of n trials, where the probability of a success is p. The probability function for the binomial distribution may be expressed as follows

$$f(x) = \binom{n}{x} p^x q^{n-x} \tag{4-136}$$

where x is an integer defined on the finite interval, 0, 1, 2, . . . n, and $q = (1-p)$.

The expected value and variance of the binomial variable X are

$$EX = np \tag{4-137}$$

$$VX = npq. \tag{4-138}$$

The second expression implies that the variance of binomial variables is always less than the mean. In addition, note that Eq. 4-136 also defines the distribution of $(n-x)$ with expected value nq.

When the mean and variance are known, then p and n can be determined by

$$p = \frac{(EX - VX)}{EX} \tag{4-139}$$

$$n = \frac{(EX)^2}{(EX - VX)}. \tag{4-140}$$

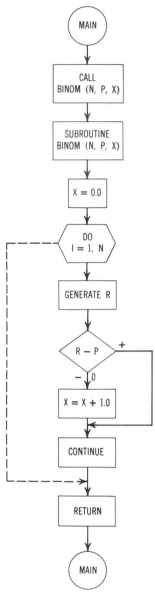

Figure 4-19. Generation of binomial variates, flow chart.

The normal distribution provides a good approximation for the binominal distribution for large n. Since it is possible to have negative values with the normal distribution, in order for the normal approximation to be useful, the probability of negative observations must be negligibly small. In practice this means that the expected value must be at least three times the standard deviation, that is,

$$np \geq 3\,(npq)^{1/2} \qquad (4\text{-}141)$$

which implies that $n \geq 9q/p$.

Binomial variates can be generated in many different ways but the simplest method, and for moderate n one of the most efficient methods, is based on the reproduction of Bernoulli trials via the rejection technique. The process starts with known values of p and n and consists of generating n random numbers after setting x_0 equal to zero. For each random number r_i, $(i = 1, 2, \ldots n)$, a check is made, and the variable x_i is incremented as follows

$$x_i = x_{i-1} + 1 \qquad \text{if } r_i \leq p \qquad (4\text{-}142)$$

$$x_i = x_{i-1} \qquad \text{if } r_i > p. \qquad (4\text{-}143)$$

After n random numbers have been generated, the value of x_n is equal to binomial variate x. This procedure can then be repeated as many times as there are binomial variates required.

A second method of generating binomial variates is based on random sums of geometric variates, thus obtaining the number of successes in n trials. When p is small, this method may be faster.

Figures 4-19 and 4-20 show a flow chart and a FORTRAN sub-

```
1. SUBROUTINE BINOM (N, P, X)
2. X = 0.0
3. DO 7 I = 1, N
4. R = RND (R)
5. IF (R − P) 6, 6, 7
6. X = X + 1.0
7. CONTINUE
8. RETURN
```

Figure 4-20. Generation of binomial variates, FORTRAN subroutine.

routine for generating binomial variates by the former of the two methods.

The Hypergeometric Distribution

Consider a population consisting of N elements such that each element belongs either to class I or class II. Let Np denote the number of elements belonging to class I and Nq the number of elements belonging to class II, where $p + q = 1$. If a random sample of n ($<N$) elements is taken from the population of N elements *without replacement*, then x, the number of class-I elements in the sample of n elements, has a hypergeometric probability distribution [31, p. 133]. Applications of the hypergeometric distribution are found in the areas of quality control and production control. For example, if the time interval between the arrival of successive customer demands for a firm's product is exponentially distributed and the quantity ordered by each customer is geometrically distributed, then the total demand in any given time period will have a hypergeometric distribution [5, p. 166].

The hypergeometric distribution is described by the following probability function

$$f(x) = \frac{\binom{Np}{x}\binom{Nq}{n-x}}{\binom{N}{n}} \qquad \begin{array}{l} 0 \le x \le Np \\ 0 \le n - x \le Nq, \end{array} \qquad (4\text{-}144)$$

where x, n, and N are integers. The expected value and variance are

$$EX = np \qquad (4\text{-}145)$$

$$VX = npq\left(\frac{N-n}{N-1}\right). \qquad (4\text{-}146)$$

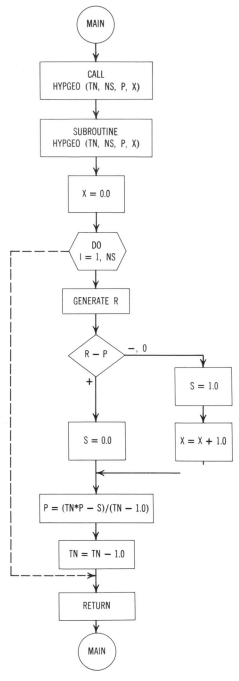

Figure 4-21. Generation of hypergeometric variates, flow chart.

1. SUBROUTINE HYPGEO (TN, NS, P, X)
2. X = 0.0
3. DO 11 I = 1, NS
4. R = RND (R)
5. IF (R − P) 6, 6, 9
6. S = 1.0
7. X = X + 1.0
8. GO TO 10
9. S = 0.0
10. P = (TN * P − S) / (TN − 1.0)
11. TN = TN − 1.0
12. RETURN

Figure 4-22. Generation of hypergeometric variates, FORTRAN subroutine.

The generation of hypergeometric variates involves simulating a sampling experiment *without replacement*. That is, we merely alter the Bernoulli trials method of generating binomial variates so that N and p vary depending respectively on the total number of elements that have been previously drawn from the population and the number of class-I elements that have been drawn. As each element in a sample of n elements is drawn, the original value of $N = N_0$ is reduced according to the formula

$$N_i = N_{i-1} - 1 \qquad i = 1, 2, \ldots, n. \qquad (4\text{-}147)$$

In a similar manner, the value of $p = p_0$ when the ith element in a sample of n elements is drawn becomes

$$p_i = \frac{N_{i-1} p_{i-1} - S}{N_{i-1} - 1} \qquad i = 1, 2, \ldots, n, \qquad (4\text{-}148)$$

where $S = 1$ when sample element $(i - 1)$ belongs to class I and $S = 0$ when sample element $(i - 1)$ belongs to class II. The starting values N_0 and p_0, of course, correspond to N, the initial population size, and p, the proportion of the total population consisting of class-I elements.

Figures 4-21 and 4-22 describe the flow chart and FORTRAN subroutine for generating hypergeometric variates. The symbols TN and NS have been used to denote respectively N and n.

The Poisson Distribution

If we take a series of n independent Bernoulli trials, in each of which there is a small probability p of an event occurring, then as

n approaches infinity, the probability of x occurrences is given by the Poisson distribution

$$f(x) = e^{-\lambda} \frac{\lambda^x}{x!} \qquad x = 0, 1, 2, \ldots \qquad (4\text{-}149)$$

$$\lambda > 0,$$

when we allow p to approach zero in such a manner that $\lambda = np$ remains fixed. We know from our previous discussion that np is the expected value of the binomial distribution, and it can be shown that λ is the expected value for the Poisson distribution. In fact, both the expected value and the variance of the Poisson distribution are equal to λ. It can be shown that if x is a Poisson variable with parameter λ, then for large values of λ, $(\lambda > 10)$, the normal distribution with $EX = \lambda$ and $VX = \lambda$ can be used to approximate the distribution of x.

Poisson distributed events frequently occur in the real world. For example, the number of aircraft arriving at an airport during a twenty-four-hour period can be very large. Yet the probability of an aircraft arriving during a particular second is very small. Hence, we might expect the probability of 0, 1, 2, . . . aircraft arriving in a given period of time to follow a Poisson distribution. The Poisson distribution is particularly useful in dealing with the occurrence of isolated events over a continuation of time, or when it is possible to prescribe the number of times an event occurs but not the number of times it does not occur.

To simulate a Poisson distribution with a parameter λ, we take advantage of the well-known relationship between the exponential and Poisson distributions. It can be shown that *if* (1) the total number of events occurring during any given time interval is independent of the number of events that have already occurred prior to the beginning of the interval and (2) the probability of an event occurring in the interval t to $t + \Delta t$ is approximately $\lambda \Delta t$ for all values of t, *then (a)*

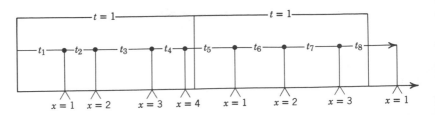

Figure 4-23. Poisson distributed events on a time scale.

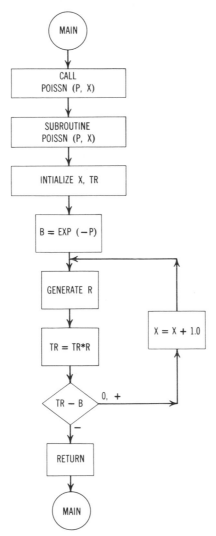

Figure 4-24. Generation of Poisson variates, flow chart.

the density function of the interval t between the occurrence of consecutive events is $f(t) = \lambda e^{-\lambda t}$, and (b) the probability of x events occurring during time t is

$$f(x) = e^{-\lambda t} \frac{(\lambda t)^x}{x!} \qquad \text{for all } x \text{ and } t. \tag{4-150}$$

Consider a time horizon (beginning at reference point 0) that has been divided into unit time intervals as illustrated in Figure 4-23. Events are assumed to occur along the time horizon and are denoted by the symbol ($\wedge$). The time interval t between events is assumed to have an exponential distribution with expected value equal to $1/\lambda$. This implies that the number of events x occurring during a unit time interval follows a Poisson distribution with expected value equal to λ. One method of generating Poisson variates involves generating exponentially distributed time intervals, $t_1, t_2, t_3, \ldots$ with expected value equal to 1. These random time intervals are accumulated as they are generated until their sum exceeds λ.

In mathematical terms the Poisson variate x is determined by the inequality

$$\sum_{i=0}^{x} t_i \leq \lambda < \sum_{i=0}^{x+1} t_i \qquad (x = 0, 1, 2, \ldots), \qquad (4\text{-}151)$$

where the exponential variates t_i are generated by the formula

$$t_i = - \log r_i \qquad (4\text{-}152)$$

with unit expectation. A faster method [28, p. 37] of generating Poisson variates x calls for the rewriting of Eq. 4-151 as

$$\prod_{i=0}^{x} r_i \geq e^{-\lambda} > \prod_{i=0}^{x+1} r_i. \qquad (4\text{-}153)$$

The FORTRAN subroutine for Eq. 4-153 appears in Figures 4-24 and 4-25. P is the FORTRAN constant for the parameter λ.

```
1. SUBROUTINE POISSN (P, X)
2. X = 0.0
3. B = EXP (−P)
4. TR = 1.0
5. R = RND (R)
6. TR = TR * R
7. IF (TR − B) 10, 8, 8
8. X = X + 1.0
9. GO TO 5
10. RETURN
```

Figure 4-25. Generation of Poisson variates, FORTRAN subroutine.

Empirical Discrete Distributions

Throughout this chapter we have been concerned with methods of generating particular probability distributions such as the normal, binomial, and Poisson distributions, to mention only a few. We now turn to a somewhat more general method that can be used to simulate: (1) any empirical distribution, (2) any discrete distribution, and (3) any continuous distribution that can be approximated by a discrete distribution. However, in general, we would not use this method to generate variates from the standard probability distributions because one of the methods described previously would be expected to yield "better" results from the standpoint of computation speeds, ease of programming, and memory requirements. In other words the method proposed in this section is a method to use when no other alternative is available.

Let X be a discrete random variable with $P(X = b_i) = p_i$, such as the random variable in the following table.

b_i	$P(x = b_i) = p_i$
b_1	0.273
b_2	0.037
b_3	0.195
b_4	0.009
b_5	0.124
b_6	0.058
b_7	0.062
b_8	0.151
b_9	0.047
b_{10}	0.044

Clearly one method of generating x on a computer is to generate a uniform $(0, 1)$ random variate r and set $x = b_i$ if

$$p_1 + \cdots + p_{i-1} < r \leq p_1 + \cdots p_i. \qquad (4\text{-}154)$$

Although a number of search techniques based on this method have been developed, most of them involve relatively complicated programs requiring excessive computational time.

A very fast procedure for generating discrete random variates has been developed by G. Marsaglia [17]. Marsaglia assumes the availability of a decimal computer that has memory blocks (words) that can be called for by number. (Most computers have this characteristic.) In memory locations 0 - 999, store 273 b_1's, 37 b_2's, 195 b_3's, $\cdots$,

44 b_{10}'s. Then if say $r = . d_1d_2d_3d_4$ is a four-digit, uniform, random number generated by the computer, the number in location $d_1d_2d_3$ will be the value of x.

Although this method is extremely fast, it requires 1000 words of memory. Marsaglia has also developed an alternative method that uses considerably less memory capacity, but it takes a little longer [17].

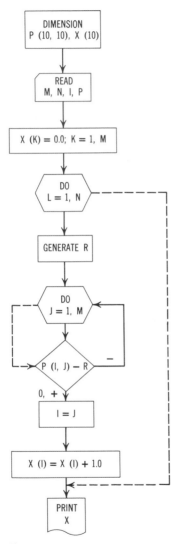

Figure 4-26. Simulation of Markov chains, flow chart.

Discrete Markov Chains

The specification of a system in terms of a sequence of distinguishable states is a frequent possibility for operational systems. For example, the state of a production facility, queue or storage facility may be adequately described by the number of items in it at any given time. If time is measurable in discrete units, we can describe the changes of the states in such systems in the following way. Every time the system is in state i at the beginning of a period, the probability that it will be in state j at the beginning of the next period is defined. This probability, p_{ij} depends only on states i and j and for each i, $\sum_j p_{ij} = 1$.

The p_{ij}'s can be arrayed in a square matrix form called the transition probability matrix $P = \|p_{ij}\|$, which completely determines the behavior of the system. This sort of behavior is called a Markov process, and a sample sequence of transitions is called a Markov chain.

There are analytical methods to evaluate the probability distribution of states of Markov processes under certain conditions, but the same can be determined by sampling estimates based on simulated Markov chains. This technique allows for frequency distribution estimates of transient as well as steady state probability vectors. Nonconstant transition probabilities can also be considered via simulation.

One of the known methods [11, p. 237] of generating Markov chains utilizes the rows of the transition matrix $||p_{ij}||$ in a manner similar to that described in the previous section. If the last state of the system was i, then the next state is j if

$$\sum_{k=1}^{j-1} p_{ik} < r \le \sum_{k=1}^{j} p_{ik}, \qquad (4\text{-}155)$$

where r is a uniform random number in the (0,1) interval. Each random number generated will cause a transition from state i to j, and the frequency of being in any of the finite states can be counted by the program.

Figures 4-26 and 4-27 describe a FORTRAN program to generate the frequency distribution of the states by simulating a Markov chain. The program is dimensional up to a ten by ten transition matrix. M indicates the actual dimension of the matrix, N is the desired length (number of transitions) of the chain, and I is the selected starting state. The FORMAT statements for reading in the data are symbolized by parentheses and are not specified further. The P matrix in the program is *not* the transition probability matrix but a matrix derived from it such that it contains the cumulative probabilities in each row. The X vector will contain the frequency distribu-

```
 1. DIMENSION P(10, 10), X(10)
 2. READ (   ), M, N, I
 3. READ (   ), P
 4. DO 5 K = 1, M
 5. X(K) = 0.0
 6. DO 12 L = 1, N
 7. R = RND (R)
 8. DO 10 J = 1, M
 9. IF (P(I,J) − R) 10, 11, 11
10. CONTINUE
11. I = J
12. X(I) = X(I) + 1.0
13. PRINT (   ), X
14. END
```

Figure 4-27. Simulation of Markov Chains, FORTRAN Program.

tion of states at the end of a sequence of N transitions. The program can be generalized by attaching subroutines which feed in reconditioned input information or by performing some computation on the X frequency vector.

AUTOCORRELATED TIME SERIES

If a stochastic process produces random variables such that there is a random variable x_t for each value of t, where t indicates time, we observe a random function of time called a time series. A common property of time series related specifically to economic and technological phenomena is the nonzero covariance of x_{t+k} and x_t, where k is the *lag*, i.e., the number of time intervals between the respective values of the time series. We shall define a covariance function $\phi(k)$ for lag k as

$$\phi(k) = E(x_t, x_{t+k}) \tag{4-156}$$

and an autocorrelation function $\rho(k)$ as

$$\rho(k) = \frac{\phi(k)}{\phi(0)}. \tag{4-157}$$

In both expressions we assume that $E(x_t) = E(x_{t+k}) = 0$ and $\phi(k)$ as well as $\rho(k)$ are functions of k only. These conditions are valid for stationary time series [31, p. 516].

It is not generally possible to generate a time series with an arbitrary autocorrelation function. There are two special functions, however, which can be used with satisfactory flexibility if the distribution of the x_t variables is normal with zero mean and identical constant variance [5, p. 169].

Linear Autocorrelation Function

Let

$$\rho(k) = 1 - \frac{k}{m} \qquad k \leq m \tag{4-158}$$

$$\rho(k) = 0 \qquad k > m$$

This is a linearly decreasing function of k and a model for autocorrelated time series where zero autocorrelation can be assumed for lags larger than m. The technique for generating a time series with this autocorrelation function is based on the process for generating normal variates described by Eq. 4-75 with the assumption that the uniform random numbers are transformed to variates with zero expectation, i.e., $E(r) = 0$. Then if

$$x_t = \sum_{j=1}^{N} r_j, \qquad (4\text{-}159)$$

x_t has zero mean and variance $N\sigma^2$, where $\sigma^2 = \text{Var}(r)$. The next variate is generated as

$$x_{t+1} = \sum_{j=p+1}^{N+p} r_j, \qquad (4\text{-}160)$$

where $(N - p)$ of the r_j random numbers are common to the successive sums.

The autocorrelation function with lag k is derived from the following identity relation:

$$(x_t - x_{t+k})^2 = {x_t}^2 - 2x_t x_{t+k} + x_{t+k}^2.$$
$$(4\text{-}161)$$

Turning to expected values and using Eqs. 4-156 and 4-159, we can write

$$E(x_t - x_{t+k})^2 = 2N\sigma^2 - 2\phi(k). \quad (4\text{-}162)$$

The parentheses on the left contain only $2kp$ nonzero r_j numbers, which are independent and have variance $2kp\sigma^2$. Consequently if $k \leq N/p$,

$$kp\sigma^2 = N\sigma^2 - \phi(k) \qquad (4\text{-}163)$$

and

$$\rho(k) = \frac{\phi(k)}{N\sigma^2} = 1 - \frac{kp}{N}. \qquad (4\text{-}164)$$

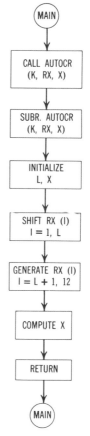

Figure 4-28. Generation of autocorrelated normal variates, flow chart.

It is customary to choose $N = 12$, which provides unit variance for x_t. The autocorrelation function is defined, however, in this case only up to $k = 12/p$ lags. Formula 4-164 corresponds to expression 4-158 with $m = N/p$.

Figures 4-28 and 4-29 describe a FORTRAN subroutine written to generate an autocorrelated time series of normally distributed variates x with zero mean and unit variance. The value of p in Eq. 4-160 corresponds to the FORTRAN variable K. The subroutine assumes twelve starting values for the uniform variates (RX) and returns one X value of the time series after each CALL statement.

Exponential Autocorrelation Function

The coefficient of correlation with lag k is expressed as

$$\rho(k) = \lambda^k; \quad 0 < \lambda < 1. \tag{4-165}$$

It can be shown that this type of autocorrelation function exists in time series obtained by exponential smoothing based on the recursion relation

$$x_0 = (1 - \lambda)r_0$$
$$x_t = \lambda x_{t-1} + (1 - \lambda)r_t, \tag{4-166}$$

where the r_t numbers are mutually independent variables with zero mean and variance σ^2.

For practical purposes, the r_t values can be generated easiest as uniform random numbers transformed to the $(-1/2, +1/2)$ interval

```
1. SUBROUTINE AUTOCR (K, RX, X)
2. DIMENSION RX(12)
3. L = 12 − K
4. X = 0.0
5. DO 7 I = 1, L
6. RX(I) = RX(I + K)
7. X = X + RX(I)
8. L = L + 1
9. DO 11 I = L, 12
10. RX(I) = RND (R)
11. X = X + RX(I)
12. X = X − 6.0
13. RETURN
14. END
```

Figure 4-29. Generation of autocorrelated normal variates, FORTRAN subroutine.

In this case, the generated x_t autocorrelated variates will have zero mean, and variance equal to

$$\sigma_{x_t}^2 \frac{1-\lambda}{1+\lambda} \sigma^2 = \frac{1-\lambda}{12(1+\lambda)}. \tag{4-167}$$

Computer programs to provide this kind of autocorrelation are well known from the literature on exponential smoothing, and they are very simple, since only one value represents the past information in Eq. 4-166 [5, p. 172].

REFERENCES AND BIBLIOGRAPHY

1. Aitchison, J., and Brown, J. A. C. *The Lognormal Distribution.* Cambridge: Cambridge University Press, 1957.
2. Anderson, T. W. *An Introduction to Multivariate Statistical Analysis.* New York: John Wiley and Sons, 1958.
3. Box, G. E. P., and Muller, M. E. "A Note on the Generation of Normal Deviates," *Annals of Mathematical Statistics,* XXIX (1958), 610–611.
4. Brockmeyer, E. H., Halstrom, L., and Jensen, A. *The Life and Works of A. K. Erlang.* Copenhagen: Copenhagen Telephone Company, 1948.
5. Brown, Robert G. *Statistical Forecasting for Inventory Control.* New York: McGraw-Hill Book Co., 1959.
6. Busch, R. R., and Mosteller, F. *Stochastic Models for Learning.* New York: John Wiley and Sons, 1955.
7. Butler, James W. "Machine Sampling from Given Probability Distributions," in *Symposium on Monte Carlo Methods.* Edited by H. A. Meyer. New York: John Wiley and Sons, 1956.
8. Cramer, Harold. *Mathematical Methods of Statistics.* Princeton, N. J.: Princeton University Press, 1947.
9. Evarts, Harry F. *Introduction to PERT.* Boston: Allyn and Bacon, Inc., 1964.
10. Feller, William. *An Introduction to Probability Theory and Its Applications.* New York: John Wiley and Sons, 1950.
11. Galliher, Herbert P. "Simulation of Random Processes," *Notes on Operations Research 1959.* Cambridge: The Technology Press, Massachusetts Institute of Technology, 1959.
12. Gupta, S. S. "Probability Integrals of Multivariate Normal and Multivariate t." *Annals of Mathematical Statistics,* XXXIV (1963).
13. Hammersley, J. M., and Handscomb, D. C. *Monte Carlo Methods.* New York: John Wiley and Sons, 1964.
14. Harling, John. "Simulation Techniques in Operations Research—A Review," *Operations Research,* VI (1958), 307–319.
15. McCracken, Daniel D. *A Guide to FORTRAN Programming.* New York: John Wiley and Sons, 1961.
16. Maguire, B. A., Pearson, E. S., and Wynn, A. H. A. "The Time Intervals Between Industrial Accidents," *Biometrika,* XXXIX (1952), 168–180.

17. Marsaglia, G. "Generating Discrete Random Variables in a Computer," *Communications of the A C M,* **VI** (Jan. 1963), 37–38.
18. Marsaglia, G. "Generating Exponential Random Variables," *The Annals of Mathematical Statistics,* **XXXII** (1961), 899–900.
19. Marsaglia, G., and MacLaren, M. D. "A Fast Procedure for Generating Normal Random Variables," *Communications of the A C M,* **VII** (1964), 4–10.
20. Morse, Philip M. *Queues, Inventories, and Maintenance.* New York: John Wiley and Sons, 1958.
21. Muller, Mervin E. "A Comparison of Methods for Generating Normal Deviates on Digital Computers," *Journal of the Association for Computing Machinery,* **VI** (1959), 376–383.
22. Organik, Elliot I. *A FORTRAN Primer.* Reading, Mass.: Addison-Wesley Publishing Co., 1963.
23. Parzen, Emanuel. *Modern Probability Theory and Its Applications.* New York: John Wiley and Sons, 1960.
24. Pearson, K. *Tables of the Incomplete Gamma Function.* London: Cambridge University Press, 1922.
25. Saaty, Thomas L. *Mathematical Methods of Operations Research.* New York: McGraw-Hill Book Co., 1959.
26. Scheuer, Ernest, and Stoller, David S. "On the Generation of Normal Random Vectors," *Technometrics,* **IV** (May 1962), 278–281.
27. Teichroew, D. *Distribution Sampling with High Speed Computers.* Ph.D. Thesis, University of North Carolina, 1953.
28. Tocher, K. D. *The Art of Simulation.* Princeton, N. J.: D. Van Nostrand Co., 1963.
29. Von Neumann, John. "Various Techniques in Connection with Random Digits," in *Monte Carlo Methods,* National Bureau of Standards, Applied Mathematics Series 12 (1951), 36–38.
30. Weibull, W. "A Statistical Distribution of Wide Applicability," *Journal of Applied Mechanics,* **XVIII** (1951), 293–297.
31. Wilks, S. S. *Mathematical Statistics.* New York: John Wiley and Sons, 1962.
32. Zung, William, Naylor, Thomas H., Gianturco, Daniel, and Wilson, William. "Computer Simulation of Sleep EGG Patterns Using a Markov Chain Model," in *Recent Advances in Biological Psychiatry.* New York: Society of Biological Psychiatry, April 30–May 2, 1965.

Chapter 5 | Computer Models of Queueing, Inventory, and Scheduling Systems

INTRODUCTION

In the preceding two chapters we have been concerned primarily with techniques for generating stochastic processes on a digital computer. We now turn our attention to the problem of formulating computer models describing large-scale, complex business and economic systems. Rather than continuing to dwell on stochastic processes themselves, we now embark on a procedure that calls for the use of the process generators described in Chapters 3 and 4 to provide the driving force for computer models of entire systems.

The emphasis of this chapter and the next will be limited strictly to the formulation of a wide variety of computer models of business and economic systems. The related problems of computer programming, validation, experimental design, and analysis of simulated data will be the subject matter of Chapters 7, 8, and 9. The purpose of Chapters 5 and 6 is to show the nature of computer models and the difficulties involved in their formulation by examining a number of different types of computer models that are applicable to business and economic systems.

We have arbitrarily decided to group our selection of computer models in the following manner. In this chapter we will develop models for queueing, inventory, and scheduling systems. In the following chapter we will formulate models that follow closely the lines of traditional economic theory—models of the firm, industry, and economy as a whole.

The formulation of a computer model generally involves a two-step procedure. First, we must formulate a mathematical model describing the system of interest. That is, we must specify the variables (exogenous, status, and endogenous) and functional relationships (operating characteristics and identities) describing the system. Second, we must convert our mathematical model into a computer flow chart that lends itself easily to the formulation of a computer program.

The flow charts we formulate in Chapters 5 and 6 will be of a general nature and can easily be programmed either in a general purpose computer language such as FORTRAN or ALGOL or a special purpose simulation language such as GPSS II [24], SIMSCRIPT [44], GASP [40], or DYNAMO [57]. In Chapter 7 we will fully explore the different programming languages available for writing simulation programs, pointing out the relative advantages and disadvantages of general purpose computer languages versus special purpose simulation languages.

Although the notion of simulating industrial systems on a computer is less than fifteen years old, the literature on simulation studies of queueing, inventory, and scheduling systems is already quite vast. (A cursory glance at the bibliography at the end of this chapter will confirm this assertion.) Therefore, in this chapter we can only hope to present a representative sample of computer models of queueing, inventory, and scheduling systems. Furthermore, due to the complexity of some of these systems, it will be necessary to restrict ourselves to relatively simple models that serve as components of more complex models, rather than treating the more elaborate systems themselves. In this manner we hope to impart some notion of the broad potential of computer models as a means of analyzing complex industrial scheduling systems.

Throughout this chapter we shall assume that the reader is either familiar with the existing terminology on queueing theory, inventory theory, and scheduling theory or has access to one or more of the standard references on these topics, which will be cited in the appropriate places throughout the chapter. In other words, we shall not attempt to develop fully the subject matter of queueing theory, inventory theory, or scheduling theory but shall merely look at a number of particular problems within each of these areas.

The approach we take in formulating computer models in this chapter is essentially a modified version of the modular or "building block" approach to model building. That is, we begin with a single block or module of the system of interest, and by adding additional blocks we construct a complex system that can either be analyzed as a whole system or in terms of its separate components. Our first block is a relatively simple single-channel queueing model. We then gradually by steps add to the complexity of our models as we progress from queueing models to inventory and scheduling models. Each new block developed is to some extent dependent on (that is, made up of) the previously constructed blocks. The flow chart of the final model in this chapter, an inventory-scheduling model, consists of a main body and a number of blocks or subprograms, each of which was developed in a previous section of the chapter.

All of the models in this chapter are fully recursive.

A model is fully recursive if it is possible to sequence one-at-a-time computation of successive values of endogenous variables in such a way that for any time period the value of each endogenous variable may be computed, given only exogenous variables, lagged endogenous variables, and preceding current endogenous variables in the sequence [53, p. 232].

The advantages of recursive models were stated in detail in Chapter 2.

There are at least three major advantages offered by the modular approach to the simulation of complex industrial systems. First, from a pedagogical standpoint the modular approach is quite appealing. Second, according to Jay Forrester,

In engineering systems, models have been built upward from available knowledge about the separate components. Designing a system model upward from identifiable and observable pieces is a sound procedure with a history of success.

In economics, models have often been constructed working backward from observed total-system results. Even as a theoretical goal, there is no evident reason to believe that the inverse process of going from total-system behavior to the characteristics of the parts is possible in the kinds of complicated, noisy systems that are encountered in business and economics [22, p. 54].

Third, it is possible to construct flow charts and computer subprograms for the building block models that can be used as library subroutines in simulating larger and more complex problems such as inventory-scheduling problems. For example, the subroutine that we formulate for simulating a single-channel queueing system can be used with both inventory and scheduling systems. In other words, the modular approach offers the model builder the possibility of considerable flexibility.

TIME FLOW MECHANISM*

One of the most important considerations in formulating a computer model of an industrial system is the method used to move the system being simulated through time. Two general types of methods have emerged for moving a model of a system through time on a computer—fixed-time increment methods and variable time increment methods. With *fixed time increment methods* a "clock" is simulated by the computer which records the instant of real time that has been reached in the system in order to maintain the correct time sequence of events [23, p. 8]. The time indicated by the "clock" is referred to as "clock time." The clock is updated in uniform discrete intervals of time, for example, minutes, hours, etc., and the system is scanned or examined every unit of clock time to determine whether there are any events due to occur at that particular clock time. With *variable time increment models* clock time is advanced by the amount necessary to cause the next most imminent event to take place. Events can occur at any desired point in clock time because time is advanced by variable increments rather than being divided into a sequence of uniform increments. When a particular event has been executed, clock time is advanced to the time at which the next significant event is to occur (according to past calculations), whether it be minutes, seconds, or hours away, and the appropriate event subroutine is automatically called and its time determined. The system is then updated to this time and so on. The intervening time periods when no changes occur in the system are skipped over [44, p. 5].

SIMPAC and DYNAMO are well-known examples of simulation languages that rely on fixed time increment methods, while SIM-SCRIPT and GASP make use of variable time increment methods. Fixed time increment methods are usually more efficient computationally speaking with systems "in which events can be expected to occur in a regular manner" [5, p. 19]. They have also been found to be useful "in the study of a system whose significant events are not well known, such as a large control system, or the initial phase of study of many systems" [62, p. 43]. On the other hand, variable time increment methods have been found to be more efficient with

* The material contained in this section as well as the material in the following two sections on fixed and variable time increment models was first published in [9] by Kong Chu and Thomas H. Naylor, "Two Alternative Methods for Simulating Waiting Line Models," *Journal of Industrial Engineering* (Nov.–Dec., 1965).

systems in which events occur unevenly in time [5, p. 19]. Variable time increment methods have the virtue that the size of the unit in which clock time is measured and recorded does not affect computation speed [64, p. 56]. Furthermore, variable time increment methods save computer running time when the simulation is static for long periods of clock time [39, p. 89]. The excellent paper by R. W. Conway, B. M. Johnson, and W. L. Maxwell entitled, "Some Problems of Digital Systems Simulation" [15] provides several concise analytical decision rules for choosing between fixed and variable time increment methods when one wants to minimize computer running time in simulating a given system.

The final decision concerning whether to use fixed time increment methods or variable time increment methods on a particular system depends on the nature of the system. Conway et al. [15] have demonstrated that the efficiency of fixed time increment methods increases with the number of status variables and that the efficiency of variable time increment methods increases with the mean length of events. Experimentation with both methods is the only sure way of determining which method minimizes computer running time for a particular problem.

In order to illustrate the differences between these two alternative time flow mechanisms we have formulated two different versions of a simple model of a single-channel queueing system—one using the fixed time increment approach and the other using the variable time increment approach. In both versions of this model arrival time and service time are assumed to be stochastic variates with known probability distributions, expected values, and variances. Arrivals are assumed to be serviced on a first-come, first-served basis. We assume the existence of a set of computer subroutines for generating stochastic variates drawn from a known probability distribution with given parameters. Those readers not familiar with the terminology of elementary queueing theory may wish to consult [11, 47, 59, 61].

A Fixed Time Increment Model [9]

In formulating a fixed time increment computer model of a single-channel queueing system we will first define the variables and functional relationships of the system in terms of a set of mathematical symbols. Then we will convert the resulting mathematical model into a computer flow chart. The variables of our fixed time increment model (which are required to be integers) are defined below:

EXOGENOUS VARIABLES

AT_i = the time interval between the arrival of the ith unit and the $(i + 1)$th unit, where $i = 1, 2, \ldots, m$. (5-1)

ST_i = the service time for the ith arrival unit, $i = 1, 2, \ldots, m$. (5-2)

PARAMETERS

$E(AT)$ = the expected time interval between arrivals. (5-3)

$Var(AT)$ = the variance of the time interval between arrivals. (5-4)

$E(ST)$ = the expected service time. (5-5)

$Var(ST)$ = the variance of the service time. (5-6)

STATUS VARIABLES

$SUMAT_i$ = total arrival time when the $(i + 1)$th unit arrives at the service station $i = 1, \ldots, m$. (5-7)

WT_i = the amount of time the ith arrival unit spends waiting to enter the service station $i = 1, 2, \ldots, m$. (5-8)

IDT_i = the amount of time the service station remains idle while waiting for the ith arrival unit to arrive $i = 1, 2, \ldots, m$. (5-9)

TWT_i = total waiting time when the ith arrival unit enters the service station $i = 1, 2, \ldots, m$. (5-10)

$TIDT_i$ = total idle time when the ith arrival unit enters the service station, $i = 1, 2, \ldots, m$. (5-11)

WL = the number of units waiting to be serviced at a particular point in time. (5-12)

$CLOCK$ = simulated time measured in unit increments. (5-13)

ENDOGENOUS VARIABLES

$E(WT)$ = expected waiting time. (5-14)

$E(IDT)$ = expected idle time. (5-15)

OPERATING CHARACTERISTICS

$f(AT)$ = the probability density function for the time interval between arrivals. (5-16)

$f(ST)$ = the probability density function for service time. (5-17)

IDENTITIES

$$E(WT) = \sum_{i=1}^{m} WT_i/m = TWT_m/m. \qquad (5\text{-}18)$$

$$E(IDT) = \sum_{i=1}^{m} IDT_i/m = TIDT_m/m. \qquad (5\text{-}19)$$

When the first input unit arrives at the service station, i.e., when $i = 1$, the following starting conditions are assumed to be in effect.

$$SUMAT_1 = AT_0 = 0 \qquad (5\text{-}20)$$
$$TIDT_1 = 0 \qquad (5\text{-}21)$$
$$TWT_1 = 0 \qquad (5\text{-}22)$$
$$WL = 0 \qquad (5\text{-}23)$$
$$CLOCK = 0. \qquad (5\text{-}24)$$

In other words, total arrival time, total idle time, total waiting time, and the lengths of the waiting line are all assumed to be equal to zero at the start of the simulation run.

The computer flow chart for this model appears in Figure 5-1. The first block of Figure 5-1 is an initialization routine in which SUMAT, TIDT, TWT, WL, and CLOCK are all set equal to zero according to Eqs. 5-20 through 5-24. In block 2 the length of the waiting line is increased by one indicating that the first input unit has arrived at the service station. Next an arrival time AT is generated by the computer according to some specified subroutine. For example, if AT has a negative exponential distribution with a given expected value, then an arrival time drawn from an exponential distribution will be generated. For the first iteration (that is, when $i = 1$) AT denotes the time interval between the arrival of the first and second input units; for the second iteration (when $i = 2$) AT denotes the time interval between the arrival of the second and third input units, etc. In block 4 a new total arrival time is computed.

Next a check is made to determine whether the service station is "empty" or "occupied" at this particular moment in time. If the service station is empty, that is, if no input unit is currently being serviced, then the waiting line is checked to determine whether there is an input unit waiting for service. If there is at least one unit waiting to be serviced, the unit at the head of the waiting line is brought into the service station, and the waiting line is decreased by one. (A first-come, first-served priority system is assumed.) In block 9 a service time ST is generated by the appropriate subroutine for the unit that has just been admitted to the service station. If, for example, service time were assumed to have a negative exponential distribution, then a negative exponential variate would be generated. One unit of waiting time is then added to the total waiting time for each input nuit in the waiting line. However, if in block 6 we find that there are no units in the waiting line, then one unit of idle time is recorded in block 7. On the other hand, if the service station is found to be "occupied" in

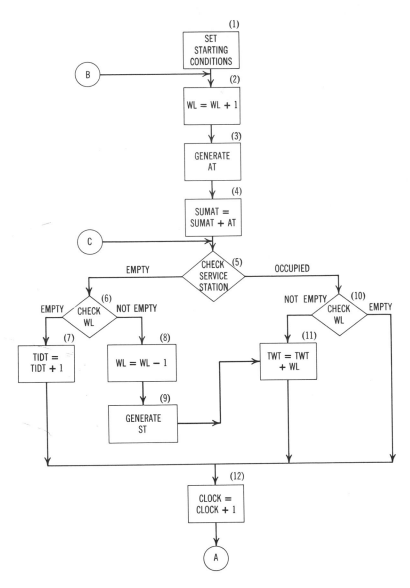

Figure 5-1. A fixed time increment model.

block 5 at this particular time, then the waiting line is checked to determine whether or not there is an input unit waiting for service. If there is at least one unit in the waiting line, one unit of waiting time is added to the total waiting time for each input unit in the waiting line.

Having considered all of the logical possibilities for the status of

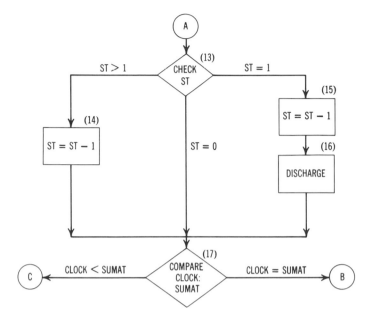

Figure 5-1. (continued)

the service station and the waiting line, we then advance the "clock" by one time unit in block 12. In block 13 the status of the service station is determined by the magnitude of the service time. (The service station check in block 5 depends entirely on the status of service time in block 13.) If service time is greater than unity, there is a unit in the service station, and the service time is decreased by one. If the service time is equal to zero, the service station is empty. If service time is equal to one, service is completed at this point. Service time is decreased by one, making it equal to zero, and the unit is discharged from the service station.

"Clock" time is compared with total arrival time in block 17. If "clock" time is equal to total arrival time, this indicates that a new input unit has arrived at the service station. Control is then transferred to block 2, and a new arrival is placed in the waiting line. An arrival time is generated corresponding to the time interval between this new arrival and the next arrival, and the whole procedure is then repeated. However, if the "clock" time is less than total arrival time, the time has not yet come for the arrival of another unit, and we must go through another iteration of updating all relevant time intervals and advancing the "clock." In other words, we return to block 5.

This procedure can be repeated for as long a period of time or for as many arrivals as are required. To terminate the simulation we merely specify in advance (when the data are read into the computer) a maximum "clock" time or some finite number of arrivals and insert a checking routine into the program that will terminate the simulation run at the appropriate time, that, is, when the maximum "clock" time is reached or when the predetermined number of arrivals have occurred.

Upon completion of a computer run using this model, we can then calculate such statistics as

1. Expected waiting time
2. Expected idle time
3. Expected queue length
4. Expected length of nonempty queues
5. Expected number of units in the system
6. Expected waiting time of an arrival who waits
7. Expected time an arrival spends in the system
8. Expected fraction of total time service station is idle
9. Expected fraction of total time service station is occupied
10. Probability that there are n units in the system
11. Maximum queue length

In order to say anything about the statistical precision of our estimates of the expected values of the aforementioned variables we must also estimate the variance of these variables. Estimates of the variance of a simulated random variable can be obtained by replicating the given simulation experiment using different starting values in the multiplicative congruential random number generators of the model for each replication. For certain special cases [61, pp. 131–133] these simulated statistics can then be compared with their theoretical counterparts as a check on the validity of the computer model. For example, the case in which both arrival time and service time have a negative exponential distribution with given expected values is a special case whose theoretical results are quite well known in the literature on queueing theory. (These theoretical results are reproduced at the conclusion of the discussion of the variable time increment model.) In addition, experiments can be performed to test the effects of changes in either the probability distribution, expected value, or variance of arrival times and service times or expected waiting time, expected idle time, etc. We can also experiment with alternative queue disciplines and restrictions on maximum queue length. However, the principal value of this model is its ability to be used as a subroutine in simulating more complex multichannel, multistation queueing systems, as well as production scheduling and inventory systems.

A Variable Time Increment Model [9]

The most obvious difference between our variable time increment queueing model and our fixed time increment model is that time is treated as a continuous variable rather than a discrete variable. Furthermore, there is no simulated "clock" in our variable time increment model. The variables, parameters, operating characteristics, and identities in this model are exactly the same as those defined in the fixed time increment model. However, the variables SUMAT, WL, and CLOCK are not essential to the operation of this model. Both arrival time and service time are again assumed to be stochastic variates with known parameters. A first-come, first-served priority system remains in effect.

Figure 5-2 contains a computer flow chart for our variable time increment model of a single-channel queueing system. In block 1 of Figure 5-2 arrival time, waiting time, idle time, total waiting time, and total idle time are all set equal to zero, indicating that the first unit has arrived at the service station. A second unit is assumed to arrive at the system, and an arrival time (that is, the time between the arrival of the first and second input units) is generated by the appropriate stochastic subroutine in block 2. Waiting time, which is equal to zero on the first iteration, is subtracted from arrival time in block 3. Next, a service time is generated and compared with the adjusted arrival time recorded in block 3. If service time exceeds arrival time, the second or $(i+1)$th input unit arrives before service is completed on the first or ith unit. Therefore, waiting time occurs, and idle time is set equal to zero. Waiting time is set equal to the difference between service and arrival time and accumulated in blocks 7 and 8, respectively. On the other hand, if service time is less than arrival time, idle time results, and waiting time is equal to zero. Idle time is then set equal to the difference between arrival time and service time and accumulated. If service time and arrival times are equal, neither waiting time or idle time occur.

This procedure can be repeated for as many arrivals as are required or for as long a period of time as necessary. For each subsequent iteration the waiting time of the previous input unit is subtracted from the arrival time before the comparison of arrival time and service time is made. At the end of each simulation run, statistics such

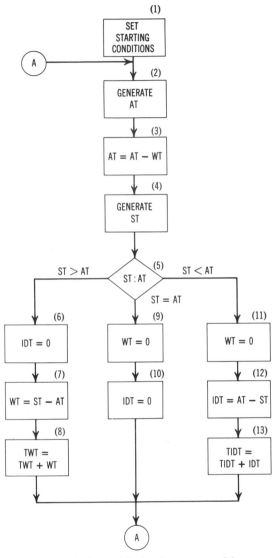

Figure 5-2. A variable time increment model.

as expected waiting time, expected idle time, etc., can be computed and compared with known theoretical values of these parameters.

In order to check the validity of our two single-channel queueing models, experimental runs can be made on the basis of certain special assumptions about the probability distributions of arrival time and service time for which there exist theoretical values for such parameters of the system as expected waiting time, expected idle time, etc. For example, it can be shown that for the case in which arrival time and service time both have negative exponential distributions with expected values equal to $1/\lambda$ and $1/\mu$, respectively, that the following relationships hold when $\mu > \lambda$ [61, pp. 131–133]:

$$\frac{\lambda}{\mu(\mu - \lambda)} = \text{expected waiting time.} \tag{5-25}$$

$$(1 - \lambda/\mu) \cdot \text{CLOCK} = \text{expected idle time.} \tag{5-26}$$

$$\frac{\lambda^2}{\mu(\mu - \lambda)} = \text{expected queue length.} \tag{5-27}$$

$$\frac{\mu}{\mu - \lambda} = \text{expected length of nonempty queues.} \tag{5-28}$$

$$\frac{\lambda}{\mu - \lambda} = \text{expected number of units in the system.} \tag{5-29}$$

$$\frac{1}{\mu - \lambda} = \text{expected waiting time of an arrival that waits.} \tag{5-30}$$

$$\frac{1}{\mu - \lambda} = \text{expected time an arrival spends in the system.} \tag{5-31}$$

$$1 - \lambda/\mu = \text{expected fraction of total time service station is idle.} \tag{5-32}$$

$$\lambda/\mu = \text{expected fraction of total time service station is occupied.} \tag{5-33}$$

$$\left(1 - \frac{\lambda}{\mu}\right)\left(\frac{\lambda}{\mu}\right)^n = \text{probability that there are } n \text{ units in the system, } n \geq 0. \tag{5-34}$$

Both single-channel queueing models have been found to yield satisfactory statistical results for the special case of exponential arrival times and service times when compared with the known theoretical values of the parameters of the system listed above. But the variable time increment model was found to consistently lead to much faster computational times than the fixed time increment model. This difference in computational performances may, in part, be attributed to the fact that with fixed time increment models the "clock" advances only one discrete unit per iteration. However, it is impossible to generalize from these two specific single-station waiting line models and infer that variable time increment methods are always faster than fixed time increment methods.

COMPLEX QUEUEING SYSTEMS

Many industrial systems are characterized by the arrival of some type of input unit to one or more service stations. These inputs may be sales orders, production orders, machine breakdowns, aircraft arriving at an airport, or automobiles arriving at a gas station. Service stations may be a battery of machines (in series or in parallel), stages in a production process, an airport, or a theater ticket booth. In many cases the time interval between inputs and the service time intervals themselves are stochastic variates or can at least be assumed to be stochastic.

From the standpoint of economic theory, a queueing problem is essentially a problem in balancing the marginal cost of waiting against the marginal cost of idle time for all service stations in a system. The costs associated with waiting include the loss of customers or potential customers as well as in-process inventory costs such as storage costs, handling costs, depreciation, deterioration, the opportunity cost of dollars invested in inventory, etc. Idle time costs represent imputed or opportunity costs, i.e., the cost of having resources tied up in a nonproductive asset rather than in an asset earning a positive return. Unfortunately, neither economists nor mathematicians have been able to develop straightforward analytical techniques for determining the conditions under which the marginal cost of waiting is equal to the marginal cost of idle time for complex, multichannel, multistation queueing systems.

In the following two sections of this chapter we describe computer models for simulating two complex queueing systems found in modern industry. First, we consider a single-channel, multistage system. Second, we analyze a multichannel system. In neither case is our objective one of finding an optimum solution (in an economic sense) to the system. Instead, our objective is merely to design a method for simulating these systems and generating the pertinent statistical data on waiting time, idle time, etc. The analyst is then free to experiment with the system by making adjustments in those parameters over which he has some degree of control and observe the effects of these changes in the light of available information on the costs and revenue associated with the system.

For a more comprehensive treatment of queueing theory and computer models of queueing systems see [11, 36, 43, 47, 59, and 61].

A SINGLE-CHANNEL MULTISTATION MODEL*

Introduction

Before the advent of the electronic computer and the development of present day mathematical and statistical techniques in the fields of operations research, econometrics, and mathematical economics, the neoclassical model of the firm formulated by J. R. Hicks [32] was probably the most widely accepted mathematical model of the firm among economists. However, over the past twenty-five years the Hicksian model of the firm has been subjected to a continuous stream of criticism (and rebuttal) by both economists and, more recently, operations researchers alike, beginning with the early attacks made by Hall and Hitch [30] as well as Lester [42] in the pre-operations research years and followed by a host of other critics in more recent years.

Our purpose is not to provide a complete survey of the arguments for and against the traditional theory of the firm, for example, the Hicksian model, or to take a position in favor of either the economist's concept of the theory of the firm or the operations researcher's approach to the problem. Instead, we merely want to point out that there is considerable need for a merger of the two alternative approaches to the problem of the firm, i.e., the traditional static equilibrium models of the economists and the more sophisticated mathematical tools of the operations researchers. Yet surprisingly, there have been very few attempts to bridge this gap between the operations research and economic theory approaches to the behavior of the firm. In this analysis we intend to go one step further in eliminating the apparent barrier that exists between economists and operations researchers.

We utilize traditional microeconomic theory and elementary queueing theory to develop a computer simulation model of a single-product, multiprocess firm. One of our objectives is to demonstrate that the body of economic theory known as the "theory of the firm"

* This section has been reproduced from a paper by Kong Chu and Thomas H. Naylor entitled, "A Dynamic Model of the Firm," *Management Science*, XI (May 1965), pp. 736–750. The paper was presented at the Winter Meetings of the Econometric Society in Chicago, Illinois, December 29, 1964.

can be used to provide a convenient frame of reference in applying some of the more powerful analytical tools of operations research and computer technology to the analysis of the behavior of the firm. The static equilibrium model formulated by J. R. Hicks is taken as the point of departure in constructing a simulation model in which (1) the time interval between the arrival of orders at the firm is a stochastic variate with a known probability distribution, (2) each order the firm receives must pass through n processes before it is transformed into a single unit of output, and (3) the time interval an order spends at the jth process ($j = 1, \ldots, n$) is a stochastic variate with a known probability distribution.

Although static equilibrium models are useful in the preliminary stages of the analysis of the problem of the firm, our simulation model possesses at least two attributes not found in the traditional models of the firm. First, the assumptions on which it rests are more flexible than the ones of the neoclassical static equilibrium models. Second, controlled experimentation is possible over extended periods of time. That is, it is possible to observe the effects on total profit (or some other measure of effectiveness) of changes in the number of orders received, the price of the product, the number of processes, the level of factor inputs, and the probability distribution of order arrival times and process times. Through computer simulation we can generate time paths reflecting and testing any number of alternative hypotheses concerning the behavior of the firm and its environment. Furthermore, this method of approach can easily be extended to the analysis of multiproduct firms whose behavior involves interactions far more complex than those of the single-product firm.

The Hicksian Model of the Firm [32, pp. 319–320]

Since one of our objectives is to compare our dynamic simulation model of the firm with Hicks' static equilibrium model, it is appropriate to begin by summarizing the important characteristics of the Hicksian model. The Hicksian model rests on the following major assumptions:

1. The prices of the firm's factors and products are fixed and known. (That is, perfect competition is assumed.)
2. The objective of the firm is to maximize profit subject to the technical constraints imposed by its production function.
3. A continuous production function exists (with nonzero first and second-order partial derivatives), which relates the set of independent factor variables to the set of independent product variables.

4. The exact nature of the firm's production function has been pre-determined by a set of technical decisions by the firm's engineers and technicians.

5. The firm's production function is characterized by: a decreasing marginal rate of technical substitution between any two factors; a decreasing marginal product for all factor-product combinations; and an increasing marginal rate of product transformation between any two products.

6. All of the firm's factors and products are perfectly divisible.

7. Neither the factor prices, product prices, nor the parameters that determine the firm's production function will change over the time period being considered. (This is a static model.)

8. Neither the factor prices, product prices, nor the parameters that determine the production function are permitted to be random variables. (Complete certainty is assumed.) [45].

The Hicksian model of the multiproduct, multifactor firm is concerned with two different types of decisions for the profit maximizing firm—output decisions and input decisions. The output decisions are concerned with "Which products to produce?" and "In what quantities should these products be produced?" The input decisions are concerned with "Which factors of production to buy?" and "In what quantities should these factors be purchased?" (Needless to say, these are by no means independent decisions.) Given the assumed information about product prices, factor prices, and production technology, the decision-maker for the firm then analytically derives a set of decision rules for maximizing total profit. The decision process for the neoclassical firm is represented in the form of a flow chart in Figure 5-3.

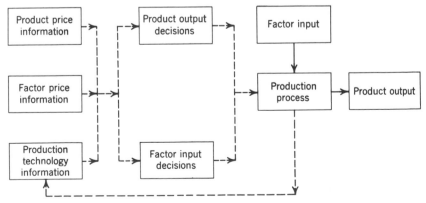

Figure 5-3. A flow chart of the decision process for the Hicksian model of the firm.

The broken lines represent informational flows, and the solid lines denote flows of factors of production and final products.

The Hicksian model can be stated mathematically as follows. The production function for the firm is given by

$$Q(X_1, \ldots, X_r, \ldots, X_v, Y_1, \ldots, Y_s, \ldots, Y_w) = 0, \quad (5\text{-}35)$$

where

$$X_r \geq 0 \text{ are products, } (r = 1, 2, \ldots, v), \quad (5\text{-}36)$$

and

$$Y_s \geq 0 \text{ are factors, } (s = 1, 2, \ldots, w). \quad (5\text{-}37)$$

For any given set of factors, $Y_1, Y_2, \ldots, Y_w$ there may be several technically feasible sets of products, $X_1, X_2, \ldots, X_v$. Assign arbitrary values to $v - 1$ of these products, and determine the largest value of the remaining product that is consistent with Eq. 5-35. This will assure a single valued production function. If all the factors and all but one of the products are assigned, then the remaining product is fully determined. Within the domain of definition the production function has continuous partial derivatives of first and second order.

If we let P_r denote the price of the rth product and P_s denote the price of the sth factor, then the firm's profit function is defined as

$$\prod = \sum_{r=1}^{v} P_r X_r - \sum_{s=1}^{w} P_s Y_s. \quad (5\text{-}38)$$

The objective of the firm is to maximize total profit subject to the technical constraints imposed by its production function. This constrained maximization problem can be solved analytically by the straightforward Lagrangian differential gradient method, which yields the following set of optimum decision rules (necessary conditions for profit maximization) for the firm.

Rule 1. The price ratio of any two products must equal the marginal rate of product transformation between the two products.

Rule 2. The price ratio of any two factors must equal the marginal rate of technical substitution between the two factors.

Rule 3. The price ratio of any factor-product combination must be equal to the marginal product for the particular factor-product combination.

Having described the Hicksian model of the firm, we now turn to a dynamic extension of this model.

A Dynamic Model of the Firm

Structure

Our dynamic model of the firm is concerned with the behavior of a single-product, multiprocess firm. The structure of this model differs from that of the Hicksian model in several ways.

First, although this model can be extended fairly easily to include multiproduct firms, for expository purposes we have elected to restrict it to the single-product case only. Hence, the question of optimum product mix no longer exists, since we have assumed away the Hicksian decision concerning, "Which products to produce?"

Second, the Hicksian model is based on the assumption of perfect competition in both the product markets and the factor markets. However, in our model we partially relax the assumption of perfect competition in the product market while retaining perfect competition in the factor markets. The quantity of output that can be sold at a particular price is assumed to be a stochastic variate. That is, the firm cannot say with complete certainty how many units of output it will sell during a particular time interval at a given price. Demand is said to be a stochastic process. This assumption appears to be at least partially borne out in the real world because the total sales of a firm depend not only on the prevailing market price but also on the effects of advertising and promotional expenditures, the marketing strategies of competitors, the national economy, and other factors over which it may be able to exercise little or no control. However, it has been found that with some firms it may be possible to find a probability density function describing the behavior of demand, or equivalently a probability density function describing the frequency with which orders are received by the firm at given price levels. In this model we assume the existence of the latter type of probability density function. We define a stochastic variate AT_i, the time interval between the arrival of the ith order and the $(i-1)$th order $(i = 1, \ldots, m)$, with a known probability density function $f(AT)$, expected value ET, and variance VT. But in order to maintain some degree of compatibility with the Hicksian model, it is convenient to assume that the firm has no control over either the density function, expected value, or variance of AT. That is, $f(AT)$, ET, and VT are fixed and known.

Third, the production process of this firm is in reality a series of n processes $P_1, P_2, \ldots, P_j, \ldots, P_n$. Each unit of final output of the firm is assumed to have passed through all n of these processes in a particular order. Furthermore, each process is assumed to have its own separate production function. The Hicksian model consists of only one process and one production function.

Fourth, the variable time was completely abstracted from the Hicksian model, since the model was entirely static in nature. That is, the rate of factor input Y_s and the rate of product outpput X_r that we specified in the Hicksian model were only applicable at a particular instant in time rather than over a continuous time interval. However, in a dynamic model of the firm the time dimension must be treated explicitly. The production function for the jth process of this model is given by

$$Q_j(t) = Q_j(Y_{1j}(t), Y_{2j}(t), \ldots, Y_{sj}(t), \ldots, Y_{wj}(t), u_j(t)) \quad (5\text{-}39)$$
$$j = 1, \ldots, n,$$

where

$$t = \text{time,} \quad (5\text{-}40)$$

$Q_j(t) = $ the rate of output of process j at time t, $j = 1$,
  $\ldots, n$, $\quad (5\text{-}41)$

$Y_{sj}(t) = $ the rate of input of factor s for process j at time t,
  $s = 1, \ldots, w_j$ $j = 1, \ldots, n$, $\quad (5\text{-}42)$

$u_j(t) = $ a stochastic variate with a known probability distribution, expected value EU and variance VU, $j = 1$,
  $\ldots, n$. $\quad (5\text{-}43)$

The production function 5-39 states that the rate of output of the ith process at time t is a function of the rate of input of factors of production at the jth process at time t and a stochastic element but independent of the rate of output of process $j - 1$. The stochastic element is an exogenous variable denoting the aggregate effect on the rate of output of the jth process of all factors over which the firm has no control. Again for the sake of compatibility with the Hicksian model, let us assume that for a particular value of t, the production function of the jth process has a decreasing marginal rate of technical substitution between any two factors and a decreasing marginal product for each factor-product combination.

Although the traditional production function in economic theory was designed to measure $Q_j(t)$ the quantity of output per unit time at time t, it is more convenient in this model to use the reciprocal relationship

$$ST_j = \frac{1}{Q_j(t)} \quad j = 1, \ldots, n, \quad (5\text{-}44)$$

where ST_j denotes the time required to produce one unit of output or one production order in the jth process. This transformation permits us to treat ST_j, the time required to produce one unit of output in the jth process, as a stochastic variate. Furthermore, the probability density function for ST_j and its parameters are completely determined by the level of factor inputs for process j and the probability density function, expected value, and variance of u_j. But the firm is assumed to know $f(u_j)$, EU, and VU. Hence, for each process ST_j may be treated as a stochastic variate with a known probability density function $f_j(ST_j)$, expected value ET_j, and variance VT_j. In other words, the firm cannot completely control the value of ST_j, but it can affect ET_j or VT_j or even $f_j(ST_j)$ by altering the rate of factor inputs for process j. For example, such factors as the frequency of machine-breakdowns and variations in employee efficiency over time are likely to affect the process time of the jth process. Although the firm may be able to reduce the frequency of breakdowns in process j by acquiring more reliable equipment (or applying preventive maintenance techniques) as well as more highly skilled employees, there is still a limit to the extent over which it can control the time required to produce one unit of output in process j. Hence, *for specified rates of factor input* at the jth process, ST_j is a stochastic variate not subject to further control by the firm.

Flow Chart

The flow chart in Figure 5-4 may serve to clarify the structure of our model. However, it should be noted that this flow chart does not include the firm's decision processes. Decision processes will be discussed after we have described the technical structure of the firm in complete detail.

In Figure 5-4 the block on the left-hand side of the flow chart de-

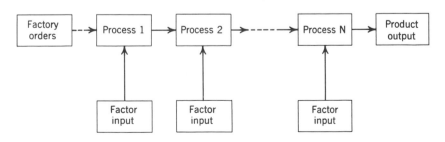

Figure 5-4. A flow chart for a dynamic model of the firm.

notes the arrival of an order to produce one unit of final output. This information is then transmitted to process 1, where factor inputs are used to produce one unit of process 1 output. The unit of output from process 1 then moves on to process 2, where it undergoes a further transformation before passing on to processes 3, 4, 5, etc., and finally reaches process N, where it is transformed into one unit of completed output. Every order received by the firm passes through these N processes in a similar manner.

Mathematical Model

We now turn to the formulation of a mathematical model describing our dynamic multiprocess firm. Let

AT_i = the time interval between the arrival of the ith order and the $(i - 1)$th order, where an order is defined as the demand by a customer for the firm to produce one unit of final output and $i = 1, \ldots, m$. $\qquad$ (5-45)

ST_{ij} = the process time for the ith order in the jth process, where $i = 1, \ldots, m$ and $j = 1, \ldots, n$. $\qquad$ (5-46)

WT_{ij} = the amount of time the ith order spends waiting to enter the jth process, where $i = 1, \ldots, m$ and $j = 1, \ldots, n$. $\qquad$ (5-47)

IDT_{ij} = the amount of time the jth process remains idle while waiting for the ith order to arrive, where $i = 1, \ldots, m$ and $j = 1, \ldots, n$. $\qquad$ (5-48)

$T_{ij} = WT_{ij} + ST_{ij}, \qquad i = 1, \ldots, m, j = 1, \ldots, n.$ $\qquad$ (5-49)
= the total time in which the ith order spends at the jth process.

When the first order arrives at the firm, i.e., when $i = 1$, the following equations are assumed to describe the multiprocesses system

$$AT_1 = 0. \qquad (5\text{-}50)$$

$$WT_{11} = 0, WT_{12} = 0, \ldots, WT_{1n} = 0. \qquad (5\text{-}51)$$

$$IDT_{11} = 0, IDT_{12} = ST_{11}, \ldots, IDT_{1n} = \sum_{j=1}^{n-1} ST_{1j}. \qquad (5\text{-}52)$$

$$T_{11} = ST_{11}, T_{12} = ST_{12}, \ldots, T_{1n} = ST_{1n}. \qquad (5\text{-}53)$$

For subsequent arrivals, i.e., when $i = 2, 3 \ldots , m$, these equations must be modified accordingly. The T-equations become,

$$
\begin{array}{ll}
T_{i1} = WT_{i1} + ST_{i1} & i = 2, \ldots , m, \qquad (5\text{-}54) \\
T_{i2} = WT_{i2} + ST_{i2} & i = 2, \ldots , m, \\
\cdots\cdots\cdots\cdots\cdots\cdots\cdots\cdots\cdots \\
T_{in} = WT_{in} + ST_{in} & i = 2, \ldots , m.
\end{array}
$$

Whether waiting time or idle time occurs at a particular process depends on the sign of the following differences, where $i = 2, \ldots ,$ m:

$$
\begin{aligned}
&DIF_1 = T_{i-1,1} - AT_i \qquad\qquad\qquad\qquad\qquad (5\text{-}55) \\
&DIF_2 = (T_{i-1,1} + T_{i-1,2}) - (AT_i + WT_{i1} + ST_{i1}) \\
&\cdots\cdots\cdots\cdots\cdots\cdots\cdots\cdots\cdots\cdots\cdots\cdots \\
&DIF_n = (T_{i-1,1} + T_{i-1,2} \cdots + T_{i-1,n}) \\
&\qquad\quad - (AT_i + WT_{i1} + ST_{i1} \cdots + WT_{i,n-1} + ST_{i,n-1}).
\end{aligned}
$$

If DIF_j is positive for the jth process, then idle time will be zero, and waiting time can be calculated by

$$
WT_{ij} = DIF_j \qquad i = 2, \ldots , m, j = 1, \ldots , n. \quad (5\text{-}56)
$$

If DIF_j is negative for a particular process, then waiting time will be zero, and idle time will be equal to

$$
\begin{aligned}
IDT_{ij} = -DIF_j \qquad &i = 2, \ldots , m, \qquad\qquad (5\text{-}57) \\
&j = 1, \ldots , n.
\end{aligned}
$$

If DIF_j is equal to zero for a particular process, then both waiting time and idle time will be equal to zero for that process.

Furthermore, AT_i is assumed to be a stochastic variate with probability density function $f(AT)$, expected value ET, and variance VT. And for each process, ST_{ij} is assumed to be a stochastic variate with probability density function $f_j(ST_j)$, expected value ET_j, and variance VT_j.

Decision Process

The decision process for our model is somewhat different from that of the Hicksian model, even though the objective of profit maximization has been retained. Although there are a number of alternative ways of viewing the decision process for our firm, we have chosen to assume that at the beginning of each planning period t, the firm decides which factors to purchase for use in planning period t and what quantities of these factors to purchase. That is, the firm is assumed to contract for a set of specific factor input rates over planning period t which can neither be increased nor decreased during the planning period. In other words, the rate of factor inputs is assumed to be fixed over each planning period but completely variable between planning periods. Once the firm specifies the rate of factor inputs for all processes for some planning period t, then the amount of total output produced in planning period t depends entirely on the arrival pattern of orders and the process times for each process in period t, both of which are stochastic variates. To be sure the firm could specify an upper limit on the number of orders it will accept in planning period t, but this would be inconsistent with the objective of profit maximization. Once the firm commits itself to a particular rate of factor inputs over planning period t, then the profit maximization objective dictates that the firm accept all orders received during the planning period, even though it may not be able to complete production, or even begin production, on all of them during the period. (This statement is based entirely on the assumption that the firm contracts for its factors at the beginning of a planning period and cannot change the rate of factor inputs during the period.) But at the end of each planning period, or equivalently the beginning of the next planning period, the firm can change the rate of input of its various factors of production. Therefore, the decision problem facing our firm is effectively reduced to "Which factors of production to purchase for use in planning period t?" and "In what quantities should these factors be purchased for each process?" Both of the output decisions of the Hicksian model have been assumed away. Since we are dealing with a single-product firm, there is no problem concerning which products to produce. Furthermore, the rate of output is completely determined by the rate of factor inputs and two stochastic variates—order arrival time and process times.

Unfortunately, there is no straightforward analytical technique available that is capable of yielding a set of optimum decision rules for the solution of this problem. Although we can specify the effect which a change in the rate of factor inputs for a particular process will have on the expected value and variance of the process time for that particular process, it is very difficult, if not impossible, to determine analytically what effect, if any, these changes will have on the firm's total profit during a given planning period. Therefore, until some type of computational algorithm (such as the simplex algorithm of linear programming) is developed which is capable of selecting factor input rates that yield maximum profits for the firm, we must necessarily resort to experimental approaches that permit us to try alternative factor input rates and test the effects that they have on total profit during a planning period. Computer simulation appears to be a reasonably satisfactory alternative for obtaining approximate solutions to this problem.

Simulation of a Dynamic Model of the Firm

Although the simulation method described here was not designed to yield precise or optimum solutions to the firm's input decision problem, it will provide a technique for testing the effects on total profit of alternative factor purchasing policies. The principal advantage of this approach is that it permits the firm to experiment with alternative decision rules within the confines of a tightly controlled laboratory without interrupting actual operations of the real system. The simulated firm can be observed either in real time, compressed time, or slow time. The firm can experiment with different levels of factor input for each process and observe the effects on idle time, waiting time, and total profit. In other words, we can specify at the outset a particular set of factor input rates for each process and hold these input rates constant over an extended time period, i.e., over a continuum of planning periods. By specifying the factor combinations for the jth process, we automatically determine $f_j(\mathrm{ST}_j)$, ET_j, and VT_j for the jth process. We then use the computer to generate the time paths of all of the variables included in our mathematical model.

The computer is also used to keep a record of waiting times, idle times, total process times, and total production output. Total profit can then be easily computed for each simulated planning period, for the product price, factor prices, and factor inputs are all given, and total output per planning period, as well as total output for the entire simulation run can be obtained from the simulation itself. Therefore, total profit for the simulation run is equal to the sum of the profits in each simulated planning period. The computer enables us to experiment with a very large number of different factor combinations for each process. Although we may not be able to determine the "optimum" factor combination for all N processes, we may be able to come very close, depending on the number of factor combinations we try and the length of each computer run. A second advantage of simulation is simplicity. Most of the computational procedures utilized here require little or no mathematical sophistication.

Figure 5-5 contains a detailed computer block diagram of the logical structure of the variable time increment method as applied to our dynamic model of the firm. This block diagram assumes the availability of computer subroutines for generating stochastic variates having known probability distributions. Given the values of the parameters describing a particular distribution as input data, the subroutine will generate variates that are distributed accordingly.

In block 1 of Figure 5-5 the parameters M (total number of orders to be considered), N (total number of processes), ET (expected order arrival time), VT (variance or order arrival time), ET1, ET2, . . . , ETN (expected process times), and VT1, VT2, . . . , VTN (variance of process times) are all read into the computer as input data. The choice of a value for M is completely arbitrary and rests primarily on statistical considerations. The total number of orders to be generated by the simulation experiment will be entirely determined by the degree of precision required in estimating such parameters as expected waiting time, expected idle time, expected output per planning period, and expected profit per planning period. The degree of statistical precision required will, of course, be dictated by the use that is to be made of the estimates.

In block 2 the index I is set equal to one denoting that the first order has been received by the firm. In block 3 process times are generated by the appropriate subroutines. Next we compute idle times and total times for each process for the initial order according to Eqs. 5-52 and 5-53. Of course Eqs. 5-50 and 5-51 must also be satisfied at this point. The total process times for all N processes are then totaled in block 5.

The arrival of a second order is indicated in block 6 by the generation of an interorder time AT_2, that is, the time that has elapsed between the arrival of order 1 and

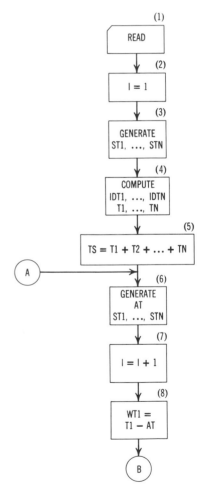

Figure 5-5. A flow chart of a simulation model of a multiprocess firm. (continued on next page)

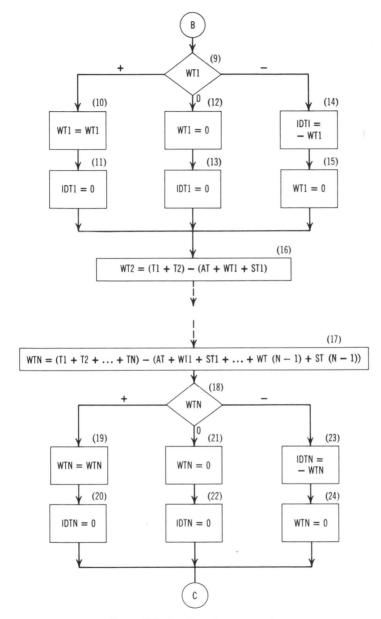

Figure 5-5. (continued next page)

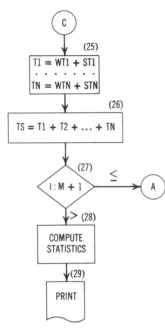

Figure 5-5. (concluded)

the arrival of order **2**. Since a new order has been received, N additional process times must also be generated. Block **7** indicates that the total number of orders should be incremented by one. In block **8** the difference indicated by the equation system 5-55 is obtained for order 2, process 1. If WT1 is positive, the idle time will be equal to zero (IDT1 = 0) and waiting time will be equal to WT1. If WT1 is equal to zero, then both waiting time and idle time are equal to zero. If WT1 is negative, waiting time will be equal to zero and idle time will be equal to —WT1. In block 16 the difference indicated by equation system 5-55 is obtained for order 2, process 2. Then WT2 is subjected to a test similar to the test applied to WT1. Sign tests must also be applied to WT3, WT4, . . . , WTN. (The sign tests for WT2, WT3, . . . , WT(N — 1) are not included in the flow chart.)

Total process times are computed in block **25** according to the formulas given by the equation system 5-54. These total process times are then added together in block **26**, yielding the total time TS (including waiting time) for an order to pass through all N processes. Finally, a test is applied to index I. If I is less than or equal to M + 1, then the procedure must be repeated. That is, we must return to block **6** and generate another interorder time and a set of N service times. However, if I exceeds M + 1 in block **27**, this implies that M order arrivals have been simulated. The computer can then compute required statistics such as expected waiting time, expected idle time, total idle time, and expected output per planning period. The statistic "expected output per planning period" cannot be generated directly from our flow chart without modifying it slightly. However, it can be computed quite easily by simple hand calculation techniques. To obtain this statistic on a computer we must use a simulated "clock" to keep track of the number of output units completed during each planning period within a simulation run. Since factor prices and factor inputs are known, as well as the price of the product output, we can then calculate total profit on the basis the number of output units generated per planning period. This calculation can either be done by hand or by the computer.

This procedure can be repeated for as many different factor input combinations as we wish to try, each time adjusting the parameters of the probability distributions describing process times accordingly. If we try a fairly large number of different factor combinations and then generate the total profits of the firm for each combination on the computer, we may be able to gradually develop an acceptable factor purchasing policy and answer the questions, "Which factors should be purchased?" and "In what quantities should they be purchased?"

A Special Case

At the outset we stated that one of our objectives was to develop a dynamic simulation model of the firm that would be as nearly compatible with the Hicksian model as possible. In order to convince the skeptical reader that we have not abandoned this objective, we now return to it. In fact, we shall show that the single-product, multifactor version of the Hicksian model is merely a special case of our model.

By assumption both factor prices and product prices are given in the Hicksian model and in our model. Furthermore, under complete certainty and static conditions, the production functions for each of our N processes have, by assumption, the exact same characteristics as the Hicksian production function. Therefore, if we assume (1) complete certainty, (2) a single-process firm, and (3) a completely static firm, that is, if we view the firm at a particular point in time, then our model is transformed into the Hicksian model. Under complete certainty the rate of output (or its reciprocal, process time per unit of output) for a single-process firm (at a particular point in time) is completely determined by the rate and combination of factor inputs. Furthermore, under perfect competition, orders are assumed to arrive at a constant rate that is greater than the production rate. Idle time is logically impossible in this special case, and for all practical purposes the waiting line is infinitely long. This special case of our model, which is in reality the Hicksian model, can be analyzed either by the Lagrangian differential gradient method discussed previously or by computer simulation. However, since we have assumed away uncertainty in both arrival times and process times and have eliminated idle time altogether, most of the features included in the flow chart found in Figure 5–5 are no longer relevant. Hence, to use simulation as a vehicle of analysis on this somewhat trivial model requires a drastic simplification in our simulation methodology.

The following simple example should serve to illustrate how we might go about treating the Hicksian model as though it were a special case of our more complicated simulation model. Consider a single-product, single-process firm operating in a world of complete certainty at a particular point in time. This firm may utilize two factors of production X and Y to produce its single product Q. The prices of X, Y, and Q are given and are denoted by the symbols P_x, P_y, and P, respectively. The production function for the single-process firm is given by

$$Q = Q(X,Y) \tag{5-58}$$

and is characterized by a decreasing marginal rate of technical substitution between X and Y and a decreasing marginal product for both X and Y. Total profit is determined by

$$\Pi = PQ - P_xX - P_yY. \tag{5-59}$$

Once we specify particular values of X and Y, then total output and total profit are completely determined. Hence, the only two decisions required of the firm are, "How much of factor X to purchase?" and "How much of factor Y to purchase?"

Two alternative methods can be used to solve this special case of our dynamic model—the Lagrangian differential gradient method or computer simulation. It can be shown quite easily by the Lagrangian differential gradient method that the optimum factor purchasing policy for the firm is a policy which leads to the purchase of quantities of X and Y which satisfy all three of the following conditions:

1. The price ratio between X and Y must equal the marginal rate of technical substitution between X and Y.

2. The price of X must be equal to the value of the marginal product of X.

3. The price of Y must be equal to the value of the marginal product of Y.

Although it is certainly possible to solve this special case of our model by computer simulation methods, the Lagrangian differential gradient method appears to be a much more suitable approach. To obtain an optimum solution to this model on a computer, we would employ a standard technique of numerical analysis-optimization of a multivariate function. That is, the computer would use a trial-and-error procedure for testing a large number of alternative values of X and Y to determine which combination yields maximum profits.

Although the solution obtained by simulation would be identical to the analytical solution, the Lagrangian differential gradient method would be by far the simpler of the two methods. Computer simulation should only be applied when there is no convenient analytical method available, such as the Lagrangian method, to solve a particular problem. The principal value of simulation is not in its ability to analyze the behavior of a firm operating under the very special static equilibrium conditions of the Hicksian model, but rather in analyzing the behavior of a more complex, dynamic, multiprocess firm operating under uncertainty.

Some Possible Extensions

Although we have gone through the painstaking task of attempting to show that our model can be considered as merely an extension of the Hicksian model rather than as a complete rejection of the Hicksian model, there are indeed a number of other equally important ways in which we can look at our model, that is, ways that depart considerably from the Hicksian perfectly competitive, static equilibrium model. We shall now briefly summarize several possible extensions of our dynamic model, which take us completely outside of the Hicksian framework.

1. The firm can be assumed to possess some degree of monopolistic power that enables it to at least partially control the arrival pattern of orders. That is, by changing either price or advertising and promotional expenditures, the firm may be able to affect either the probability distribution or the expected value of order arrival time. We can, therefore, use our simulation model as a means of testing the effects of alternative pricing and advertising policies on total profit. For example, if we know the approximate relationship between price and expected order arrival time, then we can test the effect of price changes on profit (assuming fixed factor prices and fixed rates of factor input) by simulating the behavior of the firm while operating under a number of different pricing policies.

2. We can also experiment with changes in the number of processes used by the firm, testing the effects on profit of adding a new process, eliminating a process, or combining two or more processes.

3. Experiments can also be made with changes in the nature of the production function for a particular process. There is no inherent reason whatsoever for restricting ourselves to the Hicksian concave production function [11]. Any number of other assumptions, for example, fixed proportions, indivisibility, etc., are equally acceptable and may

be included in our model. In fact, we may even want to test the sensitivity of our model to changes in the assumptions underlying our production functions.

4. In other words, we can change any parameter or function in our model that we wish (while holding other parameters constant) and test the effects of these changes by using a computer to generate the time paths of the important variables describing the behavior of the firm. The obvious advantage of this approach is it permits us to test a very large number of alternative hypotheses and decision rules concerning the behavior of the firm in a relatively short period of time without interrupting the actual operations of the firm.

A MULTICHANNEL MODEL

Consider a system consisting of n service stations operating in parallel (Figure 5-6). Input units arrive at the system and are admitted to the first vacant service station on a first-come, first-served basis. The time interval between arrivals is a stochastic variate with a known probability distribution. The service time for each of the n service stations is a stochastic variate, with each station having its own given probability distribution for service time.

When an input unit arrives at the system, the n service stations are checked to determine whether any one of them is vacant at the moment. If all n are occupied, then waiting time occurs until one station becomes vacant. When a service station becomes vacant before

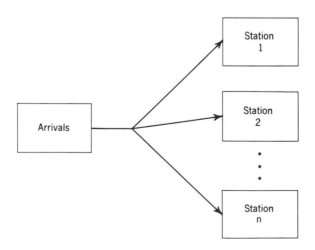

Figure 5-6. A multichannel queueing system.

another unit arrives at the system, idle time occurs until a unit arrives and enters the vacant service station.

The variables describing this system are identical to those used in the preceding model with the following exceptions:

TAT_i = total arrival time when the ith arrival unit arrives at the system, $i = 1, 2, \ldots$. (5-60)

$T_{ij} = \text{ST}_{ij} + \text{IDT}_{ij},$ (5-61)

= the time interval between the departure of the $(i - 1)$th unit and the ith unit from the jth service station, $i = 1, 2, \ldots$ and $j = 1, 2, \ldots , n$.

TT_{ij} = total time that has elapsed at the jth service station when the ith arrival unit departs from the jth service station, $i = 1, 2, \ldots ,$ and $j = 1, 2, \ldots , n$. (5-62)

SMIN = the minimum $\text{TT}_{i-1,j}$ over all j ($j = 1, 2, \ldots , n$). (5-63)

When the first unit arrives at the system, the following relationships are assumed to hold:

$$\text{AT}_1 = 0 \tag{5-64}$$

$$\text{IDT}_{1,j} = 0 \qquad j = 1, 2, \ldots , n \tag{5-65}$$

$$\text{WT}_{1,j} = 0 \qquad j = 1, 2, \ldots , n \tag{5-66}$$

$$\text{TT}_{11} = \text{ST}_{11} \tag{5-67}$$

$$\text{ST}_{1j} = 0 \qquad j = 2, \ldots , n. \tag{5-68}$$

For all subsequent arrivals the following relationships describe the system. If

$$\text{TAT}_i > \text{SMIN} \qquad i = 1, 2, \ldots , \tag{5-69}$$

then

$$\text{IDT}_{ij} = \text{TAT}_i - \text{SMIN} \qquad i = 1, 2, \ldots ; j = 1, 2, \ldots , n, \tag{5-70}$$

and

$$\text{WT}_{ij} = 0 \qquad i = 1, 2, \ldots ; j = 1, 2, \ldots , n. \tag{5-71}$$

If on the other hand,

$$\text{TAT}_i \le \text{SMIN} \qquad i = 1, 2, \ldots , \tag{5-72}$$

then

$$\text{WT}_{ij} = \text{SMIN} - \text{TAT}_i \qquad i = 1, 2, \ldots ; j = 1, 2, \ldots , n, \tag{5-73}$$

and

$$\text{IDT}_{ij} = 0 \qquad i = 1, 2, \ldots ; j = 1, 2, \ldots . \tag{5-74}$$

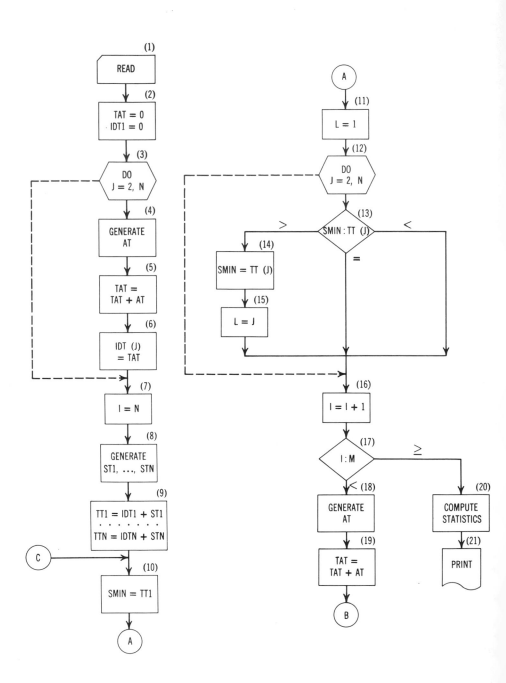

Figure 5-7. A multiple channel model.

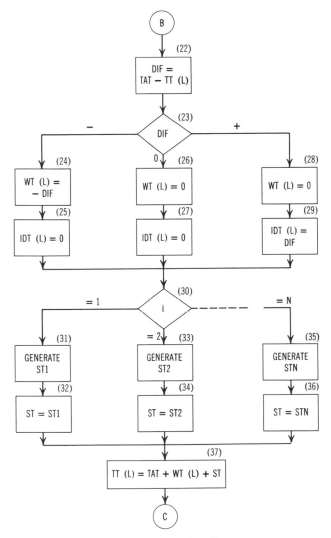

Figure 5-7. (continued)

It should be noted that the subscript i has been used in two different ways in Eqs. 5-60 through 5-74. In the case of AT_i and TAT_i, the subscript i has been used to denote the sequence of arrivals to the system as a whole. In the case of ST_{ij}, IDT_{ij}, T_{ij}, TT_{ij}, and WT_{ij}, the subscript i has been used to denote the sequence of arrivals at the jth service station.

Figure 5-7 contains a flow chart for simulating a multichannel queueing system. We begin by reading into the computer M (the total number of arrivals to be simulated), N (the number of parallel service stations), the expected value and variance of arrival time, and the expected value and variance of service time for each of the service stations. Next total arrival time and idle time for station 1 are set equal to zero. The DO-loop, which encompasses blocks 3 through 6, generates N-1 additional arrival times, as well as initial idle time values for stations 2 through N. N units must arrive before the possibility exists for waiting time. The initial idle time for the jth station is simply the total arrival time that has been accumulated before a unit is assigned to the jth station.

In the block 7 we indicate that N units have arrived. Next we generate N service times, one for each station. It should be noted that at this point each station has received only one input unit. In block 9 total idle time and service time are accumulated for each station according to Eqs. 5-61 and 5-62.

Blocks 10 through 15 represent a well-known computer subroutine for finding the minimum of a sequence of numbers. In this case we are interested in finding the minimum value of TT(J), which we call TT(L), where L is the station that becomes vacant first or equivalently has the minimum value of TT(J), which we previously defined to be SMIN.

The index I is then incremented by 1, indicating the arrival of a new unit into the system. A check is then made to determine whether M arrivals have been simulated. If I is equal to M, then the simulation has been completed, and the appropriate statistics, such as expected waiting time and idle time, are computed.

However, if I is less than M, a new arrival time is generated and added to the previous total arrival time. Then following Eqs. 5-69 through 5-74, we take the difference (DIF) between total arrival time for the system and total idle time plus service time for the Lth station, i.e., the first vacant station. Depending on whether this difference is negative, zero, or positive, waiting time and idle time are then computed according to the appropriate rule.

Finally a new service time is generated for the vacant station, and it is added to the updated total time for the Lth station in block 37. The procedure of searching for a vacant station, generating a new arrival time, checking for waiting time or idle time, and generating a new service time is then repeated until a total of M units have arrived.

An analytical solution has been developed for a special case of this model. If we have n service stations, Poisson arrivals with expected arrival rate λ, and exponential service times with expected service rate μ, then the following formulas can be derived for given values of λ, μ, and n [61, pp. 137–138]:

$$\frac{\lambda\mu(\lambda/\mu)^n P_0}{(n-1)!(n\mu-\lambda)^2} = \text{expected queue length,} \tag{5-75}$$

$$\frac{\lambda\mu(\lambda/\mu)^n P_0}{(n-1)!(n\mu-\lambda)^2} + \frac{\lambda}{\mu} = \text{expected number of units in the system,} \tag{5-76}$$

$$\frac{\mu(\lambda/\mu)^n P_0}{(n-1)!(n\mu-\lambda)^2} = \text{expected waiting time of an arrival,} \tag{5-77}$$

$$\frac{\mu(\lambda/\mu)^n P_0}{(n-1)!(n\mu-\lambda)^2} + \frac{1}{\mu} = \text{expected time an arrival spends in the system,} \tag{5-78}$$

where

$$P_0 = \text{the probability that there are no units in the system at a particular time} \tag{5-79}$$

$$= \frac{1}{\left[\sum_{k=0}^{n-1} (1/k!)(\lambda/\mu)^k\right] + (1/n!)(\lambda/\mu)^n n\mu/(n\mu-\lambda)}.$$

Simulated values of these statistics can be compared with the theoretical values to provide a check on the validity of our computer model.*

INVENTORY SYSTEMS

A second general classification of industrial systems for which computer simulation has been found to be a useful analytical tool is the area known as inventory systems. Since our objective in this chapter is to present a collection of computer models taken from a number of different applications, we shall make no attempt to treat the subjects of inventory control and inventory system analysis exhaustively in this section. Instead we have elected to formulate only one model of a particular inventory system. Hopefully, the system chosen for illustrative purposes contains a representative sample of some of the

* Michael E. Brenner has developed a special technique for this type of comparison in an article entitled, "Selective Sampling—A Technique for Reducing Sample Size in Simulation of Decision-Making Problems," *Journal of Industrial Engineering*, **XIV** (1963), 291–296.

more important elements usually found in inventory systems. The reader who is not particularly well versed in the terminology of inventory theory may wish to consult one or more of the following references on inventory theory [6, 11, 20, 29, 31, 33, 46, 47, 50, 51, 61]. These references may also suggest numerous other inventory systems that lend themselves to analysis by computer simulation.

For the most part, inventory problems are concerned with the determination or order quantities and reorder points. How much should the firm produce (or order) and how often should the firm produce (or reorder) so as to minimize the sum of the following costs?

1. Carrying costs.
2. Set-up costs.
3. Shortage costs.

Consider an inventory system in which daily demand (expressed in production days) and production lead time (in days) are both stochastic variates with known probability distributions. The inventory level is reduced each day by the total demand for that day. When the inventory level becomes less than or equal to the reorder point (ROP), then a production order is issued for an "optimum" order quantity (EOQ). When a production order is filled, the number of units of the product ordered are added to the inventory stock.

Our inventory system can be described by the following variables and functional relationships.

EXOGENOUS VARIABLES

D_i = daily demand (in production days) for the ith day,
    $i = 1, 2, \ldots .$ (5-80)
PLT_j = production lead time (in days) for the jth order,
    $j = 1, 2, \ldots .$ (5-81)

PARAMETERS

C1 = carrying cost per unit per unit time. (5-82)
C2 = set-up cost per order. (5-83)
C3 = shortage cost per unit per unit time. (5-84)
 K = a constant such that the probability of "stocking out"
    is α. (5-85)
BI = beginning inventory level. (5-86)
TT = total time period of the simulation run. (5-87)

STATUS VARIABLES

CLOCK = clock time. (5-88)
    T = time at which production order will be filled. (5-89)
    VI = inventory level. (5-90)

AD = average daily demand (in production days) calculated as a moving average for the preceding M days.   (5-91)

ALT = average lead time calculated as a moving average
of the previous N orders.   (5-92)

SDD = standard deviation of demand calculated as a
moving average for the preceding M days.   (5-93)

EOQ = economic order quantity.   (5-94)

ROP = reorder point.   (5-95)

ENDOGENOUS VARIABLES

TC1 = total carrying cost.   (5-96)

TC2 = total set-up cost.   (5-97)

TC3 = total shortage cost.   (5-98)

OPERATING CHARACTERISTICS

f(D) = the probability density function for demand.   (5-99)

f(PLT) = the probability density function for lead time.   (5-100)

IDENTITIES

$$AD = \frac{\sum_{i=1}^{M} D_i}{M} = \frac{SUMD}{M}. \qquad (5\text{-}101)$$

$$ALT = \frac{\sum_{j=1}^{N} PLT_j}{N} = \frac{SPLT}{N}. \qquad (5\text{-}102)$$

$$SDD = \sqrt{\frac{\sum_{i=1}^{M} D_i^2}{M} - \left(\frac{\sum_{i=1}^{M} D_i}{M}\right)^2}. \qquad (5\text{-}103)$$

$$EOQ = \sqrt{\frac{2 \cdot AD \cdot C2}{C1}} \cdot \sqrt{\frac{C1 + C3}{C3}}. \qquad (5\text{-}104)$$

$$ROP = ALT \cdot AD + K \sqrt{ALT \cdot SDD}. \qquad (5\text{-}105)$$

Once we have defined all of the variables and functional relationships in our mathematical model, the formulation of a flow chart for
the model follows a completely straightforward process. We begin in
Figure 5-8 by reading into the computer C1, C2, C3, K, BI, TT, and
the parameters describing the probability density functions of D and
PLT. Then we set TC1, TC2, TC3, CLOCK, and T equal to zero.
Next M values of D and N values of PLT are generated for the purpose of computing starting values for our two moving averages AD

and ALT. The inventory level is then set equal to the beginning level, and a daily demand D is generated by a subroutine. The total demand used to compute the moving average of demand is then updated, and the CLOCK is incremented by one unit of time (one day). Average lead time, average demand, the standard deviation of demand, the reorder point, and the economic order quantity are then calculated

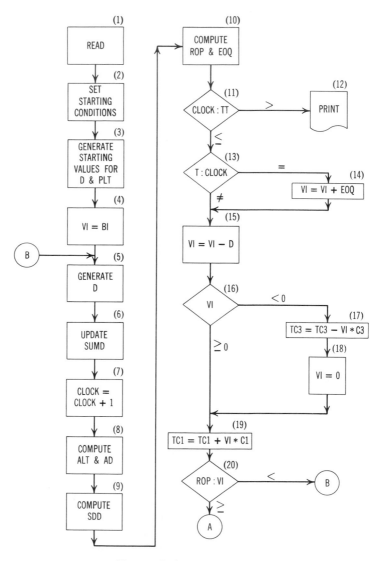

Figure 5-8. An inventory model.

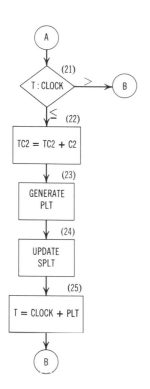

Figure 5-8. (continued)

in blocks 8 through 10. In block 11 a check is made to determine whether or not the computer run has been completed. If clock time is equal to TT, the total time period of the simulation run, then the run will be terminated and summary statistics will be tabulated and printed. If clock time does not equal TT, we check the clock to determine if sufficient time has elapsed for an outstanding production order to be filled. If sufficient time has elapsed, the inventory level is increased by an amount equal to EOQ, the optimum reorder quantity. If no order has been filled, the inventory is merely reduced by the amount of daily demand.

If the level of inventory becomes negative, a shortage occurs and a shortage cost is computed. When a shortage occurs the sale is assumed to be lost entirely. (This is just one of many possible assumptions we might make about the nature of shortages.) Hence, the inventory level must be reset to zero in block 18. Total carrying charges are then updated in block 19. If the level of inventory has not fallen to the reorder point level, then a new daily demand is generated in block 5, and the procedure is repeated. But if the inventory level is either less than or equal to the reorder point, we then proceed to block 21, where we check to see if there is an outstanding production order. If a production order remains unfilled then we return to block 5. On the other hand, if there is no outstanding unfilled order at this time, we place a production order in block 21 and update total set-up (order) costs. A lead time is then generated for the new order, and total lead time is updated for purposes of computing average lead time. The new lead time is then added to clock time indicating when the new order will be filled. We then proceed to block 5 and a new daily demand.

Among the parameters with which the analyst may wish to experiment are C1, C2, C3, K, and BI, as well as the probability distributions of lead time and daily demand. Changes can be made in any combination of these parameters or distributions, and the effects can be observed on total inventory cost, thus giving the analyst a wide range over which to experiment with the system. Examples of more complex inventory system simulations can be found in [3, 18, 46, 48, 51].

PRODUCTION SYSTEMS

The term "production scheduling" has been used to describe a wide variety of industrial problems involving decisions on the allocation of manufacturing resources at each instant of time during a given planning period.

Industrial scheduling problems differ greatly from one firm to another. Sometimes the manufacturing process consists of a series of operations at one work station on only one physical part; sometimes operations require very different labor skills and equipment on each of many thousands of subassemblies. Sometimes inventories of finished goods must be maintained to satisfy customer demands; sometimes such inventories are impossible to keep under all conceivable circumstances. Unique features of the firm's organization, of the market, of plant capabilities are always present [48, p. ix].

Among the more important factors in analyzing production scheduling problems are included the availability of resources (machines, raw materials, and manpower), process times, machine breakdowns, due dates, and demand fluctuations. Any solution to a production scheduling problem necessarily involves a compromise in satisfying the following objectives.

1. To complete all orders on time.
2. To minimize the sum of capital investment expenditures, operating costs, and in-process inventory charges.
3. To achieve an even distribution of workloads among all production facilities and a smooth (as opposed to a fluctuating) production rate.

Production scheduling problems can conveniently be partitioned into three phases: loading, scheduling, and dispatching [58, pp. 103–104].

Loading involves the comparison of demand (measured in production hours) with the capacity of the factory at a given time period. If demand exceeds capacity for a given time period, then standard operating rules cannot be applied to production scheduling. In these cases the firm can either reject the excess demand (that is, not produce or adjust its capacity by working overtime), subcontracting orders to other firms, or extending delivery schedules.

Scheduling involves assigning production orders to specific time periods. That is, specific orders or jobs are assigned to particular days according to one or more scheduling priority rules. Among the possible scheduling rules that the firm's decision makers might use are the following ones.

1. First-come, first-served.
2. First-come, first served within priority classes.
3. Sequential rule.
4. Minimum imminent processing time.
5. Maximum imminent processing time.
6. Earliest start date [58, p. 118].

The dispatching phase of production scheduling is concerned with the assignment of each order to specific machines or groups of machines at specific times within a given time period. For the multiproduct, multiprocess firm the dispatching phase of production scheduling is indeed the most complicated phase. Poor dispatching may lead to extensive waiting times for orders to be processed on particular machines, idle time and excess capacity on other machines, and a failure to meet due dates on some orders.

A special subset of scheduling problems known as the "job shop" problem has been the subject of numerous simulation studies since the early days of computer simulation [34]. The job shop problem, in its simplest form consists of the random arrival of jobs requiring work to be done in some given sequence by a set of processing facilities. The process times associated with each facility are different and usually assumed to be random variables. Associated with each job is a routing defined on a subset of facilities. The objective is to assign jobs to facilities over time in a manner consistent with the goals of the organization.

The underlying theoretical structure of job shop production systems is basically a queueing model with two or more sequential servers. The usual performance measures of queues such as state probabilities, waiting times, and facility utilization are all relevant to job shops. Typically, job shop simulations are concerned with experiments with various queue disciplines and priority rules as means of optimizing some performance index [2, 12, 13, 16, 41, 58]. The simple model described in the following section contains some of the elements of the job shop problem. This model is followed by a machine breakdown model.

A Job Shop Model

Consider a manufacturing facility for the production of a product consisting of three components. These components are produced in three separate processes, each of which is characterized by stochastic process times. The time interval between the arrival of orders at the manufacturing facility is a random variable. When an order arrives at the production facility, process times are generated for each of the three processes. When all three components are completed for a particular order, the product is assembled from the three components, and the production facility becomes "free" to receive another order. However, a new order cannot be accepted until all three components of the previous order are completed and all three processes are vacant. Otherwise, new orders are placed in a waiting line until the production facility is vacated.

A variable time increment simulation model is formulated here to simulate the arrival of orders at the facility and the production of the components of each order. Statistics are accumulated for the idle time of each of the three processes as well as the waiting time of production orders. We begin by specifying the variables and functional relationships of our model.

EXOGENOUS VARIABLES

AT_i = the time interval between the arrival of the ith order and the $(i + 1)$th order, $i = 1, 2, \ldots, m$. $\qquad$ (5-106)

ST_{ij} = the process time for the ith order at the jth process, $i = 1, 2, \ldots, m$ and $j = 1, 2, 3$. $\qquad$ (5-107)

STATUS VARIABLES

IDT_{ij} = the amount of time that the jth process remains idle while waiting for the ith order to arrive, $i = 1, 2, \ldots, m$ and $j = 1, 2, 3$. $\qquad$ (5-108)

$TIDT_{ij}$ = total idle time of the jth process when the ith order arrives at the jth process, $i = 1, 2, \ldots, m$ and $j = 1, 2, 3$. $\qquad$ (5-109)

DT_i = idle time when all three processes are idle and waiting for the arrival of the ith order, $i = 1, 2, \ldots, m$. $\qquad$ (5-110)

TDT_i = total idle time when all three processes are idle and waiting for the arrival of the ith order, $i = 1, 2, \ldots, m$. $\qquad$ (5-111)

WT_i = the amount of time that the ith order spends waiting to enter the production system, $i = 1, 2, \ldots, m$. $\qquad$ (5-112)

TWT_i = total waiting time when the ith order enters the production system, $i = 1, 2, \ldots, m$. (5-113)

TST = total time for the system. (5-114)

$SUMAT_i$ = total arrival time when the $(i + 1)$th order arrives at the system, $i = 1, 2, \ldots, m$. (5-115)

ENDOGENOUS VARIABLES

$E(WT)$ = expected waiting time. (5-116)

$E(IDT_j)$ = expected idle time of the jth process, $j = 1, 2, 3$. (5-117)

OPERATING CHARACTERISTICS

$f(AT)$ = the probability density function for the time interval between the arrival of orders. (5-118)

$f(ST_j)$ = the probability density function of the process time for the jth process, $j = 1, 2, 3$. (5-119)

IDENTITIES

$$E(WT) = \frac{TWT_m}{m}.$$ (5-120)

$$E(IDT_j) = \frac{TIDT_{mj}}{m}.$$ (5-121)

The flow chart in Figure 5-9 begins with the usual initialization routine. That is TIDT1, TIDT2, TIDT3, TDT, TWT, TST, SUMAT, and I are all set equal to zero in block 1. Then, M, the number of orders to be simulated, and the parameters describing the probability distributions of arrival time and process time are read into the computer.

Next we generate three process times, determine the maximum process time and add it to total time. This is followed by increasing the order-number index by one and checking to see if M orders have been generated. If M orders have been generated, the simulation run is terminated, and the final statistics are recorded. However, if we have not yet simulated the arrival of M orders, then total idle times are computed for each process.

A new arrival time is generated in block 14 and added to total arrival time. If the difference between total arrival time and total time is positive, then idle time has occurred at all three processes simultaneously due to the delay in the arrival of the next order. If, however, the difference between total arrival time and total time is less than or equal to zero, waiting time occurs. In either case, after updating the appropriate records, a new set of process times is generated, and the whole procedure is then repeated.

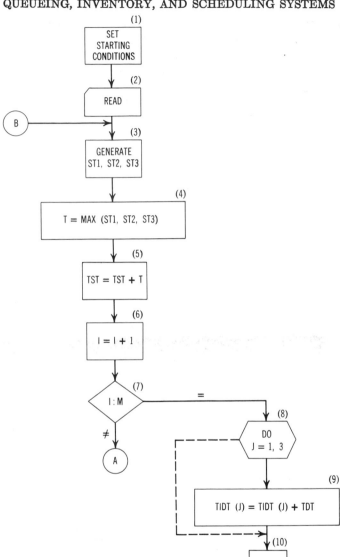

Figure 5-9. A job shop model.

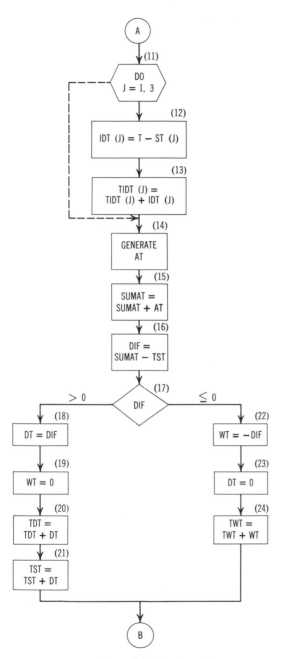

Figure 5-9. (continued)

A Machine Breakdown Model

In this model we consider N machines whose running times, that is, time intervals between breakdowns, are random variables. These machines are assumed to be maintained by M men. The time required to service the machines is also a random variable.

When a machine breaks down it is either serviced immediately or must remain idle until one of the repairmen is free to service it. Otherwise, the machines are assumed to run continuously.

In defining the variables for this model we have adopted conventional FORTRAN notation for representing subscripts on variables, since the interpretation placed on the subscripts of this model is somewhat different from that of the preceding models in this chapter.

EXOGENOUS VARIABLES

$RT(J)$ = running time (before a breakdown) for machine J,
where J = 1, 2, . . . , N.   (5-122)

$ST(J)$ = service time interval for machine J, where J = 1,
2, . . . , N.   (5-123)

PARAMETERS

N = the number of machines.   (5-124)

M = the number of maintenance men.   (5-125)

NB = the total number of machine breakdowns in the simu-
lation run.   (5-126)

STATUS VARIABLES

T = total time.   (5-127)

L = the number of machines down and under repair.   (5-128)

I = the number of machines down and waiting to be
repaired.   (5-129)

K = the number of idle repairmen.   (5-130)

$X(J)$ = 0, if machine J is in operation, where J = 1, 2,
. . . , N.   (5-131)

= 1, if machine J is down, where J = 1, 2, . . . , N.

$T(J)$ = total time for machine J, where J = 1, 2, . . . , N.   (5-132)

ENDOGENOUS VARIABLES

$DTR(L)$ = the total time period in which L machines are
down and under repair, L = 0, 1, 2, . . . , N.   (5-133)

$DTW(I)$ = the total time period in which I machines are
down and waiting to be repaired, I = 0, 1, 2,
. . . , N.   (5-134)

$RIT(K)$ = the total time period in which K repairmen are
idle, K = 0, 1, 2, . . . , M.   (5-135)

OPERATING CHARACTERISTICS

$f(RT(J))$ = the probability density function for running time (before a breakdown) for machine J, where J = 1, 2, . . . , N.   (5-136)

$f(ST(J))$ = the probability density function for the service time interval for machine J, where J = 1, 2, . . . , N.   (5-137)

IDENTITIES

The starting conditions for this model are given by the following values.

$$T = 0 \tag{5-138}$$
$$L = 0 \tag{5-139}$$
$$I = 0 \tag{5-140}$$
$$K = M \tag{5-141}$$
$$X(1) = 0, \ldots, X(N) = 0 \tag{5-142}$$
$$DTR(0) = 0, \ldots, DTR(N) = 0 \tag{5-143}$$
$$DTW(0) = 0, \ldots, DTW(N) = 0 \tag{5-144}$$
$$RIT(0) = 0, \ldots, RIT(M) = 0 \tag{5-145}$$

In Figure 5-10, the flow chart for the model, we begin by reading into the memory of the computer M, N, NB, and the expected value and variance for the running time and service time for each machine. Next the starting conditions defined by Eqs. 5-138 through 5-145 are set.

In blocks 3 through 5 a set of initial running times are generated for each of the N machines, and the total time record for each machine is then updated. In blocks 7 and 8 we determine which machine has the shortest running time and set this time equal to TMIN. The index JM is used to indicate which machine has the minimum running time. Next the difference

$$D = TMIN - T \tag{5-146}$$

is computed and added to DTR(L), DTW(I), and RIT(K) for the particular values of L, I, and K at that moment in time. In block 11 total time is set equal to TMIN.

If machine JM, that is, the machine with the minimum running time, is in operation, the dummy variable X(JM) is set equal to one, indicating that machine JM is now down. A service time is then generated for machine JM and added to total time for that machine. The index L indicating the number of machines down and under repair is then incremented by one. If there is a repairman available, the number of repairmen available is reduced by one. If there are no idle repairmen, the number of machines down and waiting to be repaired is increased by one.

If, on the other hand, in block 12, machine JM is found to be down, the procedure in blocks 17 through 25 or 26 must be followed. When

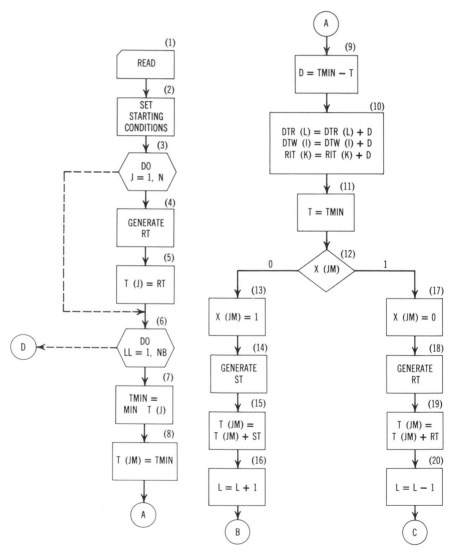

Figure 5-10. A machine breakdown model.

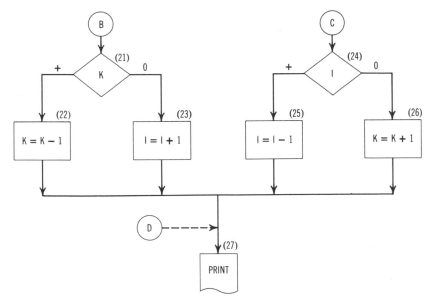

Figure 5-10. (continued)

a total of NB breakdowns have been simulated, the procedure is terminated with a print-out of the results.

A PRODUCTION-INVENTORY SYSTEM

In the preceding models we have treated inventory systems, production systems, and maintenance systems as though they were completely independent of each other. Yet in actual industrial situations we know that these problems are interrelated. Hence, there is a need to combine several of our models of specific components of industrial systems into an integrated simulation model of the firm.

Although the mechanics of integrating one or more of the models found in this chapter are not particularly difficult, the amount of space required to fully explain such a procedure cannot be justified in a book of this nature. However, for a complete discussion of the modular approach to simulating industrial systems the reader should see Jay Forrester's *Industrial Dynamics* [22].

For our purposes it will be sufficient merely to outline some of the procedures for integrating our production scheduling models and inventory control models, since these two functions can be combined rather easily.

In a production-inventory simulation for a typical firm we begin by simulating the arrival rate of the customers and the quantity of each of the firm's products demanded by each customer. Then the system by which the firm satisfies these demands in accordance with

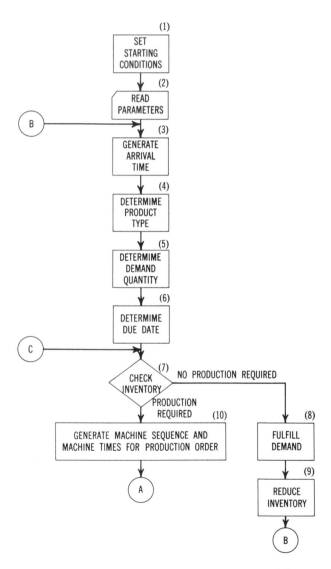

Figure 5-11. A production-inventory model.

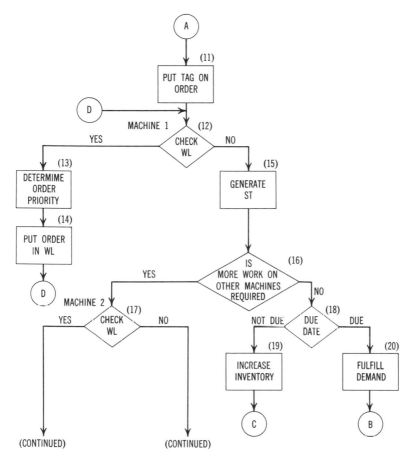

Figure 5-11. (continued)

some set of predetermined objectives would be simulated. Demand may either be satisfied by existing levels of inventory or by the issuance of production orders when the size of an order exceeds available inventory levels. Certain one-of-a-kind orders may always require special production orders, since the firm would not carry such items in its inventory of finished goods.

For each production order that is issued, a series of problems will arise. (1) When should these orders be issued and in what quantities? (2) Which rule or rules should be used for scheduling these orders? (3) How large should the labor force be? (4) How much capital equipment is required? (5) When should raw materials be purchased and in what quantities? (6) In what sequence should the capital equipment be arranged? (7) How many repairmen should be hired?

Figure 5-11 contains a flow chart describing some of the important components of a production-inventory simulation model. However, we have not attempted to describe a particular system or a complete system but merely to point out some of the elements in such a system. The simulation approach used in this integrated model is similar to that used in previous models. Subroutines are again assumed to be available for generating stochastic variates. For example, when an order is generated, its arrival time, the type of product, the quantity demanded, and the due date are simulated by the appropriate subroutines. The procedure for producing a particular order is determined by the type of product. Each product type triggers a subroutine determining the required machines, machine times, and machine sequence for that particular product. The order is then "tagged" according to the particular scheduling rule programmed for the simulation run. The remainder of the simulation consists of generating the flow of the system and the collection of statistics such as waiting time, idle time, total processing time, and total cost.

Exercises

5-1   Using the fixed time increment flow chart for a single station waiting line model (Figure 5-1) write a FORTRAN program for generating the behavior of the system when both arrival time and service time are exponentially distributed with expected values equal to 10 and 3, respectively. Simulate the system for a period of 2000 time units, i.e., until "clock" time is equal to 2000. Compute the expected value and variance of idle time, waiting time, and total time spent in the system. Compare these values with their known theoretical values.

5-2   Repeat Exercise 5-1 for the case in which the probability distributions for arrival time and service are approximated by the following probability density functions:

$f(\text{AT})$	AT	$f(\text{ST})$	ST
0.05	1	0.20	1
0.10	2	0.35	2
0.20	3	0.27	3
0.00	4	0.18	4
0.50	5		
0.15	6		

5-3   Repeat Exercise 5-1 using the variable time increment flow chart
      (Figure 5-2). Compare the results of this simulation run with
      the results obtained using the fixed time increment method in
      Exercise 5-1 on the basis of the statistical precision of the
      estimates of the expected value and variance of idle time,
      waiting time, and total time. Compare these two methods on the
      basis of computer time required to simulate 2000 units of "clock"
      time.

5-4   The number of orders X (where an order is defined as 1000
      yards of finished cloth) received each day by a cotton textile
      mill has the following probability distribution:

P(X)	X
0.30	100
0.25	200
0.20	300
0.15	400
0.05	500
0.05	600

To transform raw cotton into a completed order, a four-stage
process is required. The four stages of production are spinning,
weaving, finishing, and packaging. The process time required to
spin a sufficient amount of yarn to produce 1000 yards of finished
cloth has an exponential distribution with expected value equal
to 3 minutes. The process time required to weave 1000 yards of
cloth has an exponential distribution with expected value equal
to 6 minutes. The process time required to finish 1000 yards of
cloth is exponentially distributed with expected value equal to
8 minutes, and the packaging time for an order is also exponentially distributed with expected value equal to 1 minute. The firm
operates three shifts per day, seven days a week.

   Formulate a computer simulation model of the cotton textile
mill's production system. Simulate 30 days of production experience for the firm. What is the maximum number of orders
the firm can complete during this 30-day period? Suppose that it
is possible to acquire some high-speed looms that will reduce the
expected weaving time from 6 minutes to 4 minutes. What effect
will the new looms have on the total number of orders which can
be processed in 30 days?

5-5   A newsboy buys papers for 4¢ each and sells them for 10¢ each.
      At the end of each day the newspaper publisher will pay him 2¢

each for his unsold papers. Daily demand (D) for papers has the following probability distribution:

P(D)	D
0.08	75
0.07	80
0.02	85
0.20	90
0.09	95
0.19	100
0.12	105
0.03	110
0.14	115
0.06	120

Use computer simulation to determine the optimum number of papers for the newsboy to order each day.

5-6   The length of life of 100 vacuum tubes contained in a digital computer is normally distributed with expected value equal to 6 months and standard deviation equal to 2 weeks. If all of the tubes are replaced at one time the cost of replacing them is $2 per tube. The cost of replacing individual tubes that fail in service is $5 per tube plus the cost of computer downtime. On the average, the cost per tube for downtime is $50 during the day and $100 at night. The probability of a failure during the day is 0.7, and the probability of a failure at night is 0.3. Use computer simulation to compare the cost of the following two policies: (1) Replace the tubes individually as they fail, and (2) replace all 100 tubes every five months and replace the tubes that fail during the interim period individually. Determine an optimum replacement policy for the firm.

5-7   A gas station opens each morning at 7:00 A.M. and closes at 7:00 P.M. Gas station attendants are normally paid $30 for a 12-hour day. Cars arrive at the gas station for service in a Poisson fashion at an expected rate of 10 cars per hour. The service time per car is exponentially distributed with expected service time equal to 5 minutes. When the number of cars waiting for service exceeds three, arrivals angrily depart without waiting for service. Use computer simulation to determine the optimum number of gas station attendants to hire if the expected revenue per car serviced is $2.

5-8   Manufacturing a certain type of product consists of three basic steps. The time required to complete the first step is exactly 10

minutes, the time required to complete the second step is exponentially distributed with mean equal to 8 minutes, and the
time required to complete the third step is normally distributed
with mean equal to 5 minutes and variance equal to 4 minutes.
Use computer simulation to estimate the expected time to produce the product.

5-9   Customers at a supermarket arrive at the checkout counters
in a Poisson fashion at an average rate of 20 customers per
hour. The checkout time per customer is exponentially distributed with expected value equal to 10 minutes. If the store's
policy is such that it will permit a customer to wait on the
average at most 5 minutes at a checkout counter, use computer
simulation techniques to estimate the required number of
checkout counters. Also estimate the expected waiting time of
the customers and the expected idle time for each checkout
counter.

5-10 The following is a tabulation of demand experience for a
particular product produced by a manufacturing firm based
on last years' performance.

Units Demanded per Day	Frequency (in Days)
1000	10
1500	50
2000	25
2500	49
3000	85
3500	73
4000	37
4500	31

Production lead time, that is, the time required to produce
an order, had the following frequency distribution last year.

Number of Days to Produce an Order	Number of Orders
1	5
2	18
3	26
4	33
5	7
6	10

The set-up per order is $100, and the carrying charge is 5¢ per unit per day. The cost of a shortage is $185 per unit per day. On the basis of last year's operating experience use computer simulation to compute a minimum cost reorder point and a minimum cost order quantity.

5-11   Develop a computer flow chart for simulating a waiting line system consisting of M parallel channels each consisting of a series of N processes.

5-12   Formulate a FORTRAN program for simulating the inventory system described by the flow chart in Figure 5-8. Assume that both daily demand and production lead time are normally distributed with given expected values and variances. Design a simulation experiment for testing the effects of changes in C1, C2, C3, K, M, N, and the expected value and variance of daily demand and production lead time on total inventory cost (TC1 + TC2 + TC3).

5-13   Write a FORTRAN program for simulating the behavior of the system described in Figure 5-9. Assume particular probability distributions (either theoretical or empirical) for arrival times and process times.

5-14   Write a FORTRAN program for simulating the behavior of the machine shop described by the machine breakdown model in Figure 5-10.

5-15   The production-distribution system for textile mill products typically follows a pattern similar to the flow chart found in Figure 5-12. Assume that we are concerned with the production-distribution system for a particular textile consumer product, for example, men's shirts of a given size, style, and color.

When the consumer goes into a retail store and asks for some specified number of shirts, the clerk in the store will simply remove that number of shirts from the retail store's present stock and exchange them with the consumer for cash (or credit). As long as the retail store has sufficient inventory to cover the consumer's order, the time required to process such an order is assumed to be negligible. (This is indicated by the zero in the delay circle for the retail store stage of the textile production-distribution system in Figure 5-12.) The retail store is assumed to use a fixed reorder point system for replenishing its inventory of shirts. That is, whenever the level of inventory drops below the reorder point (ROP), the retail store will order an economic order quantity (EOG) of shirts from the cutter.

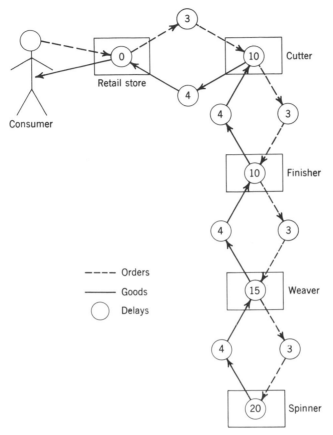

Figure 5-12. A production-distribution system for textile mill products.

However, it usually takes 3 days' mailing time for an order from the retail store to reach the cutter. (This is indicated by the 3 in the order delay circle on the broken line connecting the retail store and the cutter in Figure 5-12.) If the cutter has sufficient finished cloth on hand to produce enough shirts to satisfy the retail store's order, it will take 10 days to make up the order. (This is indicated by the 10 in the delay circle for the cutting stage in Figure 5-12.) Furthermore, it takes 4 days for the goods produced by the cutter to reach the retail stores because of shipping delays.

The cutter also operates on a fixed ROP system and reorders an EOQ of finished cloth from the finisher whenever his inventory of finished cloth falls below the ROP. The finisher and the weaver also have fixed ROP's and EOQ's. The spinner is assumed to carry an inventory of raw cotton that is sufficient to prevent the possibility of not being able to satisfy the weaver's demands, that is, it will never take the spinner any longer than 20 days to process an order from the weaver.

Design a computer simulation experiment for testing the effects of various delay, ROP, and EOQ patterns on orders and inventories for each of the stages in the textile mill production-distribution system for some particular product.

REFERENCES AND BIBLIOGRAPHY

1. Allen, Morton. "The Efficient Utilization of Labor under Conditions of Fluctuating Demand," *Industrial Scheduling*. Edited by John F. Muth and Gerald L. Thompson. Englewood Cliffs, N.J.: Prentice-Hall, 1963.
2. Baker, C. T., and Dzielinski, B. P. "Simulation of a Simplified Job Shop," *Management Science*, VI (1960), 311–323.
3. Balintfy, Joseph L. "On a Class of Multi-Item Inventory Problems," *Management Science*, X (Jan. 1964), 787–797.
4. Baumol, William J. *Economic Theory and Operations Analysis*. Englewood Cliffs, N.J.: Prentice-Hall, 1961.
5. Blake, K., and Gordon, G. "Systems Simulation with Digital Computers," *IBM Systems Journal*, III, No. 1 (1964), 14–20.
6. Bowman, Edward H., and Fetter, Robert B. *Analysis for Production Management*. Homewood, Illinois: Richard D. Irwin, 1961.
7. Brown, R. G. *Statistical Forecasting for Inventory Control*. New York: McGraw-Hill Book Co., 1959.
8. Brown, R. G. *Smoothing, Forecasting and Prediction of Discrete Time Series*. Englewood Cliffs, N.J.: Prentice-Hall, 1963.
9. Chu, Kong, and Naylor, Thomas H. "Two Alternative Methods for Simulating Waiting Line Models," *Journal of Industrial Engineering*, (Nov.–Dec. 1965).
10. Chu, Kong, and Naylor, Thomas H. "A Dynamic Model of the Firm," *Management Science*, XI (May 1965), 736–750.
11. Churchman, C. West, Ackoff, Russell L., and Arnoff, E. Leonard. *Introduction to Operations Research*. New York: John Wiley and Sons, 1957.
12. Conway, R. W. An Experimental Investigation of Priority Dispatching," *Journal of Industrial Engineers*, XI (1960), 221–230.
13. Conway, R. W. *An Experimental Investigation of Priority Assignment in a Job Shop*, The RAND Corporation, RM-3789-PR (Feb. 1964).
14. Conway, R. W., Johnson, B. M., and Maxwell, W. L. "A Queue Network Simulator for the Burroughs 220," *Communications of the Association for Computing Machinery*, II (1959), 20–23.
15. Conway, R. W., Johnson, B. M., and Maxwell, W. L., "Some Problems of Digital Systems Simulation," *Management Science* (October 1959).

16. Conway, R. W., and Maxwell, W. L. "Network Scheduling by the Shortest-Operation Discipline," *Industrial Scheduling*. Edited by John F. Muth and Gerald L. Thompson. Englewood Cliffs, N.J.: Prentice-Hall, 1963.
17. Doyle, V. *General Electric Simulation Test* (Gest). General Electric Technical Information Series No. D591S15, Schenectady, N.Y. (Feb. 1959).
18. Dzielinski, B. P., and Manne, A. S., "Simulation of a Hypothetical Multi-Item Production and Inventory System," *Journal of Industrial Engineering*, XII (1961), 417–421.
19. Eilson, S. "Economic Batch-Size Determination for Multi-Product Scheduling," *Operational Research Quarterly*, IX (Dec. 1958) 217–227.
20. Fetter, Robert B., and Dalleck, Winston C. *Decision Models for Inventory Management*. Homewood, Ill.: Richard D. Irwin, Inc. 1961.
21. Fischer, H., and Thompson, G. L. "Probabilistic Learning Combinations of Local Job-Shop Scheduling Rules," *Industrial Scheduling*. Edited by John F. Muth and Gerald L. Thompson. Englewood Cliffs, N.J.: Prentice-Hall, 1963.
22. Forrester, Jay. *Industrial Dynamics*. Cambridge: The M.I.T. Press, 1961.
23. *General Purpose Systems Simulator*, Program Library, Reference 7090-CS-05x, International Business Machines Corporation.
24. *General Purpose Simulator II*, Program Library, Reference 7090-CS-13x, International Business Machines Corporation.
25. Giffler, B. "Mathematical Solution of Production Planning and Scheduling Problems," IBM ASDD Technical Report (Oct. 1960).
26. Giffler, B. *SIMPRO I: An IBM 704-7090 Simulation Program for Planning Scheduling and Monitoring Production Systems*, IBM ASDD Technical Report (Dec. 1961).
27. Gordon, G. "A General Purpose Systems Simulator," *IBM Systems Journal*, I (1962).
28. Gross, Donald, and Ray, Jack. "A General Purpose Forecast Simulator," *Management Science*, XI (April 1965), 119–135.
29. Hadley, G., and Whitin, T. M. *Analysis of Inventory Systems*. Englewood Cliffs: Prentice-Hall, 1963.
30. Hall, R. L. and Hitch, C. J. "Price Theory and Business Behavior," *Oxford University Papers*, II (May 1939), 12–45.
31. Hanssmann, F. *Operations Research in Production and Inventory Control*. New York: John Wiley and Sons, 1962.
32. Hicks, J. R. *Value and Capital*. Oxford: Clarendon Press, 1939.
33. Holt, C. C., Modigliani, F., Muth, J. F., and Simon, H. A. *Planning Production, Inventories and Work Force*. Englewood Cliffs, N.J.: Prentice-Hall, 1960.
34. Jackson, James R. "Simulation Research on Job Shop Production," *Naval Research Logistics Quarterly* IV (Dec. 1957).
35. Jackson, James R. "Machine Shop Simulation Using SWAC: A Progress Report," Management Sciences Research Project, Discussion Paper No. 67, University of California, Los Angeles (April 1958).
36. Jackson, James R. "Simulation of Queues with Dynamic Priorities," Management Sciences Research Project, Research Report No. 71, University of California, Los Angeles, March 20, 1961.
37. Jackson, James R. "Queues with Dynamic Priority Discipline," *Industrial Scheduling*. Edited by John F. Muth and Gerald L. Thompson. Englewood Cliffs, N.J.: Prentice-Hall, 1963.

38. *The Job Simulator: An IBM 704 Program,* IBM Mathematics and Applications Department, International Business Machines Corporation, New York (1960).
39. Kelley, D. H., and Buxton, J. N. "Montecode—An Interpretive Program for Monte-Carlo Simulations," *The Computer Journal,* V (1962).
40. Kiviat, Philip J. "GASP-A General Activity Simulation Program," Project No. 90. 17-019 (2), Applied Research Laboratory, United States Steel, Monroeville, Pennsylvania, July 8, 1963.
41. Kurantani, Yoshiro, and Nelson, R. T. "A Pre-Computational Report on Job-Shop Simulation Research, Management Sciences Research Project, University of California, Los Angeles (Oct. 1959).
42. Lester, R. A. "Shortcomings of Marginal Analysis for Wage-Employment Problems," *American Economic Review,* XXXVI (March 1946).
43. Malcolm, D. G. *Report of System Simulation Symposium.* Baltimore, Md.: Waverly Press, 1957.
44. Markowitz, H. M., Hausner, Bernard, and Karr, H. W. *SIMSCRIPT: A Simulation Programming Language,* The RAND Corporation, RM-3310 (Nov. 1962).
45. Mauer, William A., and Naylor, Thomas H. "Monopolistic-Monopsonistic Competition: The Multi-Product, Multi-Factor Firm," *The Southern Economic Journal,* XXXI (July 1964).
46. Miller, D. W., and Starr, Martin K. *Inventory Control: Theory and Practice.* Englewood Cliffs, N.J.: Prentice-Hall, 1962.
47. Morse, Phillip M. *Queues, Inventories, and Maintenance.* New York: John Wiley and Sons, 1958.
48. Muth, John F., and Thompson, Gerald L. editors. *Industrial Scheduling.* Englewood Cliffs, N.J.: Prentice-Hall, 1963.
49. Muth, John F. "The Effect of Uncertainty in Job Times on Optimal Schedules," *Industrial Scheduling.* Edited by John F. Muth and Gerald L. Thompson. Englewood Cliffs, N.J.: Prentice-Hall, 1963.
50. Naddor, E. "A Comparison of (t, Z) and (z, Z) Policies," *Operations Research* X (1962), 401–403.
51. Naddor, E. "Markov Chains and Simulations in an Inventory System," *Journal of Industrial Engineering,* XIV (1963), 91–98.
52. Naddor, E. and Saltzman, S. "Optimal Reorder Periods for an Inventory System with Variable Costs of Ordering," *Operations Research,* VI, No. 5 (1958), 670–685.
53. Orcutt, Guy H. "Views on Simulation and Models of Social Systems," in *Symposium on Simulation Models.* Edited by Austin C. Hoggatt and Frederick E. Balderston. Cincinnati: South-Western Publishing Co., 1963.
54. Palm, C. "The Distribution of Repairmen in Servicing Automatic Machines," *Industritidningen,* LXXV (1947).
55. Phipps, T. E., Jr. "Machine Repair as a Waiting-Line Problem," *Operations Research,* IV (1956), 76–85.
56. *The Production Simulator.* Westinghouse Corporation, East Pittsburgh, Pa. (July 1960).
57. Pugh, Alexander L. *DYNAMO User's Manual.* Cambridge, Mass.: The M.I.T. Press, 1963.
58. Rowe, Alan, J. "Toward a Theory of Scheduling," *Contributions to Scientific Research in Management.* The Proceedings of the Scientific Program

following the Dedication of the Western Data Processing Center, Graduate School of Business Administration, Univ. of Calif., Los Angeles, Jan. 29–30, 1959.

59. Saaty, T. *Elements of Queueing Theory*. New York: McGraw-Hill Book Co., 1961.

60. Sandeman, J. "Empirical Design of Priority Waiting Times for Jobbing Shop Control," *Operations Research*, IX (1961), 446–455.

61. Sasieni, Maurice, Yaspin, Arthur, and Friedman, Lawrence. *Operations Research*. New York: John Wiley and Sons, 1959.

62. *SIMPAC User's Manual*. TM 602/000/00, Systems Development Corporation, Santa Monica, California, April 15, 1962.

63. Thompson, G. L. "Recent Developments in the Job Shop Scheduling Problem," *Naval Research Logistics Quarterly*, VII (1960), 585–589.

64. Tocher, K. D., and Owen, D. G. "The Automatic Programming of Simulations," *Proceedings of the Second International Conference on Operational Research* (1960).

Chapter 6 | Simulation of Economic Systems

This book is concerned primarily with the development of computer simulation methods for use in analyzing and solving problems in business administration and economics. To the extent that business administration can be considered as a subset of economics, it can be argued that this is a book on economics. Although all the applications of simulation in this book are in one sense economic applications of simulation techniques, in this chapter the term "economics" has a more specific meaning. Rather than treating economics as an all encompassing discipline of which business administration is an important subset, it is limited to an interpretation that is widely accepted among economists, namely, Samuelson's definition of economics.

Economics is the study of how men and society choose, with or without the use of money, to employ scarce productive resources to produce various commodities over time and distribute them for consumption, now and in the future, among various people and groups in society [57, p. 5].

In other words, this chapter is written primarily with economists in mind.

Such being the case, it is appropriate to use the language of economists, economic theory, as a vehicle of analysis. Economic theory not unlike other theories, consists of three basic elements—definitions, assumptions, and conclusions. As an example of the use of theory in economics we might consider the classical theory known as the "theory of the firm." *If* we define such terms as price, profit, factor, product, production function, etc., in the usual manner and *if* we postulate a multiproduct, multifactor competitive firm whose objective is to maximize profit subject to the technical constraints imposed by a production function characterized by (1) a decreasing marginal rate of technical substitution between any two factors, (2) a decreasing marginal product for all factor-product combinations, and (3) an increasing marginal rate of product transformation between any two products, *then* it follows logically that the firm will behave in such a manner that (1) the price ratio of any two products will be equal to their rate of technical substitution, (2) the price of each factor will be equal to the marginal revenue product of each product, and (3) the price ratio of any two products will be equal to their rate of product transformation. The tautological nature of this statement is self-evident; the conclusions follow directly from the definitions and assumptions.

Economic theory usually assumes one of three alternative forms—verbal, graphical, or mathematical. The literature on methodology in economics is rich in arguments, both pro and con, concerning the relative merits of each of these forms of logic. For example, the nonmathematical economists contend that mathematical economics requires too high a degree of simplification and abstraction. "It is claimed that the degree of generality achieved and the violence done to observation restricts its usefulness to a point of very limited returns" [60, p. 72]. On the other hand, the mathematical economists reply that

Economic facts are extraordinarily complicated so that . . . mathematics is to be expected to be the most efficient way of delving into them. To maximize the relation of theory to fact, to minimize the simplification away from reality, it is usually safer to operate in mathematical terms. An economist who ventures to set up a theoretical model of empirical content is well advised to do so in explicit mathematical form. He risks failure if he does not; or, at least, he is liable to overlook some cases or possibilities which may be important, and to make empirical testing of his model more difficult [3, p. xvii].

However, there are indeed two major shortcomings of mathematical economics that are quite apparent to practitioners. First, most economic problems are so complex that techniques do not exist for solving them, or if solution techniques do exist they may very well exceed the capabilities of our present-day computers. Models used to develop theories of the business cycle and market behavior both give rise to difficulties of this type. Since the 1930's economists have relied on solutions to differential and difference equations as the standard analytical technique for investigating the behavior of business cycles. But as nonlinearities were introduced into these models and higher order equation systems were considered, solutions by straightforward analytical techniques became increasingly difficult, if not impossible, to handle. Under these circumstances, business cycle economists have almost been forced to turn to computer simulation as an alternative technique of numerical analysis. Computer simulation permits the analysis of much larger and much more complex economic systems than do the standard mathematical techniques.

The second major shortcoming of mathematical economics stems from the fact that "mathematical economics may lack a richness of descriptive power" [60, p. 73]. For example, the mathematical notation required to handle such entities as, "the quantity of the ith product produced by the jth firm for shipment to the kth customer via the lth shipping terminal," soon becomes quite unwieldly [60, p. 73].

Yet in spite of its major shortcomings mathematical economics is capable of achieving a much higher degree of precision than either verbal or graphical economic models. However, for many problems in economics, neither verbal, graphical, nor mathematical models are entirely satisfactory as tools of analysis. We are convinced that the analysis of most of the more complex dynamic problems in economics, which frequently involve stochastic elements also, calls for a united effort of all three forms of economic analysis (verbal, graphical, and mathematical) in conjunction with the high-speed computer. That is, rather than limiting ourselves to only one language (for example, mathematics), we may very well require as many as five languages to achieve an optimal form of analysis. For example, we would always begin with a verbal description of the economic system under consideration. The verbal description could then be translated into a set of mathematical models, which would in turn provide the basis for a flow chart from which a computer code could be written in a special language, such as FORTRAN, ALGOL, DYNAMO, SIMULATE, etc., and then be translated by the computer into actual machine language [61, p. 914].

Directly related to the problem of choosing a mode of analysis within the framework of theoretical economics is the problem of testing and experimenting with alternative economic theories. Since economic theory, whether expressed in the form of verbal, graphical, or mathematical models, is merely a species of logical deduction, which has been clothed in "economic garb," any particular economic theory must be tested empirically before it can be said that the theory "proves" anything about the real world in which we live [13, p. 115]. As has been often stated by both logicians and philosophers, it is simply not possible to "prove" the validity of a particular axiom, theorem, corollary, etc., on purely a priori grounds.

The value of deduction is grounded in its emptiness. For the very reason that the deduction does not add anything to the premises, it may always be applied without a risk of leading to a failure. More precisely speaking, the conclusion is no less reliable than the premises. It is the logical function of deduction to transfer truth from given statements to other statements—but that is all it can do. It cannot establish synthetic truth unless another synthetic truth is already known [55, pp. 37–38].

Or stated even more strongly,

It cannot be overemphasized that logical deduction cannot create independent results. It is merely an instrument of connection; it derives conclusions from given axioms, but cannot inform us about the truth of the axioms [55, p. 57].

As is the case with any nonlaboratory science (for example, sociology, psychology, and political science), controlled experimentation and testing are very difficult in the study of economic phenomena. Rarely is it possible to observe cases in the real world in which an independent and a dependent variable can be analyzed under *ceteris paribus* conditions. For example, it would be very difficult to find a situation in which we could observe the effects of changes in price on the quantity demanded by consumers while holding consumers' tastes, income, etc., constant. However, with the advent of the computer, the possibilities for experimenting with and testing alternative hypotheses regarding the behavior of economic systems have been extended considerably. The principal advantage of using computer simulation as a tool of economic analysis is to provide not only a procedure for formulating alternative economic theories but also testing these theories. All too frequently accusations that economic models are unrealistic are well founded because the addition of realism to an economic model usually results in a corresponding increase in the degree of complexity of the model.

Computer models, however, can be made as complex and realistic as our theories permit, for analytical solutions to these models are unnecessary. No matter how complicated the formulation of the model, simulation techniques enable us to trace out the consequences of the model. Hence, economic theories can be cast into a precise model without distortion of the meaning embodied in the theories, and the descriptions of the world implied by these theories can be determined [12, p. 82].

However, in no sense does this imply that simulation models will completely replace the more traditional verbal, graphical, and mathematical models of economists, but it does imply that economists will no longer be limited to just these models.

Since prior to the acquiescence of simulation models in economics, a subset of economic models known as "econometric models" has provided the "least ambiguous descriptions of the economic world" [12, p. 8], it is appropriate that we compare simulation models with econometric models and point out their differences and similarities. In comparing simulation models with traditional econometric models, we shall rely heavily on the work of Cohen [12, pp. 8–9] [13, pp. 118–119] because he was among the first writers to clearly differentiate between these two forms of analysis.

In an econometric model we view the economic system as describable by a set of simultaneous equations expressing all the interrelationships among the measurable economic magnitudes which guide economic behavior. The variables in this set of equations are classified into two main types, endogenous and exogenous. The endogenous variables are those variables which are determined within the system of economic forces in a narrow sense . . . The exogenous variables are those which represent forces outside the confines of the economic system [44, p. 2].

Econometric models are usually interpreted as "one-period-change" models.

Any lagged values of the endogenous variables are, in effect, treated as exogenous variables. They are assumed to be predetermined by outside forces rather than by earlier applications of the mechanisms specified in the model. Hence, the output of econometric models is the determination of the values of the endogenous variables for a given time period. To determine these values for the next period, new values would have to be assigned to the lagged endogenous variables. For this reason, most econometric models should be regarded as determining the changes which take place in the world from one period to another [13, pp. 118–119].

Computer simulation models of economic systems or "process models" [12, p. 13] differ from traditional econometric models primarily in the treatment of lagged endogenous variables. "The equations of the model, together with the observed time paths of the exogenous variables, are treated as a closed dynamic system; each period, the values of the predetermined endogenous variables are the values generated by the model, not the known or actually observed values" [12, p. 13]. The computer is used to trace out the time paths of each endogenous variable over extended periods of time in sharp contrast to the single-period time paths of econometric models.

In the one-period-change model, it is assumed that each period any errors resulting from the "determination" of last period's endogenous variables are corrected, so that there is a tendency for the one-period-change model to be kept on course by the fact that it always has a correct starting place. The process model on the other hand, is forced to live with any errors that may have been made by the model, in "determining" the values of the endogenous variables in previous periods; there is no automatic resetting of the error terms to assure a correct jumping off place for each period [12, p. 13].

Cohen and Cyert [13, p. 118] have described two alternative approaches for simulating economic systems—"synthesis" and "analysis." The choice between these alternatives depends entirely on the type of information that is available and the kinds of questions that are being raised about the system.

If considerable information is available concerning the operating characteristics of the components of the system and if one is interested in observing or predicting the behavior of the total system, then the "synthesis" approach will be the preferred alternative. That is, we may be able to specify with a high degree of accuracy the operating characteristics of the components of the system, but the mathematics involved may be so intricate that mathematics alone can provide little or no assistance in determining the behavior of the over-all system. In situations of this type, computer simulation may prove to be an effective means of generating time paths of variables describing the total system. Actually, the problems discussed in Chapter 5 come closer to satisfying these requirements than do the economic systems investigated in this chapter. In fact, this approach is the generally accepted methodology of operations research and management science.

On the other hand, in social sciences we often find that the situation is completely reversed. For example, in economics it is easy enough to observe the behavior of the total system as measured by Gross National Product, National Income, or per capita income for the economy as a whole or total profits, total cost or total physical output for a firm or industry.

The problem is to derive a set of component relations which will lead to a total system exhibiting the observed characteristics of behavior. The usual procedure is to construct a model which specifies the behavior of the components, and then to analyze the model to determine whether or not the behavior of the model corresponds with the observed behavior of the total system [13, p. 118].

Again, computer simulation may be the only practicable method for generating the time paths of the endogenous variables of the system if the model is overly complex because of the large number of variables in it or the nature of the functional relationships describing the operating characteristics.

In this chapter we have decided to classify simulation models of economic systems on the basis of whether they apply to a firm or industry or to the economy as a whole. In each case we describe what we consider to be a representative sample of models of each type, that is, models of the firm and industry and models of the economy. In a survey book of this type, it is impossible to include detailed descriptions of large-scale simulation models; that is, our examples are necessarily limited to simplified special cases of more complex models. It is felt, however, that the procedures outlined for analyzing the small-scale models can easily be extended to the larger models. Although we do not include detailed descriptions of any of the existing large-scale simulation models, we do include brief summaries of some of the characteristics of the more important and more complex simulation models that have been developed in recent years.

SIMULATION MODELS OF THE FIRM AND INDUSTRY

Introduction

Four simulation models of the firm and the industry are investigated in this section. Equations are specified in detail for each model, and flow charts are also included. The models are presented in order of increasing difficulty. We begin by formulating computer simulations for several variations of the "classical" cobweb model. The cobweb model is then followed by a relatively simple model of a competitive industry and a classical duopoly model. Finally, we consider a type of model known in the field of business administration as a "management game." This "game" is a simulation of a three-firm industry in which firms are required to make decisions each time period concerning price and expenditures for marketing, production, research and development, and plant improvement. Immediately following these models is a brief and somewhat more general description of several well-known, large-scale models of the firm and industry. Among these are included the models of Balderston and Hoggatt [5], Bonini [8], Cohen [12], Cyert and March [18], and Forrester [26].

Cobweb Models

A classical example of economic dynamics is a type of model known as the "cobweb model." Although there are many variations of this familiar model, all have certain basic characteristics. Typically the quantity demanded of a particular product (usually assumed to be an agricultural product) in a specified time period depends on the

price (and other factors) in that time period. The quantity supplied
is assumed to depend on the price in the preceding time period. And,
finally, the market is assumed to be cleared at the end of each period
[25, 58]. We shall consider three separate variations of the cobweb
model—a stochastic model, a learning model, and a model with stocks.

Cobweb Model 1

The variables, operating characteristics, and market clearing condition for the stochastic model are given as follows.

EXOGENOUS VARIABLES

U_T = a stochastic variate with a known probability distribution, expected value equal to zero, and variance VU.   (6-1)

V_T = a stochastic variate with a known probability distribution, expected value equal to zero, and variance VV.   (6-2)

W_T = a stochastic variate with a known probability distribution, expected value equal to zero, and variance VW.   (6-3)

ENDOGENOUS VARIABLES

$$P_T = \text{price in period T.} \tag{6-4}$$

$$D_T = \text{quantity demanded in period T.} \tag{6-5}$$

$$S_T = \text{quantity supplied in period T.} \tag{6-6}$$

OPERATING CHARACTERISTICS

$$D_T = A - BP_T + U_T. \tag{6-7}$$

$$S_T = C + DP_{T-1} + V_T. \tag{6-8}$$

MARKET CLEARING CONDITION

$$S_T = D_T + W_T. \tag{6-9}$$

(The constants A, B, C, and D are assumed to have been estimated
by standard estimating techniques, such as ordinary least squares.)

The operating characteristics for this model can be interpreted as
follows. The quantity supplied in period T is a linear function of the
price in period T-1 and a stochastic variate V_T. The stochastic
variate, which has a known probability distribution, is assumed to
represent the net effect on the supply quantity in period T of weather
conditions, technology, production efficiency, etc., in period T. The
supply quantity in period T is assumed to be cleared subject to random fluctuations in the stochastic error term W_T. Price in period T
is a linear function of the quantity demanded in period T and a
stochastic variate U_T. This stochastic variate is assumed to reflect

changes in consumers' tastes and income as well as any other random element that might affect the price in period T.

By substituting the values of D_T and S_T in Eqs. 6-7 and 6-8 into Eq. 6-9 and solving for P_T, we obtain,

$$P_T = 1/B(A - C - DP_{T-1} + U_T + W_T - V_T) \qquad (6\text{-}10)$$

Then for a given initial price P_0 and known probability distributions for U_T, V_T, and W_T with variances VU, VV, and VW, respectively, we can generate time paths for P_T, S_T and D_T. These time paths can then be compared with actual time series data to determine the "goodness of fit" of the model. A flow chart for generating the time paths for Model 1 appears in Figure 6-1.

Since negative prices are not defined in economics, it will usually be necessary to include a sign test in computer programs for simulating prices in a market economy. For example, if P_T as generated by Eq. 6-10 in Figure 6-1 is found to be negative, it could automatically be set equal to zero. Although sign tests are usually necessary,

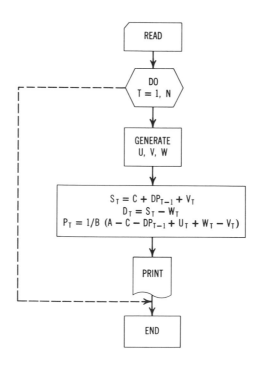

Figure 6-1. Flow chart for Cobweb Model 1.

we have elected to conserve space and not include them in any of the flow charts in this chapter.

It may be of interest to the reader to compare the time path of P_T generated by Model 1 with the well-known theoretical results for the static version of this model, that is, when U_T, V_T, and W_T are assumed to be equal to zero. Under complete certainty the time path of P_T is completely determined by the magnitude of the constants D and B according to the following formula given by Eq. 6-11 [3, p. 5]. Whether P_T oscillates in a manner that is explosive, regular, or damped depends entirely on D and B.

(1) If $D > B$, then oscillations of P_T are explosive.
(2) If $D = B$, then oscillations of P_T are regular.   (6-11)
(3) If $D < B$, then oscillations of P_T are damped.

As might be expected, by introducing uncertainty into the model, the time paths of P_T, S_T, and D_T are altered considerably by comparison to their certainty equivalents.

Cobweb Model 2

Model 1 was based on the implicit assumption that suppliers never learn. In each period the supplier behaved in a manner consistent with the expectation that the price of the previous period would continue in the next period. Yet this expectation was continuously disappointed each period. In this model we alter Model 1 only slightly. We now assume that the supplier is capable of learning or that the expected price of the supplier is $P_{T-1} - \rho \Delta P_{T-2}$, where

$$\Delta P_{T-2} = P_{T-1} - P_{T-2} \qquad (6-12)$$

and ρ is a constant $(0 \leq \rho \leq 1)$, indicating the importance the supplier attaches to the tendency of price movements to be reversed (or continued) [3, pp. 13–14]. Equation 6-9 therefore becomes

$$S_T = C + D(P_{T-1} - \rho \Delta P_{T-2}) + V_T. \qquad (6-13)$$

Since all of the other assumptions of Model 1 are assumed to hold, the procedure for generating time paths for P_T, S_T, and D_T differs only slightly from that of Model 1 and will not be repeated.

Cobweb Model 3

In Models 1 and 2 price was set to clear supply, implying that either there was no inventory on hand (for example, a perishable good) or that inventory was maintained at a constant level. In this

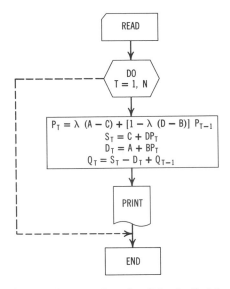

Figure 6-2. Flow chart for Cobweb Model 3.

model we introduce a third group of individuals called "merchants," whose function is distinguished from that of buyers and suppliers. Merchants can hold inventory and make sales. As a matter of notational convenience, we assume complete certainty in this model. We let

$$Q_T = \text{the level of inventory at the end of period T,} \qquad (6\text{-}14)$$

and

$$\Delta Q_T = Q_T - Q_{T-1} = S_T - D_T. \qquad (6\text{-}15)$$

The merchants are assumed to set the price in period T according to the rule that the price is set higher if inventories in the previous period fall and the amount of increase is proportional to the decrease in inventory [3, pp. 15–16]. That is,

$$P_T = P_{T-1} - \lambda \Delta Q_{T-1}, \qquad (6\text{-}16)$$

where λ is a positive constant. The supply and demand functions are expressed as

$$S_T = C + DP_T, \qquad (6\text{-}17)$$

$$D_T = A + BP_T. \qquad (6\text{-}18)$$

But since

$$\Delta Q_{T-1} = Q_{T-1} - Q_{T-2}$$
$$= S_{T-1} - D_{T-1}$$
$$= (C - A) + (D - B)P_{T-1}, \tag{6-19}$$

then by substitution

$$P_T = P_{T-1} - \lambda(C - A) - \lambda(D - B)P_{T-1}$$
$$= \lambda(A - C) + [1 - \lambda(D - B)]P_{T-1}. \tag{6-20}$$

The procedure for generating the time paths of P_T, S_T, D_T, and Q_T would follow a straightforward process. (See Figure 6-2.) Once we specify starting values for P_0 and Q_0, then P_T, S_T, D_T, and Q_T are completely determined for any value of T (T = 1, . . . , N).

A Model of a Competitive Industry

This model provides us with an example of a simulation of a three-firm competitive industry in which each firm must decide each period how much it is going to produce and sell. That is, the output the firm produces each period is considered as a controllable exogenous variable. The output decision for each firm is made by the individual firms themselves rather than by some mathematical decision rule that has been programmed into the computer. This is in contrast to the cobweb models in which output decisions were controlled entirely by mathematical formulas based on particular behavioral assumptions as to how firms or industries make their output decisions. Variables that are subject to human control of this type are said to be "instrumental" or "decision" variables. This model is essentially a variation of a small-scale experimental business game developed by Austin C. Hoggatt [34]. The variables, operating characteristics, and identities for this model are outlined below.

DECISION VARIABLE

X_{iT} = the quantity produced and sold by the ith firm in the
    Tth period, $i = 1, 2, 3$. $\tag{6-21}$

EXOGENOUS VARIABLES

U_{iT} = a stochastic variate with a given expected value, variance and probability distribution. $\tag{6-22}$

V_T = a stochastic variate with a given expected value, variance, and probability distribution. $\tag{6-23}$

A_i = a scale parameter for the ith firm, i = 1, 2, 3.   (6-24)

B = a technological parameter.   (6-25)

C = a technological parameter.   (6-26)

D, E, F, G = constants.   (6-27)

ENDOGENOUS VARIABLES

S_T = quantity supplied by the entire industry in period T.   (6-28)

D_T = quantity of the industry's output demanded in period T.   (6-29)

P_T = industry price in period T.   (6-30)

C_{iT} = total cost of production of the ith firm in the Tth period.   (6-31)

Π_{iT} = total profit of the ith firm in period T.   (6-32)

OPERATING CHARACTERISTICS

$$C_{iT} = (X_{iT} - A_i)^2 + BA_i{}^2 + C + U_{iT}.$$ (6-33)

$$P_T = D - ED_T - FD_{T-1} - GD_{T-2} + V_T.$$ (6-34)

IDENTITIES

$$S_T = \sum_{i=1}^{3} X_{iT}.$$ (6-35)

$$S_T = D_T.$$ (6-36)

$$\Pi_{iT} = P_T X_{iT} - C_{iT}.$$ (6-37)

In making its output decisions, each firm is assumed to have the following information available to it.

1. Each firm knows the coefficients of its own cost function (Eq. 6-33).

2. Each firm knows the functional form of the cost functions of other firms but not the coefficient values.

3. Each firm knows the demand function (Eq. 6-34) facing the industry and the values of its parameters.

4. Each firm knows the total industry output for the two previous periods.

5. Each firm knows the industry price of the previous period.

Since collusion is not permitted, the information available to each firm is strictly limited to the five items listed above. After each firm makes its output decision on the basis of the given information available, the outputs of the three firms are added together to obtain the total quantity supplied by the industry as indicated by Eq. 6-35. The market is forced into short-run equilibrium each period by the identity (Eq. 6-36). Once the quantity demanded D_T, is established by Eq. 6-36, then Eq. 6-34 (the industry demand function) yields P_T the market clearing price. The industry demand curve expresses price as a function of the quantity actually sold in periods T, T-1, and T-2, as well as a stochastic variate. Once the industry price is determined, total profit is computed for each firm according to Eq. 6-37. A firm's profit depends, therefore, on the industry price, the firm's output, the scale of the plant as measured by the parameter A_i, the present state of technology as measured by B and C, and the stochastic variate U_{iT}. (The values of B and C are the same for all three firms.)

A flow chart for this three-firm industry simulation can be found in

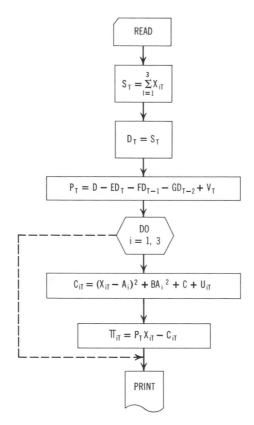

Figure 6-3. Flow chart of a three-firm competitive industry.

Figure 6-3. The data which must be read into the computer include X_{iT}, A_i, B, C, the mean and variance of U_{iT} and V_T, and the constants D, E, F, G.

This simulation can be easily extended to an N-firm industry. Experiments can also be performed on the birth and death of firms. That is, we might begin with, say, ten firms in the industry. In each period when at least one firm operates at a loss (that is, has negative profit), the firm that has the greatest loss is eliminated from the industry. In each period when at least one firm has a positive profit, then a new firm will enter the industry. This new firm enters the industry at an optimum scale (as measured by A_i) based on the assumption that the price in the previous period will continue in the future. Another way in which the model could be modified would be to use mathematical decision rules to determine each firm's output in a particular period. One possible rule might be stated as follows: each firm assumes that its competitors will not change their output in the following period. That is, each firm assumes that the only changes in output for the industry in the next period (over the previous period) will be attributed only to its changes (the particular firm's changes) in output and not that of its competitors. Each firm would then produce at the optimum level each period, based on its cost function and the industry demand function in which the output of the firm's competitors is held constant. Such a rule can easily be determined by applying simple differential calculus to Eq. 6-37. It is also possible to make interesting comparisions between the behavior of our simulated industry and that of industries whose behavior is based on classical duopoly and oligopoly models as well as industries in the real world.

A Duopoly Model

One of the most fertile fields for the application of computer simulation in economics is in the area of economic theory known as oligopoly theory. The theory of oligopoly, of which duopoly theory is a special case, is one of the oldest of all economic theories concerning competition and monopoly and the behavior of the individual firm. Although the theory of oligopoly began with the work of Cournot in 1838 [16] and Edgeworth in 1897 [24], its usefulness in economics has until quite recently been limited primarily to that of a pedagogical device rather than a theory that describes or predicts the behavior of firms in the real world. Before the advent of the computer, practical necessity dictated that theories of oligopoly and duopoly be based on rather strong (and frequently unrealistic) assumptions, since to do otherwise would lead to models of such a complex nature that they would be impossible to solve or interpret. Needless to say, there has not been a very high degree of correlation between the behavior of actual business firms and the behavior of the hypothetical firms described by the mathematical constructs of classical oligopoly and duopoly theory. However, with the arrival of the computer, the necessity of basing oligopoly and duopoly theories on assumptions that are completely incompatible with the real world no longer exists, as has been demonstrated by the recent work of Cyert, Feigenbaum, and March [17]. These workers, by using a set of highly detailed assumptions about the behavior of the decision processes of firms, and by specifying particular values for the parameters of their model, have achieved a relatively high degree of success in simulating some aspects of the behavior of the tin can industry from the time when Continental Can Company entered as a competitor to American Can Company.

To illustrate the applicability of computer simulation to oligopoly and duopoly theory, we have chosen to use a slightly modified version of Cournot's duopoly model as an example. Although the model is quite unrealistic and is based on a set of rather gross assumptions, it can be easily extended to include more detailed and more realistic assumptions. Several possible extensions of the model are suggested following the explanation of the model and the simulation procedure. Furthermore, our only purpose in restricting the model to the special case of duopoly is to conserve time and space in explaining the model. The model works equally well for any number of firms.

The following assumptions underlie our particular interpretation of the Cournot model.

1. The industry consists of two firms, A and B.
2. Both firms are profit maximizers.
3. Both firms decide in each time period how much they will produce during that time period. This is the only decision made by the firms.
4. The demand function for the industry as a whole is known by both firms.
5. The industry demand function is a linear function in which price is expressed as a function of total industry output plus a stochastic variate.
6. Firm A assumes that Firm B's output in period T will be the same as it was in period T — 1. Firm B assumes that Firm A's output in period T will be the same as it was in period T — 1.

7. The total output of Firm A and Firm B combined is sold each period at the market price, i.e., the price at which the market can absorb the entire industry output.

8. Unit costs are constant for both firms and equal.

9. The firms produce a perfectly homogeneous product, in no way differentiated.

10. There are no limitations on the production capacity of either firm.

The variables and functional relationships for our model are specified below.

EXOGENOUS VARIABLES

U_T = a stochastic variate with a given mean and variance and a known probability distribution. $\qquad$ (6-38)

PARAMETERS

$$C = \text{unit cost for Firm A and Firm B.} \qquad (6\text{-}39)$$

$$D \text{ and } E = \text{constants.} \qquad (6\text{-}40)$$

ENDOGENOUS VARIABLES

$$A_T = \text{output of Firm A in period T.} \qquad (6\text{-}41)$$

$$B_T = \text{output of Firm B in period T.} \qquad (6\text{-}42)$$

$$Q_T = \text{industry output in period T.} \qquad (6\text{-}43)$$

$$P_T = \text{industry price in period T.} \qquad (6\text{-}44)$$

$$\Pi A_T = \text{profit of Firm A in period T.} \qquad (6\text{-}45)$$

$$\Pi B_T = \text{profit of Firm B in period T.} \qquad (6\text{-}46)$$

OPERATING CHARACTERISTICS

$$P_T = D - EQ_T + U_T. \qquad (6\text{-}47)$$

$$A_T = \frac{D - EB_{T-1} + U_T - C}{2E}. \qquad (6\text{-}48)$$

$$B_T = \frac{D - EA_{T-1} + U_T - C}{2E}. \qquad (6\text{-}49)$$

IDENTITIES

$$Q_T = A_T + B_T. \qquad (6\text{-}50)$$

$$\Pi A_T = P_T A_T - CA_T. \qquad (6\text{-}51)$$

$$\Pi B_T = P_T B_T - CB_T. \qquad (6\text{-}52)$$

A word of explanation is in order concerning the derivation of Eqs. 6-48 and 6-49. Firm A's expected profit is given by the expression

$$\Pi A_T = P_T A_T - CA_T. \tag{6-53}$$

By substituting the value of P_T in Eq. 6-47 for P_T in Eq. 6-53, we obtain

$$\Pi A_T = (D - EQ_T + U_T)A_T - CA_T \tag{6-54}$$

or equivalently,

$$\Pi A_T = DA_T - EQ_T A_T + U_T A_T - CA_T. \tag{6-55}$$

But Firm A assumes that Firm B's output in period T will be equal to B_{T-1}. Therefore,

$$Q_T = A_T + B_{T-1} \tag{6-56}$$

represents Firm A's expectation concerning total industry output in period T. Substituting Eq. 6-56 into Eq. 6-55 we get,

$$\Pi A_T = DA_T - EA_T(A_T + B_{T-1}) + U_T A_T - CA_T. \tag{6-57}$$

Taking the first derivative of Eq. 6-57 with respect to A_T and setting it equal to zero, we obtain

$$\frac{d(\Pi A_T)}{dA_T} = D - 2EA_T - EB_{T-1} + U_T - C = 0. \tag{6-58}$$

And solving for A_T we arrive at Firm A's output decision,

$$A_T = \frac{D - EB_{T-1} + U_T - C}{2E}. \tag{6-59}$$

Firm B's output quantity Eq. 6-48 can be derived in a similar manner.

A flow chart for generating the time paths for this hypothetical industry over N time periods appears in Figure 6-4. Given the values of C, D, E, A_0, and B_0, as well as the parameters describing U_T, the simulation of the behavior of this industry follows a straightforward process. However, it may be necessary to insert a test for negative price into the flow chart for reasons stated previously in this chapter.

At the outset we indicated that the real source of power underlying simulation as a tool of analysis in the area of oligopoly and duopoly theory was the flexibility in assumptions that is possible with this approach. The oligopoly model developed by Cyert, Feigenbaum, and

March [17] is one of the most interesting recent extensions of classical oligopoly theory from the standpoint of the degree of detail incorporated into the assumptions underlying the model. Their model is considered by some economists as an indication of the direction in which research on the theory of oligopoly will take in the future. The assumptions of the Cyert, Feigenbaum, and March model [17] are summarized as follows:

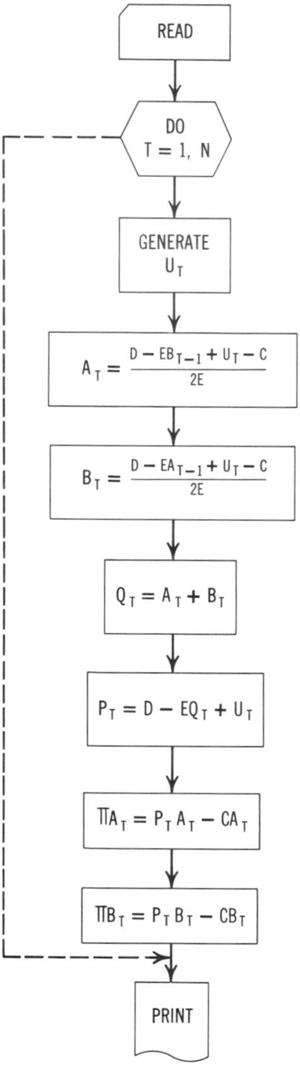

Figure 6-4. Flow chart for a duopoly model.

In rough outline, each firm is assumed to: (1) forecast the reactions of its competitor, (2) revise its estimate of the demand curve, (3) revise its estimates of its own curve, (4) specify its profit goal (on the basis of its profit achievement in the past), (5) evaluate the alternatives available to it. If no alternatives which meet its goal are available, the firm (6) searches for opportunities for cost reduction, (7) re-examines its estimates of demand, and (8) lowers its profit goal to a more modest level. Finally, the firm (9) sets its output for the coming period [11, p. 926].

In contrasting their model with classical oligopoly models Cyert, Feigenbaum, and March have stated that,

(1) The models are built on a description of the decision-making process . . . . (2) The models depend on a theory of search as well as a theory of choice. They specify under what conditions search will be intensified . . . . They also speicfy the direction in which search will be undertaken . . . . (3) The models describe organizations in which objectives change over time as a result of experience . . . . (4) Similarly, the models describe organizations that adjust forecasts on the basis of experience. Organizational learning occurs . . . . (5) The models introduce organizational biases in making estimates . . . . (6) The models all introduce features of organizational slack [17, pp. 93–94], [11, p. 926].

A Management Decision-Making Game

In Chapter 1 we defined the term "game" or "operational gaming" as a special type of simulation in which human participants act as decision-makers within the framework of the system being simulated. Although the concept of gaming originated many centuries ago in the form of military war games (used for training puposes), its use in business and economics only goes back to 1956 when the American Management Association developed the first so-called management decision-making game, called the Top Management Decision Game [7]. Since 1956 hundreds of management games have been developed by various universities, business firms, and research organizations, both for research purposes and for training persons in such diverse disciplines as management, business operation, economics, organization theory, psychology, production management, finance, accounting, and marketing. These games range in degree of complexity from the simple competitive game described earlier in this chapter to the extremely complex Carnegie Tech Management Game [14, 15, 20]. The degree of realism and the level of abstraction also vary considerably among the existing management games. However, most games involve decisions which would be made only by rather high level executives as opposed to operating employees.

Most business games are built around a hypothetical oligopolistic industry consisting of three to six firms, whose decision-makers or managers are the "players" of the game. At the outset of the game each firm or "team" is allocated a specified amount of resources in the form of cash, inventories, raw materials, plant and equipment, etc. Then before each operating period (usually assumed to be a quarter) the players make decisions concerning price, output, advertising, marketing, raw material acquisition, changes in plant capacity, wage rates, to mention only a few possibilities. This information is then read into a computer that has been programmed on the basis of a set of mathematical models that provide a link between the operating results of the individual firms (for example sales, profits, and levels of inventory) and the individual firms' operating decisions, as well as the external environment (the market). On the basis of (1) a set of operating characteristics, such as demand and cost functions, and a set of accounting formulas that have been programmed into the computer and (2) the individual decisions of each firm, operating results are generated by the computer in the form of printed reports, such as profit and loss statements, balance sheets, production reports, sales reports, and total industry reports at the end of each operating period. The environment can usually be changed by the administrator of the game by altering the parameters of the operating characteristics of the game. For example, it may be possible to change parameters that affect the rate of growth of the economy, the rate of taxation, the rate of depreciation of fixed assets, the industry wage rate, the prices of raw materials, and production lead time. In each case the firms find it necessary to react according to the magnitude and the nature of the change imposed by the external environment, i.e., by changing the parameters of the game. Some of the more complicated and more realistic games even permit multiple products, plants, and marketing areas, stochastic production periods, stochastic demand, labor negotiations, and the sale of common stock.

In this section a simplified version of a well-known management game, which has been widely used by colleges and universities and businessmen alike as a training tool—the International Business Machines Management Decision-Making Game [37]—will be outlined. Since we are merely attempting to survey several different types of applications of computer simulation in economics in this chapter, it is not possible to present a highly complex game within the confines of a few pages. Although this scaled-down version of the IBM Game is not nearly as realistic or as complicated as, for instance, the Carnegie Tech Management Game, it does contain most of the basic features of business games. Furthermore, after careful study of the description of this game, anyone who is knowledgeable in economic theory and standard accounting techniques should be able to design his own management game, incorporating whatever degree of realism is desired, subject to constraints imposed by computer technology and the analyst's knowledge of the mathematical forms and parameter estimates of the operating characteristics of the real world.

Our reduced form of the IBM Game consists of three firms producing a single homogeneous product for sale in a single marketing area. Each firm begins the period of play with equal endowments of cash, inventory, and plant capacity. The net worth of each firm is equal to the total assets of the firm since firms are not permitted to borrow money or incur debts in this game. At the beginning of each operating period, the three firms make separate decisions regarding:

1. Price.
2. Marketing expenditures.
3. Plant improvement expenditures.
4. Production expenditures.
5. Research and development expenditures.

However, the total expenditures of a firm in a particular period cannot exceed the amount of cash which it has available at the beginning of

Firm 1 Report

Sales Analysis

Orders	253
Sales	253
Unit price	$40
Sales revenue	$10,119
Marketing expenses	$600

Production

	Inventory	Plant Capacity	Current Production
Quantity	9	260	216
Unit cost	$35.49	$34.44	$35.49
Total cost	$304	$8,955	$7,650

Profit and Loss Statement

Total revenue		$10,119
Cost of goods sold	$8,881	
Marketing	$600	
Research and development	$100	
Depreciation	$104	
Total expenses		$9,685
Profit before taxes		$434
Taxes		$217
Net profit		$217

Cash Statement

Old balance		$8,500
Total revenue		$10,119
Production cost	$7,650	
Marketing	$600	
Research and development	$100	
Plant improvement	$104	
Taxes	$217	
Total outlay		$8,671
New cash balance		$9,948

Balance Sheet

Cash balance		$9,948
Current inventory		$304
Old plant	$5,200	
Depreciation	$104	
Plant improvement	$104	
New plant		$5,200
Total assets		$15,452
Net worth		$15,452

Figure 6-5. A sample firm report.

Industry Report

Firm 1 Balance Sheet

Cash	$ 9,948
Inventory	304
Plant	5,200
Total assets	$15,452

Firm 2 Balance Sheet

Cash	$ 9,948
Inventory	304
Plant	5,200
Total assets	$15,452

Firm 3 Balance Sheet

Cash	$ 9,948
Inventory	304
Plant	5,200
Total assets	$15,452

Total Market Survey

Total orders	759
Total sales	759
Total marketing expenditure	$ 1,800
Firm 1 price	$40
Firm 2 price	$40
Firm 3 price	$40

Figure 6-6. A sample industry report.

the period. The decisions are punched into cards and read into the computer, which processes the decisions according to the flow chart in Figure 6-7. The computer simulates the behavior of each firm and generates reports showing the operating results of the activity in the period. This cycle can be repeated for as many periods or quarters as are desired.

At the start of play each firm receives an identical set of reports—a confidential report and an industry report. Figures 6-5 and 6-6 contain sample copies of a confidential report and an industry report for the start of play. After each period of play the three firms receive a new set of confidential and industry reports. After the first period of play, the confidential reports are no longer identical for each firm because they depend entirely on the decisions made by the three firms in preceding periods, as well as any changes that have been made in the parameters of the operating characteristic functions by the administrator of the game. However, the industry reports are always identical for each firm in a particular period.

A total of 37 variables and more than 30 parameters are required to describe this game. The variables have been categorized as decision variables, status variables, and output variables and are specified below. We have not listed the parameters or specified their initial values because they are to a large extent arbitrary. The set of mathematical equations describing the behavior of this hypothetical industry consists of 15 operating characteristic functions and 18 accounting formulas. We shall not attempt to elaborate on the assumptions underlying the equations for the operating characteristics or discuss the accounting formulas. The operating characteristics are based on a set of fairly arbitrary assumptions about the real world, which are self-evident upon careful examination of the equations. The accounting formulas are based on standard accounting practices and are relatively easy to interpret.

DECISION VARIABLES

$$P_i = \text{Price of the } i\text{th firm.} \tag{6-60}$$

$$M_i = \text{Marketing expenditure of the } i\text{th firm.} \tag{6-61}$$

$$PI_i = \text{Plant improvement expenditure of the } i\text{th firm.} \tag{6-62}$$

$$PC_i = \text{Production expenditure of the } i\text{th firm.} \tag{6-63}$$

$$RD_i = \text{Research and development expenditure of the } i\text{th firm.} \tag{6-64}$$

STATUS VARIABLES

$$X = \text{Effect of research and development expenditures on total orders for the industry.} \tag{6-65}$$

$$Y = \text{Effect of marketing expenditures on total orders for the industry.} \tag{6-66}$$

$$Z = \text{Effect of price on total orders for the industry.} \tag{6-67}$$

$$EM_i = \text{Effective marketing expenditure of the } i\text{th firm.} \tag{6-68}$$

$$ERD_i = \text{Effective research and development expenditure of the } i\text{th firm.} \tag{6-69}$$

$$V_i = \text{Share of market of the } i\text{th firm.} \tag{6-70}$$

$$W_i = \text{Overall order-producing effect of decisions of the } i\text{th firm.} \tag{6-71}$$

S = Research and development factor. $\qquad$ (6-72)

V = Quantity factor. $\qquad$ (6-73)

F = Penalty factor for producing less than capacity. $\qquad$ (6-74)

OUTPUT VARIABLES

O_i = Number of orders received by the ith firm. $\qquad$ (6-75)

$SALES_i$ = Number of units actually sold by the ith firm. $\qquad$ (6-76)

$SREV_i$ = Sales revenue of the ith firm. $\qquad$ (6-77)

IQ_i = Quantity of inventory of the ith firm. $\qquad$ (6-78)

UIC_i = Unit cost of inventory of the ith firm. $\qquad$ (6-79)

IC_i = Total cost of inventory of the ith firm. $\qquad$ (6-80)

C_i = Production capacity (in units) of the ith firm. $\qquad$ (6-81)

UPC_i = Unit production costs of the ith firm. $\qquad$ (6-82)

PQ_i = Production quantity of the ith firm. $\qquad$ (6-83)

CGS_i = Cost of goods sold of the ith firm. $\qquad$ (6-84)

DEP_i = Depreciation charges of the ith firm. $\qquad$ (6-85)

TE_i = Total expenses of the ith firm. $\qquad$ (6-86)

PBT_i = Profit before taxes of the ith firm. $\qquad$ (6-87)

T_i = Taxes of the ith firm. $\qquad$ (6-88)

NP_i = Net profit of the ith firm. $\qquad$ (6-89)

$CASH_i$ = Cash balance of the ith firm. $\qquad$ (6-90)

TOL_i = Total outlay of the ith firm. $\qquad$ (6-91)

PV_i = Plant value of the ith firm. $\qquad$ (6-92)

TA_i = Total assets of the ith firm. $\qquad$ (6-93)

NW_i = Net worth of the ith firm. $\qquad$ (6-94)

TS = Total sales for the industry. $\qquad$ (6-95)

TM = Total marketing expenditures for the industry. $\qquad$ (6-96)

OPERATING CHARACTERISTICS

Total Orders

$$TO_T = rT_1X_TY_TZ_T. \qquad (6\text{-}97)$$

Marketing Effects

$$Y_T = b_1 - \frac{sT_3 b_2}{x_2 \sum_{i=1}^{3} EM_{i,T}} \qquad \text{if } \sum_{i=1}^{3} EM_{i,T} > 125{,}000$$

(6-98)

$$= \frac{\sum_{i=1}^{3} EM_{i,T}}{125{,}000} \qquad \text{if } \sum_{i=1}^{3} EM_{i,T} \leq 125{,}000.$$

$$EM_{i,T} = a_1 M_{i,T} + a_2 M_{i,T-1} + a_3 M_{i,T-2}.$$

(6-99)

Research and Development Effects

$$X_T = b_3 + \frac{\sum_{i=1}^{3} ERD_{i,T}}{b_4}.$$

(6-100)

$$ERD_{i,T} = gERD_{i,T-1} + RD_{i,T}.$$

(6-101)

Price Effects

$$Z_T = \frac{x_1 T_2}{P_{Min}}.$$

(6-102)

Market Share

$$O_{i,T} = V_{i,T} TO_T.$$

(6-103)

$$V_{i,T} = \frac{W_{i,T}}{\sum_{i=1}^{3} W_{i,T}}.$$

(6-104)

$$W_{i,T} = \left(\frac{EM_{i,T}}{\overline{EM}_T} - y_1 \right) \left(\frac{\overline{P}_T}{P_{i,T}} - y_2 \right) \left(c_1 + y_3 \frac{ERD_{i,T}}{SALES_{i,T-1}} \right).$$

(6-105)

Plant Capacity

$$C_{i,T} = \frac{0.98 PV_{i,T-2} + PI_{i,T-1}}{20}.$$

(6-106)

Production Quantity

$$PQ_{i,T} = \frac{(PC_{i,T}/T_4) - SK_2 - C_{i,T}K_3}{SK_1 - K_3}.$$

(6-107)

$$S = d_3 - \frac{Z_2 ERD_{i,T}}{d_4}.$$

(6-108)

Unit Production Cost

$$UPC_{i,T} = T_4(VS + F). \tag{6-109}$$

$$V = \left(d_1 + \frac{d_2}{PQ_{i,T}}\right) Z_1. \tag{6-110}$$

$$F = \left(\frac{C_{i,T} - PQ_{i,T}}{PQ_{i,T}}\right) K_3. \tag{6-111}$$

ACCOUNTING FORMULAS

Sales

$$\begin{aligned} SALES_{i,T} &= O_{i,T} && \text{if } O_{i,T} \leq PQ_{i,T} + IQ_{i,T-1} \\ &= PQ_{i,T} + IQ_{i,T-1} && \text{if } O_{i,T} > PQ_{i,T} + IQ_{i,T-1}. \end{aligned} \tag{6-112}$$

Sales Revenue

$$SREV_{i,T} = P_{i,T} \cdot SALES_{i,T}. \tag{6-113}$$

Inventory Quantity

$$IQ_{i,T} = PQ_{i,T} + IQ_{i,T-1} - SALES_{i,T}. \tag{6-114}$$

Inventory Cost

$$IC_{i,T} = [(PQ_{i,T} + IQ_{i,T-1}) - O_{i,T}]UPC_{i,T}, \tag{6-115}$$

when $IQ_{i,T-1} \leq O_{i,T} < (IQ_{i,T-1} + PQ_{i,T})$.

$$IC_{i,T} = [(IQ_{i,T-1} - O_{i,T})UIC_{i,T-1}] + PC_{i,T},$$

when $O_{i,T} < IQ_{i,T-1}$.

$$IC_{i,T} = O,$$

when $PQ_{i,T} + IQ_{i,T-1} < O_{i,T}$.

Unit Inventory Cost

$$UIC_{i,T} = \frac{IC_{i,T}}{IQ_{i,T}}. \tag{6-116}$$

Cost of Goods Sold

$$CGS_{i,T} = IC_{i,T-1} + (SALES_{i,T} - IQ_{i,T-1})UPC_{i,T}, \tag{6-117}$$

when $IQ_{i,T-1} \leq SALES_{i,T} < (IQ_{i,T-1} + PQ_{i,T})$.

$$CGS_{i,T} = SALES_{i,T} \cdot UIC_{i,T-1}$$

when $SALES_{i,T} < IQ_{i,T-1}$.

$$CGS_{i,T} = IC_{i,T-1} + PC_{i,T}$$

when $\text{SALES}_{i,T} = \text{IQ}_{i,T-1} + \text{PQ}_{i,T}$.

Depreciation

$$\text{DEP}_{i,T} = 0.02\text{PV}_{i,T-1}. \tag{6-118}$$

Total Expenses

$$\text{TE}_{i,T} = \text{CGS}_{i,T} + \text{M}_{i,T} + \text{RD}_{i,T} + \text{DEP}_{i,T}. \tag{6-119}$$

Profit Before Taxes

$$\text{PBT}_{i,T} = \text{SREV}_{i,T} - \text{TE}_{i,T}. \tag{6-120}$$

Taxes

$$\text{T}_{i,T} = 0.5\text{PBT}_{i,T}. \tag{6-121}$$

Net Profit

$$\text{NP}_{i,T} = \text{PBT}_{i,T} - \text{T}_{i,T}. \tag{6-122}$$

Total Outlay

$$\text{TOL}_{i,T} = \text{PC}_{i,T} + \text{M}_{i,T} + \text{RD}_{i,T} + \text{PI}_{i,T} + \text{T}_{i,T}. \tag{6-123}$$

Net Cash Balance

$$\text{CASH}_{i,T} = \text{CASH}_{i,T-1} + \text{SREV}_{i,T} - \text{TOL}_{i,T}. \tag{6-124}$$

Plant Value

$$\text{PV}_{i,T} = \text{PV}_{i,T-1} - \text{DEP}_{i,T} + \text{PI}_{i,T}. \tag{6-125}$$

Total Assets

$$\text{TA}_{i,T} = \text{CASH}_{i,T} + \text{IC}_{i,T} + \text{PV}_{i,T}. \tag{6-126}$$

$$\text{NW}_{i,T} = \text{TA}_{i,T}. \tag{6-127}$$

Industry Totals

$$\text{TS} = \sum_{i=1}^{3} \text{SALES}_{i}. \tag{6-128}$$

$$\text{TM} = \sum_{i=1}^{3} \text{M}_{i}. \tag{6-129}$$

Figure 6-7 shows a computer flow chart for our modified version of the IBM Game. The input data for this computer program consist of history cards and decision cards. The history cards contain the values of the lagged output and decision variables required by Eqs.

6-97 through 6-129. For the first period of play, a set of initial values must be specified and punched on cards that become the starting history deck. However, at the end of each computer run a new history deck is punched by the computer. This output deck then becomes part of the input data for the next period.

For the reader interested in developing his own business game, the

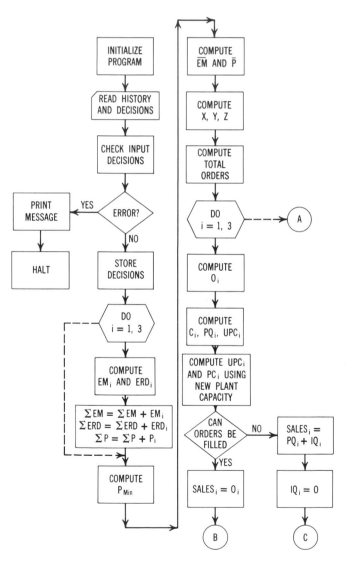

Figure 6-7. Flow chart for a management decision-making game.

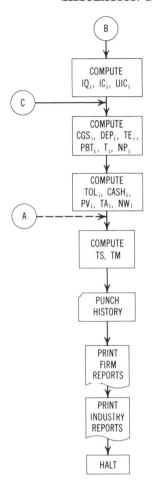

Figure 6-7. (continued)

following procedure may be helpful. Begin by writing a computer program for the game described in this section, using the flow chart in Figure 6-7 as a guide. Experiment with the game by observing the effect on operating results of various changes in the parameters of the operating characteristics. Finally, gradually, step by step, relax some of the assumptions of the model by making the appropriate changes in the operating characteristics and accounting formulas. By following this simple procedure it may be possible to develop a fairly realistic management game. Undoubtedly, those readers who elect to develop their own game will find the experience to be extremely rewarding, since one cannot possibly write a computer program for a business game without a clear understanding of the complex interactions involved in the operation of a business firm. Such an experience is highly recommended for students in business administration and economics who want to test their real knowledge of the behavior of business firms in a dynamic world.

Other Models of the Firm and Industry

For the most part the models presented in this chapter have been relatively simple, based on assumptions that are not entirely realistic. Although we have repeatedly pointed out that these models can easily be extended so as to include more complex and realistic assumptions, we have not provided any specific examples of these extensions. Hence, an objective of completeness requires that we at least mention a number of well-known large-scale simulation models of the firm and industry, which may serve to illustrate how the simple concepts outlined in this chapter can be extended. Several different studies involving the simulation of the behavior of the firm and industry on a digital computer will be summarized briefly in the following paragraphs. However, in each of these simulation studies primary emphasis is placed on the behavior of the firm or industry as a whole rather than on some particular decision-making component thereof. Because of the complexity of these studies it will not be possible to treat them in detail.

Balderston and Hoggatt

The joint work of Balderston and Hoggatt [5] is a simulation study of the United States' West Coast lumber industry and attempts "to show how limits on market information, decentralization of market decisions, and institutional alignments affect and are affected by economic forces" [6, 183]. This study grew out of the initial investigations by Balderston [4] of the communication networks in intermediate markets of the West Coast lumber industry and Hoggatt's doctoral dissertation, *Simulation of the Frm* [32], which employed simulation techniques to analyze several problems in microeconomic theory.

Three sets of participants were involved in this industry simulation—manufacturers, wholesalers, and retailers. The IBM 709 FORTRAN computer code for this simulation utilized six different classes of variables (of which there were 16,000) and functional relationships: economic, physical commodity flow, accounting and cash-flow, decision, information, and institutional. Manufacturers are assumed to sell to wholesalers who resell to customer firms who in turn sell to final consumers according to explicit decision rules concerning price and output. However, physical shipments go from the manufacturer directly to the retailer (bypassing the wholesaler) and from the retailer to the final consumers. Complete accounting records (balance sheet, cash flow, net revenue, etc.) are maintained for each firm in the industry. Manufacturers and retailers obtain information from wholesalers in the form of "messages" concerning possible transactions. Messages are a prerequisite for a transaction to take place and must be paid for by the manufacturers and the retailers. They are analogous to long-distance telephone calls and telegraph messages between manufacturers and wholesalers, and retailers and wholesalers concerning prices and commodity supplies. Decision-making is autonomous and completely decentralized among firms following a set of institutional decision rules for all transactions.

The principal value of this study lies not in its empirical accuracy in describing the behavior of the West Coast lumber industry but rather in the information it yields concerning the effects of changes in two key experimental parameters: "(1) the unit cost of sending a message . . . and (2) the choice of a method for setting the preference ordering by each firm on its potential partners in transactions"

[6, p. 187]. This type of information could not have been otherwise obtained, if at all, without copious and laborious computations. Although this study provides a valuable linkage between economics, sociology, and marketing, it possesses four features that are of primary interest to economists in particular.

(1) it represents a multi-stage rather than a single-stage market; (2) the firms constituting the market face uncertainty and operate with limited information; (3) transactions occur by means of sequences of steps that are reminiscent of the Walrasian "tatonnements" though not identical with them; and (4) the system is dynamic in the strict, technical sense that its path develops, period by period, as a consequence of the interactions that occur [5, p. 16].

Bonini

Another interesting simulation model was developed by Charles Bonini for his doctoral dissertation entitled "Simulation of Information and Decision Systems in the Firm" [8]. This simulation model of a hypothetical business firm differs from the other models discussed in this chapter in that it represents a synthesis of some of the important theory from a number of disciplines, among which are economics, accounting, organization theory, and behavioral science, instead of concentrating exclusively on economic theories of behavior. The Bonini model consists of a series of difference equations which are used to

specify in quantitative terms the behavior of individuals or groups within the organization as a function of the behavior of other individuals and of the information available, both past and present. The sum of these behavior parts for individuals represents the total model [8, p. 11].

The essential elements of the Bonini hypothetical business organization include: decision centers, information centers, decision rules, information links, information systems, and decision systems. The purpose of the model was to study the effects of three types of changes on the behavior of the firm—changes in the external environment, changes in the information system, and changes in the decision system. This analysis was accomplished by a factorial experimental design in which the main effects and the various interactions of eight specific changes in the model on prices, inventory levels, costs, sales, profits, and organizational pressure were estimated. In addition, the factorial experimental design yielded estimates of the effects on the behavior of the firm of differences in the initial starting conditions of the firm. The eight types of alterations that were made on the model and whose effects on firm behavior were analyzed included:

1. Low versus high variability in the external environment of the firm. More specifically, we are interested in the effect of small versus large standard deviations in the probability distributions for sales and production costs.

2. Two different market trends for the firm; one a slow (2 per cent per year) growth upon which is imposed a three-year cycle; the other a fast (10 per cent per year) but irregular growth.

3. A "loose" versus "tight" industrial engineering department in the matter of changing standards.

4. An organization that is contagious to pressure as opposed to one that is not.

5. An organization in which the individuals are sensitive to pressure as opposed to one in which they are not.

6. An average cost method of inventory valuation versus a LIFO method.

7. Knowledge on the part of the sales force about the inventory position of the company versus the absence of such knowledge.

8. The reliance primarily upon request versus past information for control within the firm [8, pp. 86–87].

Bonini then tested null hypotheses that these changes taken both one at a time and two at a time had no significant effect on the behavior of the firm as measured by changes in prices, inventory levels, costs, sales, profits, and organizational pressure.

Cohen

In his doctoral dissertation, entitled *Computer Models of the Shoe, Leather, Hide Sequence,* Kalman Cohen formulated and experimented with two mathematical models, a "one-period-change model" and a "process model," describing the aggregate behavior of shoe retailers, shoe manufacturers, and cattlehide leather tanners between 1930 and 1940 [12]. The principal exogenous variables included in Cohen's models were the Bureau of Labor Statistics consumers' price index, disposable personal income, and the stocks of hides held by hide dealers. After dividing the industry vertically into five segments—consumers, shoe retailers, shoe manufacturers, cattlehide leather tanners, and hide dealers, two major classes of endogenous variables were defined—price and physical flow. Among the endogenous variables analyzed by Cohen were: the retailers' selling price, sales, and shoe receipts; the manufacturers' selling price, production, and leather receipts; the tanners' selling price, finished production, hide wettings, and hide receipts; and the hide dealers' selling price [12, p. vii]. Both of Cohen's models consisted of lagged simultaneous nonlinear difference equations subject to boundary constraints, with one month used as the unit of time.

. . . a "one-period-change model," is intended to explain the values of the endogenous variables for only one time period ahead into the future;

this model assumes, as is usually done in econometrics, that lagged endogenous variables refer to their actually observed values . . . . A "process model," is designed to explain the determination of the endogenous variables for an arbitrarily large number of future time periods. The equations of the process model, together with the observed time paths of the exogenous variables, are treated as a closed dynamic system; each month, the values of the pre-determined endogenous variables are the values generated by the model, not the actually observed values [12, p. vii].

A computer was used to generate the time paths from 1930 to 1940 of each endogenous variable for each of the two models. These results were in turn compared with the actual time paths of these variables. A very close correspondence was found between the simulated time paths and the actual time paths on an annual basis.

Cyert and March

In their book, entitled *A Behavioral Theory of the Firm,* Cyert and March describe three complex simulation models of the firm and in-dustry—a duopoly model, an oligopoly model, and a model of a de-partment store [18]. We have previously described the main features of the duopoly model in an earlier section of this chapter [17]. The oligopoly model [18, pp. 149–236] is essentially an extension of the duopoly model and represents an attempt to describe and analyze a general behavioral theory of price and output determination in an oligopoly.

The model portrays the process of decision making in terms consistent with a behavioral theory of the firm. The firm uses multiple, changing, aspira-tion-level goals; it solves problems in each of its decision areas more or less independently; it searches for solutions in a manner learned from experience; it adjusts its decision rules on the basis of feedback on experience. Decisions on price, output, and sales strategy are made on the basis of profit, inventory, production-smoothing, sales, market share, and competitive position goals [18, p. 182].

One unique feature of this model is the use of multiple regression analysis "to determine the extent to which behavior in the model is sensitive to variations in various internal parameters" [18, p. 173]. The department store model is used to illustrate how a general behavioral theory of the firm can be applied to a particular type of firm, namely, a department store.

Forrester

Of the existing simulation models of the firm and industry, perhaps the "industrial dynamics" project of Jay Forrester is the best known [26]. Actually "industrial dynamics" is not a simulation model at all but rather a methodology for studying business and economic systems that utilize computer simulation as a tool of analysis. Forrester defines industrial dynamics as

the study of the information-feedback characteristics of industrial activity to show how organizational structure, amplification (in policies), and time delays (in decisions and actions) interact to influence the success of the enterprise. It treats the interactions between the flows of information, money, orders, materials, personnel, and capital equipment in a company, an industry, or a national economy [26, p. 13].

The industrial dynamics approach to simulation is similar to the other methods discussed in this chapter in the sense that the mathematical models used to describe a firm, an industry, or an economy must be expressed in the form of a set of lagged difference equations. However, in the case of industrial dynamics, a special computer language, DYNAMO, has been developed for writing programs for difference equation simulation models. In his book *Industrial Dynamics* Forrester describes three industrial dynamics models of the firm that have been programmed in DYNAMO. These include a production-distribution model, an advertising model, and a customer-producer-employment model. The DYNAMO output for these models takes the form of a series of graphs of the time paths of the endogenous variables of the models. In addition to the hypothetical models included in *Industrial Dynamics*, DYNAMO has also been applied to a number of simulations of firms and industries in the real world, e.g., the Sprague Electric Company [26, p. ix], the shoe, leather, hide, industry [67] and the textile industry [64].

SDC Model

In 1959 under the leadership of A. J. Rowe, the System Development Corporation initiated the Management Control Systems Project, whose objective was to accomplish the following.

1. Develop a well-formulated model of the elements, characteristics, and structure of management control systems.
2. Develop a general-purpose computer model for simulation.
3. Design the decision rules for management controls.
4. Study the behavior of the computer model to gain insight into the problem and validate experimental conclusions [40].

In order to accomplish this objective a computer model of a prototype firm producing durable industrial hard goods was formulated and was christened "Mark I" [39, 40].

The specific product produced by the Mark I Corporation was assumed to be similar to an electric motor for industrial machines. The sales for the firm typically total $30 million annually. The Mark I Corporation is organized into seven functional areas including accounting, purchasing, sales, engineering, manufacturing, personnel, and warehousing. Each functional area is staffed by a manager and his staff and a complement of operating personnel. Net profits for the firm (after taxes) amount to $2.5 million annually. The firm maintains a raw material inventory consisting of stocks of eight different materials used to manufacture the motors that the firm produces. The firm also maintains a work-in-process inventory which includes largely the four standard models produced by the firm and to a lesser extent the eleven custom-design (job-shop) models. The firm's finished-goods-inventory consists of standard models only.

Mark I focuses on two different types of general activities—budgeting and the processing of customer orders. The corporate budget is prepared by the accounting department and is based on past experience and forecast sales. There are two different general types of customer orders—standard orders and special orders—each of which requires different scheduling, routing, and dispatching procedures. Special orders are treated in a manner similar to that found in a typical job-shop.

The environment of the Mark I Corporation consists of a set of assumptions about sales, share of market, vendor behavior, customer behavior, labor behavior, and machine breakdown patterns.

A special purpose simulation language called SIMPAC was developed by C. A. Kribs, M. R. Lackner, and others at System Development Corporation to simulate the Mark I model. SIMPAC will be discussed in Chapter 7.

Textile Models

Several computer models have been developed for simulating a number of subindustries within the textile industry in the United States. Manuel Zymelman [70] has developed an analog computer model of the cotton textile gray-goods industry for the U.S. Department of Commerce. The operating characteristics of the model were based on data analysis of the industry and personal interviews. The simulation runs based on data for the time period 1948 to 1960 showed that "it is possible to reduce the amplitude of the cotton textile gray-goods cycle by introducing a simple policy in the production decision-making process whereby greater attention is paid to changes in inventories than to changes in unfilled orders" [70].

Zymelman's analog computer model has also been programmed for use on a digital computer using the DYNAMO simulation language in conjunction with the Civilian Industrial Technology (CIT) Program in Textiles at the U.S. Department of Commerce in Washington, D.C. In addition, the CIT Program in Textiles has also formulated DYNAMO computer models for the tufted textile industry and the ladies seamless hosiery industry [64].

SIMULATION OF THE ECONOMY

Introduction

In the preceding sections of this chapter we concentrated on simulation models of the firm and industry. However, now let us turn to an even more difficult problem, namely, the problem of simulating the entire economy of a sociopolitical unit such as a state or a country. From a strictly technical standpoint the mechanics of simulating an economy on a computer are no different from the techniques required to simulate a firm, an industry, or some component thereof. That is, we still have to define the economic system, define the pertinent exogenous and endogenous variables, formulate mathematical models describing the system, formulate a computer flow chart of the simulation procedure, and write a computer program. But there remain a number of very big differences between simulating the behavior of an economy and simulating the behavior of a microeconomic system, and all of these differences are related to the problem of obtaining meaningful mathematical formulations of the operating characteristics of an economy.

First, the endogenous variables of a macrodynamic system, such as national income, national product, and total employment, are likely to depend on the magnitude of a very large number of significant variables (both exogenous and endogenous to the system), considerably more than are usually found in microeconomic models. Second, if aggregative variables are used to describe the behavior of the system, then an acceptable theory of aggregation must be developed for the system, relating microeconomic variables to their aggregative counterparts. The so-called aggregation problem in economics has continuously plagued economists, both theoreticians and empiricists alike, throughout the history of economic thought [3, pp. 694–724]. Third, there are likely to be complicated interactions and feedback effects among the endogenous variables of a macrodynamic system. Fourth, the formulation of realistic hypotheses concerning the behavior of a dynamic economy requires a considerable knowledge of macroeconomic theory. The analyst who attempts to use simulation techniques as a substitute for a thorough grounding in macroeconomic theory is very likely to find that he has simulated his own ignorance rather than the real world. Fifth, the econometric problem of estimating the parameters for multiple-equation, dynamic, aggregative models is indeed a formidable one. Sixth, suitable data for constructing mathematical models of macrodynamic systems may even be more difficult to obtain than data for microeconomic systems.

In a book such as this we cannot possibly attempt to solve these problems or even elaborate on them to any extent, since volumes have been written on each of them. However, we are obligated to at least forewarn the reader of the potential pitfalls he may face in attempting to simulate macrodynamic systems unless he has first acquired more than a superficial knowledge of macroeconomic theory, mathematical economics, and econometrics.

Any attempt to classify the existing macrodynamic simulation models is likely to be quite arbitrary because there are simply not that many full-fledged simulation models of the economy available at this time for taxonomical purposes. However, in the remainder of this chapter we analyze what we consider to be four different simulation models of the economy. First, we investigate a very simple theoretical model of the economy that consists of only a few variables but is fairly typical of a broad range of models found in the macroeconomic literature. Second, we present an example of a multivariable, multiequation econometric model that is a simplified version of some of the more complex large-scale econometric models of the economy. Third, we briefly describe the most ambitious econometric model to date, *The Brookings-SSRC Quarterly Econometric Model of the United States* [23]. Finally, we consider two somewhat unique approaches to the simulation of an economy, the models of Orcutt et al. [51] and Holland and Gillespie [35].

Macrodynamic Models: Theoretical

Since the beginning of the Keynesian Revolution [42] and the advent of the Swedish School of economic thought in the 1930's [68], we have witnessed in economics a steady stream of literature dealing with macrodynamic models of the economy. For the most part these models have been relatively simple and highly aggregative, consisting of a small number of variables and a small number of lagged difference or differential equations. (We will consider more realistic, large-scale econometric models in the next section.) Standard analytical techniques have been used to determine the nature of the time paths of the endogenous variables of these models under conditions of complete certainty. A partial listing of some of the more important contributions to the literature on macrodynamic models (which consists primarily of business cycle and economic growth models) include: Kalecki [41], Samuelson [56], Metzler [49], Domar [21], Harrod [30], Hicks [31], Goodwin [29], Phillips [52 and 53], and Smithies [62].

Although we will demonstrate that these models can be treated as small-scale simulation models, their principal value is pedagogical because when most of the original formulations of these macrodynamic models were developed, computers did not even exist. (The models of Phillips [52 and 53] and Smithies [62] are exceptions to this rule.)

[However,] they are useful in illustrating some basic theoretical points, either numerical or general, about the economy; they show how fluctuations might take place and be sustained; they show why the economy tends to grow and something about the pace of growth. However, these models are not suitable for persons who require results for practical decisions in public or business policy. A working model must be one that has the ability to do more than illustrate a fine point in theory; it must be able to describe the actual workings of the everyday economy with an accuracy that will suit the needs of decision makers . . . . A working model must bring in many institutional characteristics of an economy and be sufficiently disaggregated to enable the decision maker to form judgments about sectors of interest to him. Generally, it will be much larger and more complicated model than those discussed so far [46, p. 222].

To be sure, computer simulation is not capable of making any of the theoretical models listed above more realistic or more accurate so long as they remain in their original form. However, with computer simulation it is possible to trace the time paths of the endogenous variables of more complicated versions of these models. For example, we could take any one of the models of this type and introduce additional variables, introduce additional equations, and increase the complexity of the original equations. We could then compare the time paths of the original model and the modified model with the actual time paths of the economic system. It would appear that such a procedure would be an extremely useful pedagogical device in a course in intermediate macroeconomic theory because a sure test of one's understanding of a particular economic model is whether or not he can write a computer program for the model.

To illustrate how we might go about simulating a modified version of one of the aforementioned macrodynamic models, we have selected the well known Samuelson-Hicks [3, pp. 209–239; 56; 31] "multiplier-accelerator" model as an example. This model is fairly typical of the entire class of models included in this section. Hence, the methods used to simulate the Samuelson-Hicks model can easily be applied to any of the other models mentioned above.

The Samuelson-Hicks model consists of the following variables and functional relationships.

EXOGENOUS VARIABLES

u_T = a stochastic variate with a known probability distribution, expected value equal to zero, and a given standard deviation. (6-130)

v_T = a stochastic variate with a known probability distribution, expected value equal to zero, and a given standard deviation. (6-131)

PARAMETERS

b = accelerator coefficient. (6-132)

c_1 = marginal propensity to consume in period $T - 1$, $0 < c_1 < 1$. (6-133)

c_2 = marginal propensity to consume in period $T - 2$, $0 < c_2 < 1$. (6-134)

STATUS VARIABLES

c = overall marginal propensity to consume. (6-135)

w = reduced investment coefficient. (6-136)

s = marginal propensity to save. (6-137)

ENDOGENOUS VARIABLES

C_T = consumption in period T. (6-138)

I_T = investment in period T. (6-139)

Y_T = national income in period T. (6-140)

IDENTITIES

$$Y_T = C_T + I_T. \qquad (6\text{-}141)$$

$$c = c_1 + c_2. \qquad (6\text{-}142)$$

$$w = b - c_2. \qquad (6\text{-}143)$$

$$s = 1 - c. \qquad (6\text{-}144)$$

OPERATING CHARACTERISTICS

$$C_T = c_1 Y_{T-1} + c_2 Y_{T-2} + u_T. \tag{6-145}$$

$$I_T = b(Y_{T-1} - Y_{T-2}) + v_T. \tag{6-146}$$

Substituting the values of C_T and I_T from Eqs. 6-145 and 6-146 into Eq. 6-141, we obtain

$$Y_T = cY_{T-1} + w(Y_{T-1} - Y_{T-2}) + u_T + v_T. \tag{6-147}$$

Figure 6-8 contains a computer flow chart for generating the time paths of the three endogenous variables on a computer.

If we let u_T and v_T be equal to zero, then we can determine the time path of Y_T analytically according to the following formula [3, p. 211].

	Condition	Time Path of Y_T
(i)	$w < (1 - \sqrt{s})^2$	Non-oscillatory and damped
(ii)	$(1 - \sqrt{s})^2 < w < 1$	Oscillatory and damped
(iii)	$1 < w < (1 + \sqrt{s})^2$	Oscillatory and explosive
(iv)	$(1 + \sqrt{s})^2 < w$	Non-oscillatory and explosive

It may be of interest to compare the results of the simulated time paths with the theoretical time paths.

Macrodynamic Models: Econometric

As we have previously indicated, the relatively unsophisticated Samuelson-Hicks type of theoretical models of the economy described in the preceding section were not met with overwhelming enthusiasm on the part of economists, whose major interest was in the area of governmental economic policy decisions. There was still a definite need for a type of model that could be used to describe the behavior of an economy within a fairly close tolerance range, a type of model that could be used to predict the effect of various decisions made by the household, business, and governmental sectors of an economy on such aggregative variables as total output, total employment, and consumer price levels for the economy as a whole. To partially fulfill this vacuum a second type of macrodynamic model came into being, the so-called aggregate econometric model.

The first large-scale (12 equations or more) aggregate econometric model of any real consequence was developed by Tinbergen [66] in 1939. Tinbergen's model evolved from a number of schools of intellectual thought, including Walras' work with simultaneous equations and general equilibrium analysis, Frisch's theory of economic dynamics,

King and Kuznets' numerical estimates of national income and expenditures, and Keynes' theory of aggregate income, consumption, and investment [42]. Tinbergen's model of the U.S. economy for the period 1919–1932 consisted of 48 equations and 48 endogenous variables, including 4 consumption variables, 4 investment components, 5 output variables, 11 income components, 11 price variables, 2 real stocks, and 11 finance stocks. The main exogenous variables included exports and imports building costs, required reserves, 5 financial stocks, 3 financial flows, and agricultural supply. Ordinary least squares was used to estimate the parameters for the model that featured lags up to 4 years and cumulated profits and investment. Tinbergen's contribution is particularly noteworthy, since large-scale computers did not become available until the early 1950's.

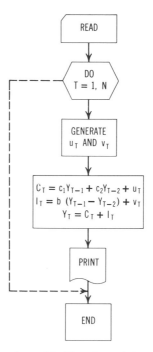

Figure 6-8. Flow chart of the Samuelson-Hicks model.

Following in Tinbergen's footsteps, a number of large-scale aggregate econometric models has been forthcoming since 1939. Among the more important ones are: Klein's Model [44], Christ's Model [9], the Klein-Goldberger Models [48], the Dutch Model [59], the Duesenberry, Eckstein, and Fromm Model [22], the United Kingdom Model [47], and the Research Seminar in Quantitative Economics Model [63]. With the exception of the Duesenberry, Eckstein, and Fromm Model, all the econometric models listed above were estimated and tested in such a manner that they may be considered to be what Cohen has called "one-period-change" models. That is, they were designed to make assertions about the behavior of the economy for one and only one time period in the future. Given the observed values of the lagged endogenous variables for periods $T - 1$, $T - 2$, etc., and the values of the exogenous variables for periods T and $T + 1$, then the equations of these models assert something very definite about the state of the economy in period T, but they assert nothing about that state of the economy in period $T + 1$.

The problem of obtaining satisfactory estimates of the parameters contained in large-scale econometric models is a formidable task. If the model contains equations that are interdependent, then the application of ordinary least-squares estimating techniques to each equation separately will lead to estimates that are biased and inconsistent. When this is the case, we must resort to techniques that explicitly take into account the simultaneous nature of the equations of the model. Some of the more important estimation methods that can be used for estimating parameters of simultaneous equation systems include indirect least squares, limited information methods, least-variance ratio methods, two-stage least squares, full-information maximum likelihood methods, and three-stage least squares. Unfortunately, these methods are considerably more complex, computationally speaking, than ordinary least squares [38]. The choice of an estimation method necessarily involves a compromise between the desired statistical properties of the estimator and computational simplicity. However, if an econometric model of an economic system is a completely recursive model, then ordinary least squares can be used without the inherent risk of statistical bias and inconsistency. Hence, there is considerable incentive to formulate models of aggregate economic systems that are completely recursive rather than interdependent.

Although most of the work on large-scale aggregative econometric models has been concentrated on one-period-change models, there have been several studies in which major emphasis was placed on computer simulation rather than on one-period-changes. These studies include the work of Duesenberry, Eckstein, and Fromm [22], Adelman and Adelman [1, 2], and *The Brookings-SSRC Quarterly Econometric Model of the United States* [23]. In each of these studies a computer was used to generate the time paths of each endogenous variable over extended periods of time, substituting the generated values of the endogenous variables for the lagged endogenous variables of future time periods rather than using the actual observed values of the lagged endogenous variables. In addition, these studies make use of stochastic shocks in one or more of the behavioral equations describing the economy, which in this case happens to be the the economy of the United States.

To illustrate some of the concepts and problems involved in simulating the behavior of an economy using an aggregative econometric model, let us consider a modified version of a relatively simple model developed by Klein for expository purposes [44, pp. 58–80]. Although Klein's use of this model was limited to the one-period-change type of analysis, we shall treat it as a simulation model. (This will also necessitate certain changes in the methods used to estimate the

parameters of the model, which will be discussed later.) The variables
and functional relationships for the model are defined as follows:

EXOGENOUS VARIABLES

$W2_T$ = governmental wage bill in period T. (6-148)

G_T = governmental and net foreign demand in period T. (6-149)

ENDOGENOUS VARIABLES

C_T = consumption in period T. (6-150)

$W1_T$ = private wage bill in period T. (6-151)

Π_T = nonwage income (profits) in period T. (6-152)

I_T = net investment in period T. (6-153)

K_T = capital stock at the end of period T. (6-154)

Y_T = output in period T. (6-155)

TX_T = business taxes in period T. (6-156)

OPERATING CHARACTERISTICS

$$C_T = a_0 + a_1(W1_T + W2_T) + a_2\Pi_T + u_T. \tag{6-157}$$

$$I_T = b_0 + b_1\Pi_T + b_2\Pi_{T-1} + b_3K_{T-1} + v_T. \tag{6-158}$$

$$W1_T = c_0 + c_1(Y_T + TX_T - W2_T) \\ + c_2(Y_{T-1} + TX_{T-1} - W2_{T-1}) + c_3T + w_T. \tag{6-159}$$

$$\Pi_T = d_1Y_{T-1} - d_2K_{T-1} + x_T. \tag{6-160}$$

IDENTITIES

$$K_T = K_{T-1} + I_T. \tag{6-161}$$

$$Y_T = W1_T + W2_T + G_T. \tag{6-162}$$

$$TX_T = C_T + I_T + G_T - Y_T. \tag{6-163}$$

The symbols u_T, v_T, w_T, and x_T denote normally distributed stochastic variates with expected value equal to zero and a standard
deviation equal to the standard error of estimate for the equation in
question, and a_i, b_i, c_i, and d_i are parameters whose values must be
estimated.

Given a set of starting values for the lagged endogenous variables,
as well as values for the exogenous variables W2 and G (extrapolated,
or otherwise), the simulation of this economic system is completely
straightforward. Since the model is nonrecursive, the seven simultaneous linear equations must be solved for the seven endogenous variables

each period. This means that if we want to generate time paths for the endogenous variables over N time periods, then 7N equations must be solved to obtain the values of the 7N endogenous variables. (Again the advantage of using completely recursive models is quite obvious.) Computationally, this calls for N inversions of a 7×7 matrix. A computer is an absolute necessity for handling problems of this size and larger. The generated values of the endogenous variables are merely substituted back into the system each period for the lagged endogenous variables, whereas new values of the stochastic variates and the exogenous variables must be generated and extrapolated, respectively, each period. Figure 6-9 contains a computer flow chart for this procedure.

Now that we have indicated how to go about simulating the behavior of an economy with an aggregative econometric model, we must return briefly to the sticky problem of estimating the values of the parameters of the structural equations of the model. Since this is a nonrecursive model, even if we had chosen to use it as one-period-change model rather than a simulation model, it would have been necessary to apply simultaneous equation estimating techniques rather than ordinary least squares to insure against the possibility of biased and inconsistent estimates. This, in itself, would have required the consideration of seven equations. However, by choosing to use the model as a simulation model (which is not self-correcting each period), it becomes necessary to incorporate all 7N equations into the model to obtain estimates of the structural parameters that are unbiased and consistent. Hence, the task of obtaining unbiased and consistent parameter estimates for simulation models is several orders of magnitude more difficult for simulation models than it is for one-period-change models [12, p. 15]. For this reason it is usually necessary to compromise between

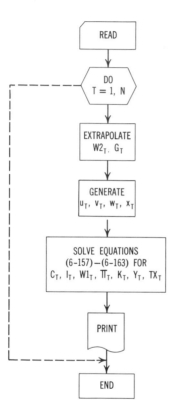

Figure 6-9. Flow chart for Klein's model.

the conflicting objective of computational feasibility and unbiased estimates.

Since our modified version of Klein's model represents the only non-recursive model discussed in any degree of detail in this book, it seems advisable to reiterate the advantages of recursive simulation models. First, the problem of estimating the parameters of the structural equations is grossly simplified, since it is possible to obtain unbiased and consistent estimates of parameters by applying ordinary least squares to each equation separately. Second, the generation of the time paths of the endogenous variables does not require the solution of simultaneous equations.

The Brookings-SSRC Model

Probably the most elaborate computer model of an economic system in existence today is the *Brookings-SSRC Quarterly Econometric Model of the United States* [23]. The Brookings-SSRC model is a block-recursive model consisting of over 250 equations and represents a composite of the theories and empirical findings of a large number of econometricians scattered across the United States. The parameters for the operating characteristics of the model were estimated using ordinary least squares, two-stage least squares, and limited information estimating methods using quarterly data for the period 1949 to 1960. The model consists of over 150 behavioral equations and over 75 mathematical identities.

Through the efforts of Holt [36] and others a special simulation language called "Program SIMULATE" has been developed to generate the time paths of the endogenous variables of the model. Program SIMULATE is capable of handling block-recursive systems of equations in which the maximum number of linear or nonlinear simultaneous equations in a given block does not exceed 50.

Although it is still too early to properly evaluate the potential usefulness of the Brookings-SSRC model, it is aimed primarily at forecasters, policy-makers, and research economists whose principal goal is a better understanding of economic systems. Perhaps months and years of experimentation with the model will be required before a definitive judgment can be rendered on the ultimate value of the Brookings-SSRC model.

Other Simulation Models of the Economy

Two recent studies involving the simulation of an economy do not lend themselves to either of the two previously defined categories and, hence, will briefly be described separately in this section. The two studies are Orcutt, Greenberger, Korbel, and Rivlin's [51] computer simulation of a demographic model of the United States household sector and Holland and Gillespie's simulation of the economy of India [35].

Orcutt

The Orcutt study represents the first step in the development of a general simulation model consisting of the ten flow-of-funds sectors used in national income accounting. This model differs from the other models of the economy described in this chapter because it was constructed in terms of microcomponents rather than aggregative components. Individuals and combinations of individuals such as married couples and families, serve as the basic components of this model.

The family units form, grow, diminish, and dissolve as married couples have children and get divorced and individuals age, marry and die. These outputs of the basic components in a given month depend on the status variables that characterize each component as of the beginning of the month and on the inputs into each component during the month. The operating characteristics, which serve to relate outputs of components to input and status variables, are stochastic in nature; i.e., it is the probabilities of occurrence of certain outputs rather than the outputs themselves which are regarded as functions of input and status variables . . . . The model is recursive in that the probabilities determined for the possible outputs of each component in any period depend only on previously determined input and status variables. [50, p. 903].

A number of computer simulation runs were carried out covering the time interval from April 1950 to April 1960. The operating characteristics for these runs were estimated from data that were available. Experiments were made changing some of the critical operating characteristics. The results were tabulated and compared with available aggregative data about the United States population and its composition.

Holland and Gillespie

This study was an outgrowth of an unsuccessful attempt to simulate the Indian economy on an analog computer. The objective of the study was to develop and experiment with a number of alternative policies which an underdeveloped country might pursue in order to reach the so-called "take-off point" for economic growth. The economic model of the Indian economy constructed by Holland and Gillespie consisted of a multiplicity of economic sectors, functional relationships, and controls. The six major sectors of the economy were as follows.

1. Manufactured consumer goods using power.
2. Agricultural products.
3. Capital and intermediate goods.
4. Nonpower manufactured consumer goods.
5. Public overhead services.
6. Services without explicit supply functions.

The functional relationships included short-run supply functions, a fixed demand for food, and various other demand and supply relationships. The controls included investment controls and tariff and exchange rate controls. The model was programmed for the DYNAMO compiler at the Massachusetts Institute of Technology and utilized numerical values based on statistical data on India for 1951 to 1952. The output of the simulation took the form of a series of graphs depicting the time paths of the endogenous variables. A period of twenty years was simulated and used to test the effects of several different policies on the exchange rates, the rate of inflation, the balance of payments, gross national product, per capita income, and gross real investment in each sector.

Exercises

6-1   Write a FORTRAN program that will generate the values of the time paths of P_T, D_T, and S_T for *Cobweb Model 1* for $T = 1$, 2, . . . 50 when

   $A = 10,000$
   $B = 2.00$
   $C = 0$
   $D = 0.10$
   $U_T = $ a normally distributed variate with expected value equal to zero and variance equal to 1.00
   $V_T = $ a normally distributed variate with expected value equal to zero and variance equal to 0.50
   $W_T = $ a normally distributed variate with expected value equal to zero and variance equal to 0.20
   $P_0 = 4738.$

   Repeat the simulation experiment for $D = 2.00$ and $D = 2.50$. Test the effect on P_T of increasing the variance of V_T from 0.50 to 10.00 and from 10.00 to 15.00.

6-2   Formulate a FORTRAN program and generate the time paths for P_T, D_T, and S_T for *Cobweb Model 2* using the data given in Exercise 6-1, where $\rho = 0.30$, $P_0 = 4000$, and $P_1 = 4500$.

6-3   Formulate a FORTRAN program and generate the time paths
for P_T, S_T, D_T, and Q_T for *Cobweb Model 3* using the data given
below.

$$A = 5000$$
$$B = -0.05$$
$$C = 100$$
$$D = 0.10$$
$$\lambda = 0.001$$
$$P_0 = 1000$$
$$Q_0 = 1200$$
$$T = 1, 2, \ldots 100.$$

6-4   Write a FORTRAN program for the three-firm competitive industry model outlined in Figure 6-3, where

$A_i = 2$
$B = 2$
$C = 24$
$D = 1000$
$E = 0.5$
$F = 0.2$
$G = 0.03$
$U_T =$ a uniformly distributed variate with expected value
    equal to zero and variance equal to 1.0
$V_T =$ a uniformly distributed variate with expected value
    equal to zero and variance equal to 0.5
$D_0 = 200$
$D_1 = 150$
$T = 1, 2, \ldots , 100.$

6-5   Modify the FORTRAN program for Exercise 6-4 so that the
three firms in the competitive industry use the following decision
rule for determining their output each period. *Decision Rule:*
each firm assumes that its competitors will not change their
output in the following period. That is, each firm assumes that
the only changes in output for the industry in the next period
(over the previous period) will be attributed only to its changes
(the particular firm's changes) in output and not that of its
competitors. Each firm then produces at the optimum level each
period based on its cost function and the industry demand function in which the output of the firm's competitors is held
constant.

6-6   Design a computer simulation experiment for testing the effects of changes in C, D, E, A_0, and B_0 on the endogenous variables of the *Cournot Duopoly Model* described by the flow chart in Figure 6-4.

6-7   Write a FORTRAN program for the *Management Decision-Making Game* described in this chapter (Figure 6-7). Suggest several changes which might be made in this game to make it more "realistic."

6-8   Formulate a FORTRAN program for the Samuelson-Hicks model found in Figure 6-8. Experiment with the model in its stochastic form as well as its deterministic form. Test the effects of changes in b, c_1, c_2, Var (u), and Var (v) on national income. For the nonstochastic form of the model compare the simulated time paths for Y_T with the theoretical time paths for Y_T.

6-9   Write a FORTRAN program for generating the time paths for the endogenous variables in Klein's econometric model (Figure 6-9). Test the effects of changes in the model's parameters on the endogenous variables of the model. (Use Gaussian elimination to perform the matrix inversions.)

REFERENCES AND BIBLIOGRAPHY

1. Adelman, Irma. "Long Cycles—A Simulation Experiment," *Symposium on Simulation Models*. Edited by Austin C. Hoggatt and Frederick E. Balderston. Cincinnati: South-Western Publishing Co., 1963.
2. Adelman, Irma, and Adelman, Frank L. "The Dynamic Properties of the Klein-Goldberger Model," *Econometrica*, XXVII (October 1959), 596–625.
3. Allen, R. G. D. *Mathematical Economics*. New York: Macmillan and Co., 1960.
4. Balderston, F. E. "Communication Networks in Intermediate Markets," *Management Science*, IV (1958), 154–171.
5. Balderston, F. E. and Hoggatt, Austin C. *Simulation of Market Processes*. Berkeley: Institute of Business and Economic Research, 1962.
6. Balderston, F. E., and Hoggatt, Austin C. "Simulation Models: Analytic Variety and the Problem of Model Reduction," *Symposium on Simulation Models*. Edited by Austin C. Hoggatt and Frederick E. Balderston. Cincinnati: South-Western Publishing Co., 1963.
7. Bellman, Richard, et al. "On the Construction of a Multi-Person, Multi-Stage Business Game," *Operations Research*, V (1957), 469–503.
8. Bonini, Charles P. *Simulation of Information and Decision Systems in the Firm*. Englewood Cliffs, N.J.: Prentice-Hall, 1963.
9. Christ, C. F. "A Test of an Econometric Model for the United States," *Conference on Business Cycles*. New York: National Bureau of Economic Research, 1951.
10. Christ, C. F. "Aggregate Econometric Models," *American Economic Review*, XLVI (June 1956), 385–408.
11. Clarkson, Geoffrey P. E., and Simon, Herbert A. "Simulation of Individual

and Group Behavior," *American Economic Review*, **L** (Dec. 1960), 920-932.

12. Cohen, Kalman J. *Computer Models of the Shoe, Leather, Hide Sequence.* Englewood Cliffs, N.J.: Prentice-Hall, 1960.

13. Cohen, Kalman J., and Cyert, Richard M. "Computer Models in Dynamic Economics," *Quarterly Journal of Economics*, **LXXV** (Feb. 1961), 112-127.

14. Cohen, Kalman J., et al. "The Carnegie Tech Management Game," *Simulation in Social Science.* Edited by Harold Guetzkow. Englewood Cliffs: Prentice-Hall, 1962.

15. Cohen, Kalman, J. and Rhenman, Eric. "The Role of Management Games in Education and Research," *Management Science*, **VII** (1961), 131-166.

16. Cournot, Augustin. *Researches into the Mathematical Principles of the Theory of Wealth.* trans. Nathaniel T. Bacon. New York: Macmillan, 1897, reprinted 1927.

17. Cyert, R. M., Feigenbaum, E. A., and March, J. G. "Models in a Behavioral Theory of the Firm," *Behavorial Science*, **IV** (April 1959), 81-95.

18. Cyert, Richard M., and March, James G. *A Behavioral Theory of the Firm.* Englewood Cliffs, N.J.: Prentice-Hall, 1963.

19. De Leeuw, Frank. "Financial Markets in Business Cycles: A Simulation Study," *American Economic Review*, **LIV** (May 1964), 309-323.

20. Dill, William R., and Doppelt, Neil. "The Acquisition of Experience in a Complex Management Game," *Management Science*, **X** (Oct. 1963), 30-46.

21. Domar, E. D. "Capital Expansion, Rate of Growth, and Employment," *Econometrica*, **XIV** (1946), 137-147.

22. Duesenberry, James S., Eckstein, Otto, and Fromm, Gary. "A Simulation of the United States Economy in Recession," *Econometrica* **XXVIII** (Oct. 1960), 749-809.

23. Duesenberry, James, Fromm, Gary, Klein, Lawrence R., and Kuh, Edwin (editors). *The Brookings-SSRC Quarterly Econometric Model of the United States.* Chicago: Rand McNally and North-Holland Press, 1965.

24. Edgeworth, F. Y. "La teoria pura del monopolio," *Giornale degli Economisti*, **XV** (1898), 13-31.

25. Ezekiel, M. "The Cobweb Theorem," *Quarterly Journal of Economics*, **LII** (1938), 255-280.

26. Forrester, Jay W. *Industrial Dynamics.* New York: The M.I.T. Press and John Wiley and Sons, 1961.

27. Goldberger, Arthur S. *Economertic Theory.* New York: John Wiley and Sons, 1964.

28. Goldman, Morris R., Marimont, Martin L., and Vaccara, Beatrice N. "The Interindustry Structure of the United States," *Survey of Current Business*, **XLIV** (Nov. 1964), 10-29.

29. Goodwin, R. M. "The Non-linear Accelerator and the Persistence of Business Cycles," *Econometrica*, **XIX** (1951), 1-17.

30. Harrod, R. F. *Towards a Dynamic Economics.* London: Macmillan and Co., 1948.

31. Hicks, J. R. *A Contribution to the Theory of the Trade Cycle.* Oxford: Clarendon Press, 1950.

32. Hoggatt, Austin C. *Simulation of the Firm*, I.B.M. Research Paper, RC-16, Aug. 1957.

33. Hoggatt, Austin C. "A Simulation Study of an Economic Model," *Contributions to Scientific Research in Management.* The Proceedings of the Sci-

entific Program Following the Dedication of the Western Data Processing Center, Graduate School of Business Admin., Univ. of Calif., Los Angeles, Jan. 29–30, 1959.

34. Hoggatt, Austin C. "An Experimental Business Game," *Behavioral Science,* IV (1959), 192–203.

35. Holland, Edward P. and Gillespie, Robert W. *Experiments on a Simulated Underdeveloped Economy: Development Plans and Balance of Payments Policies.* Cambridge: The M.I.T. Press, 1963.

36. Holt, Charles C.; Shirey, Robert W.; Steward, Donald V.; Midler, Joseph L.; and Stroud, Arthur. "Program SIMULATE, a User's and Programmer's Manual," Social Systems Research Institute, University of Wisconsin, May 1964. (Mimeographed.)

37. "IBM Management Decision-Making Laboratory Administrator's Reference Manual," International Business Machines Corporation, B20-8099 (1963).

38. Johnston, J. *Econometric Methods.* New York: McGraw-Hill Book Co., 1963.

39. Kagdis, J. "The Mark I Business System Simulation Model," System Development Corporation, TM-708/200/00 (Dec. 1, 1962).

40. Kagdis, J., and Lackner, M. R. "Introduction to Management Control Systems Research," System Development Corporation, TM-708/100/00 (Oct. 15, 1962).

41. Kalecki, M. "A Macrodynamic Theory of Business Cycles," *Econometrica,* III (1935), 327–344.

42. Keynes, John Maynard. *The General Theory of Employment Interest and Money.* London: Macmillan and Co., 1936.

43. Klein, L. "The Use of Econometric Models as a Guide to Economic Policy," *Econometrica* XV (April 1947), 111–151.

44. Klein, Lawrence. *Economic Fluctuations in the United States, 1921–1941.* Cowles Commission for Research in Economics, Monograph No. 11. New York: John Wiley and Sons, 1950.

45. Klein, L. *A Textbook of Econometrics.* Evanston, Illinois: Row Peterson and Co., 1953.

46. Klein, Lawrence R. *An Introduction to Econometrics.* Englewood Cliffs, N.J.: Prentice-Hall, 1962.

47. Klein, L. R., Ball, R. J., Hazelwood, A., and Vandome, P. *An Econometric Model of the United Kingdom.* Oxford: Basil Blackwell, 1961.

48. Klein, L., and Goldberger, A. S. *An Econometric Model of the United States, 1929–1952.* Amsterdam: North-Holland Publishing Co., 1955.

49. Metzler, L. "The Nature and Stability of Inventory Cycles," *The Review of Economic Statistics,* XXIII (1941), 113–129.

50. Orcutt, Guy H. "Simulation of Economic Systems," *American Economic Review.* L (Dec. 1960), 893–907.

51. Orcutt, Guy., Greenberger, Martin, Korbel, John, and Rivlin, Alice M. *Microanalysis of Socioeconomic Systems: A Simulation Study.* New York: Harper and Brothers, 1961.

52. Phillips, A. W. "Stabilization Policy in a Closed Economy," *The Economic Journal,* LXIV (1954), 290–323.

53. Phillips, A. W. "Stabilization Policy and the Time-Form of Lagged Responses," *The Economic Journal,* LXVII (1957), 265–277.

54. *Proceedings of the Conference on Business Games.* Sponsored by the Ford Foundation and School of Business Administration. Tulane University. April 26–28, 1961.

55. Reichenbach, Hans. *The Rise of Scientific Philosophy.* Berkeley: University of California Press, 1951.
56. Samuelson, Paul A. "Interactions between the Multiplier Analysis and the Principle of Acceleration," *Review of Economic Statistics,* XII (May 1938), 75–78.
57. Samuelson, Paul A. *Economics: An Introductory Analysis,* 6th ed. New York: McGraw-Hill Book Co., 1964.
58. Schultz, H. *Theory and Measurement of Demand.* Chicago: University of Chicago Press, 1938.
59. *Scope and Methods of the Central Planning Bureau.* The Hague: Central Planning Bureau, 1956.
60. Shubik, Martin. "Simulation and the Theory of the Firm," *Contributions to Scientific Research in Management.* The Proceedings of the Scientific Program Following the Dedication of the Western Data Processing Center, Graduate School of Business Admin., Univ. of Calif., Los Angeles, Jan. 29–30, 1959.
61. Shubik, Martin. "Simulation of the Industry and the Firm," *American Economic Review,* L, No. 5 (Dec., 1960), 908–919.
62. Smithies, A. "Economic Fluctuations and Growth," *Econometrica,* XXV (January 1957), 1–52.
63. Suits, Daniel B. "Forecasting and Analysis with an Econometric Model," *American Economic Review,* LII (March 1962), 104–132.
64. U. S. Department of Commerce, Civilian Industrial Technology Program in Textiles. *Textile Industry Behavioral Information,* Washington, D.C., March 15, 1965.
65. Theil, H. *Economic Forecasts and Policy.* Amsterdam: North-Holland Press, 1958.
66. Tinbergen, J. *Statistical Testing of Business Cycle Theories.* Geneva: League of Nations, 1939.
67. Yance, J. V. "A Model of Price Flexibility," *American Economic Review,* L (June 1960), 401–418.
68. Yohe, William P. *The Wicksellian Tradition in Swedish Macroeconomic Theory.* Unpublished Ph.D. dissertation, University of Michigan, 1958.
69. Yohe, William P. "An Experimental Model of Federal Open Market Committee Voting Behavior," Unpublished paper, Duke University, 1965.
70. Zymelman, Manuel. "A Stabilization Policy for the Cotton Textile Cycle," *Management Science,* XI (March 1965), 572–580.

Chapter 7 | Simulation Languages

INTRODUCTION

In Chapters 5 and 6 we have been concerned primarily with the formulation of mathematical models and flow charts describing the logic underlying certain systems in business and economics. However, we have said very little about how to convert a flow chart of a particular economic system into a computer program that will, in turn, be used to carry out simulated experiments. It is the purpose of this chapter to focus on the all-important problem of writing computer programs for performing simulation experiments.

Clearly one way to approach programming simulation experiments is to write a special program for simulating each system to be studied in one of the well-known, general-purpose languages such as FORTRAN, ALGOL, COBOL, or IBM's PL/I. To be sure, this alternative offers the programmer maximum flexibility in (1) the design and formulation of the mathematical model of the system being studied, (2) the type and format of output reports generated, and (3) the kinds of simulation experiments performed with the model. However, the principal shortcoming of this approach is the difficulty we encounter in writing simulation programs in a general purpose programming language.

. . . the central difficulty of the problem is the control of the sequence in which the interdependent actions forming the model occur. If one attempts to write a simulation program using only a general-purpose language, one rapidly becomes enmeshed in the complexities of this sequencing control, which is not of great interest but nevertheless affords surprisingly fertile ground for minor errors. Moreover, mistakes here are liable to produce obscure effects, and are correspondingly difficult to eradicate [34, p. 328].

However, recent years have witnessed the development of a number of so-called "simulation languages" that are aimed at simplifying the task of writing simulation programs for a variety of different types of models and systems. Among the simulation languages that have been developed are the ones below.

1. GPSS II [13].
2. SIMSCRIPT [25].
3. GASP [22].
4. SIMPAC [29].
5. DYNAMO [28].
6. SIMULATE [18].

These programs have been developed with the following objectives in mind:

1. To produce a generalized structure for designing simulation models.

2. To provide a rapid way of converting a simulation model into a computer program.

3. To provide a rapid way of making changes in the simulation model that can be readily reflected in the machine program.

4. To provide a flexible way of obtaining useful outputs for analysis [10, p. 4].

The simulation languages that are available today differ considerably in the extent to which they can be applied to particular types of systems and in the extent to which they can render the simulation procedures more or less automatic. For example, although GPS II "can be applied generally to a broad class of systems while maintaining a relatively fixed set of procedures for carrying out the simulation automatically" [1, p. 20], it is best suited to certain types of scheduling and waiting line problems. On the other hand, DYNAMO and SIMULATE lend themselves best to simulations of large-scale economic systems that are described by econometric models involving complex feedback mechanisms.

The simulation program best suited for a particular simulation study depends upon the nature of the system and upon the programming skill of the individual conducting the study. As a general rule, an increase in the flexibility of a simulation program is obtained at the cost of requiring more understanding of programming procedures [1, p. 20].

Likewise, reductions in programming time achieved through the use of simulation languages are usually associated with increases in computer running time and computer costs.

In the final analysis the decision whether to use a particular simulation language rests primarily on economic considerations such as these:

1. Availability of computer hardware.

2. Availability of programmers knowledgeable in particular computer languages.

3. Cost of programming per unit time.
4. Cost of computer time.

Although we cannot possibly hope to answer the question, "Which simulation language is best suited for a particular business or economic system?" we can describe some of the well-known simulation languages and indicate how they differ from each other.

One alternative method of achieving such a comparison of simulation languages would be to take a particular case and write a program for that case in each of the languages under consideration and simply compare the results on the basis of programming time, computer running time, type of reports generated, etc. Unfortunately, such a comparison leads to completely biased results because the choice of a particular system to simulate tends to place some of the simulation languages in a favorable light while making other languages appear quite inadequate. On the other hand, the choice of a second example system might lead to completely opposite results.

In this chapter we attempt to compare the various simulation languages on the basis of the following criteria

1. Special flow chart symbols.
2. Instruction types.
3. Language components.
4. Available subroutines.
5. Computer hardware requirements.
6. Compiler requirements.
7. Error checking.
8. Simulation procedure.
   a. Initial values.
   b. Data generation procedure.
   c. Time flow mechanism.
   d. Output reports.
9. Applications.

In addition to comparing each language on the basis of each of these characteristics, we also include sample programs written in some of the languages in order to provide the reader with the flavor of the different languages. However, the decision of which language is best suited for a particular system under study will remain unanswered in this book, but the reader is encouraged to pursue the answer to this question by consulting the references at the end of the chapter and experimenting with one or more simulation languages on his own.

We begin our comparison of simulation languages by first applying the aforementioned criteria to FORTRAN, an example of a general purpose language that is not specifically oriented toward simulation. The purpose in discussing FORTRAN in this manner is to provide a frame of reference for discussing the simulation languages. Although we shall attempt to follow the criteria outlined above in our discussion of GASP, SIMPAC, DYNAMO, and SIMULATE, we deviate slightly from this approach in the treatment of GPSS II and SIMSCRIPT. We have chosen to reprint two articles by the authors of GPSS II and SIMSCRIPT, respectively, as a means of presenting these two languages.

GENERAL PURPOSE LANGUAGES, FORTRAN

Although a discussion of general purpose computer languages might well include ALGOL, COBOL, FORTRAN, IBM'S PL/I, as well as other computer languages, we have arbitrarily elected to limit this section to a treatment of FORTRAN, since it is indeed the most widely used computer language for scientific applications. Our objective is to demonstrate the use of a particular general purpose computer language in writing simulation programs and then to compare the general purpose language with several of the special purpose simulation languages. This objective could have been accomplished just as easily by choosing any of the other general purpose languages.

The key word in comparing FORTRAN with the simulation languages is flexibility, since this is the principal advantage to be gained by writing simulation programs in FORTRAN rather than in GPSS, SIMSCRIPT, GASP, etc. The flexibility of FORTRAN can easily be seen in its complete independence of flow charting. That is, FORTRAN programs can be written with or without the use of a flow chart and without any regard for the particular form of the flow chart if one is used. FORTRAN instructions come in four varieties:

1. Arithmetic formulas.
2. Control statements.
3. Input/output statements.
4. Specification statements.

The language consists of five major components: variables, constants, subscripts, expressions, and functions. The number of different subroutines or functions available with FORTRAN is limited only by the memory capacity of the particular machine configuration being utilized. That is, the programmer has the flexibility of being able to write almost any subroutine that he may need for a particular simulation program using a main program to call the specific subroutines when they are needed. The FORTRAN programs for generating stochastic variates that were outlined in Chapter 4 might prove to be a useful set of subroutines to incorporate into one's library of FORTRAN subroutines. Likewise, some of the models described in Chapter 5 could also be formulated as FORTRAN subroutines.

Clearly one alternative to the use of simulation languages is to develop a flexible "main program" written in FORTRAN that can be used to "call a wide variety of FORTRAN subroutines. Rather than attempting to write a unique FORTRAN program for each simulation problem, it may be possible to build up a FORTRAN simulation program for a complex system from a set of existing FORTRAN subroutines. Needless to say a modular approach of this type necessarily requires that there be some degree of similarity in the basic structure of the systems being simulated by this procedure. It may be recalled that a modular approach to simulation was suggested in Chapter 5. Although such a procedure may require a great deal of programming time to write all of the subroutines, as well as the FORTRAN main program, it offers the investigator a maximum of flexibility in the design of simulation experiments. Furthermore, for the investigator who does not have access to a large-scale computer of the magnitude of the IBM 7090/94, this may prove to be the only alternative available to him, since most of the existing simulation languages have been written exclusively for large-scale machines.

The simulation language known as GASP has incorporated these principles into its design because programs written in GASP consist of a FORTRAN "main program" associated with an elaborate set of FORTRAN subroutines which when combined yield a very powerful simulation programming package. The advantage to this modular approach is that each person can design his own simulation language in a manner that is best suited to his particular simulation requirements.

Another advantage which FORTRAN has over the special purpose simulation languages is its almost universal availability, since FORTRAN compilers exist for almost every type of computer (both large and small) that is being marketed today. Until the time comes when everyone has access to a large-scale computer, the majority of the practitioners in the field of computer simulation are likely to find it necessary to resort to the type of modular approached outlined above, using either FORTRAN or some other general purpose compiler rather than a special purpose simulation language.

Most FORTRAN compilers include a fairly elaborate diagnostic or error checking program that checks programs written in FORTRAN for either FORTRAN rule violations or capacity violations. However, these diagnostic programs as a rule do not possess the ability to check for logical errors in simulation programs. This represents a decided disadvantage of FORTRAN when compared to GPSS, SIMSCRIPT, DYNAMO, etc., because all of the special purpose simulation languages have error-checking programs that can detect logical errors as well as rule violations and capacity violations.

Having examined a number of simulation models of business and economic systems in Chapters 5 and 6, it should be fairly obvious that four elements are basic to all simulation procedures whether they be written in FORTRAN or one of the special purpose simulation languages. These four elements include:

1. Initial values.
2. Data generation.
3. Time flow mechanism.
4. Output reports.

At the beginning of any simulation run a set of input values or starting conditions must either be read into the memory of the computer in the form of constants or generated internally by the computer itself. That is, the system being simulated is assumed to be a "running" dynamic system, and our simulation program is assumed to take over control of this "running" system at a particular point in time. The initial values we select are necessarily a reflection of the point in time at which we decide to enter the system. With FORTRAN the programmer has complete flexibility in terms of the method of either reading in starting values for the system or generating them using FORTRAN subroutines such as those described in Chapter 4.

On the basis of the initial values or starting conditions under which the system is assumed to operate and the values of the system's exogenous variables, which are either read into the computer during a simulation run or generated internally while the run is taking place, endogenous variables are generated by the computer according to the logic of the particular system under study (which has previously been read into the memory of the computer in the form of a computer program). With FORTRAN the generation of exogenous variables is again a matter that depends entirely on the programmer's ingenuity in writing subroutines capable of yielding the desired types of exogenous data. The kinds of FORTRAN subroutines that can be written to generate exogenous variables are almost without limits.

In Chapter 5 we have previously pointed out the importance of selecting a method to move the system being simulated through time. The reader will recall that there are two types of time flow mechanisms in use today—fixed time increment programming methods and variable time increment methods. Throughout this chapter we will have occasion to compare various programming languages on the basis of the type of time flow mechanism utilized.

The decision whether to use a fixed time increment programming method or variable time increment programming method on a particular system depends on the nature of the system [6]. Trial and error is the only sure way of determining which method minimizes computer running time for a particular system. With FORTRAN we have the freedom to choose either of these two methods whereas the special simulation languages force the programmer to choose whatever method the particular language happens to use.

Turning now to the fourth basic element in a simulation procedure, we consider output reports. By comparison with the special purpose simulation languages, FORTRAN offers the maximum in terms of flexibility in the design of output reports, whether they be of a graphical or a tabular nature. With FORTRAN, we are not restricted to a particular output format as is the case with GPSS, SIMSCRIPT, etc.

To illustrate the applicability of FORTRAN to a particular simulation problem we consider the simulation model of a multiprocess firm described by the flow chart in Figure 5-5. A FORTRAN program based on the flow chart in Figure 5-5 is included in Figure 7-1. This program assumes that arrival times are exponentially distributed with an expected value equal to EAT. Process times are also assumed to have a negative exponential distribution with expected values equal to EST(J), $J = 1, \ldots, N$. A subroutine for generating negative exponential variates is included in the FORTRAN program (statements 60 through 67). The parameters M1 and N1 are constants satisfying the requirements of the multiplicative congruential method of generating random numbers described in Chapter 3.

The program begins with a dimension statement indicating that the program will accommodate at most 100 processes. (This number will depend entirely on the memory capacity of the particular computer.) The symbols DT, TWT, TDT, EWT, EDT denote, respectively, idle time, total waiting time, total idle time, expected waiting time, and expected idle time for the jth process, $j = 1, \ldots, 100$. The given input parameters for the model are read into the computer by statement 3. Statement 5 corresponds to block 2 of Figure 5-5, which causes an index I to be set equal to 1 denoting that the first order has been received by the firm. Statements 6-8 cause total waiting time and total idle time for each process to be set equal to zero. Next, process times

```
1    COMMON N1, M1
2    DIMENSION EST(100), ST(100), T(100), WT(100), DT(100),
     TWT(100), TDT(100), EWT(100), EDT(100)
3    READ 4, N1, M1, M, N, EAT, (EST (J), J = 1, N)
4    FORMAT (2 I 10, I 5, I 2/ (10 F 8.2) )
5    I = 1
6    DO 8 J = 1, N
7    TWT (J) = 0.
8    TDT (J) = 0.
9    DO 11 J = 1, N
10   A = EST (J)
11   ST (J) = EXPVAR (A)
12   N2 = N − 1
13   DT (1) = 0.
14   DO 16 J = 1, N2
15   DT (J + 1) = DT (J) + ST (J)
16   TDT (J + 1) = DT (J + 1)
17   TS = 0.
18   DO 21 J = 1, N
19   T (J) = ST (J)
20   TS = TS + T(J)
21   WT (J) = 0.
22   PRINT 23, TS, (WT (J), DT (J), T(J), J = 1, N)
23   FORMAT (F15.2/(8F15.2))
24   AT = EXPVAR (EAT)
25   DO 27 J = 1, N
26   A = EST (J)
27   ST (J) = EXPVAR (A)
28   I = I + 1
29   B = T(1)
30   C = AT
31   DO 43 J = 1, N
32   WT (J) = B − C
33   I F (WT (J)) 34, 34, 37
34   DT (J) = − WT (J)
35   WT (J) = 0.
36   GO TO 38
37   DT (J) = 0.
38   T (J) = WT (J) + ST (J)
39   TWT (J) = TWT (J) + WT (J)
```

Figure 7-1. A FORTRAN program for a simulation model of a multiprocess firm.

```
40    TDT (J) = TDT (J) + DT (J)
41    B = B + T (J + 1)
42    C = C + WT (J) + ST (J)
43    CONTINUE
44    TS = 0.
45    DO 46 J = 1, N
46    TS = TS + T (J)
47    PRINT 23, TS, (WT (J), DT (J), T(J), J = 1, N)
48    IF (I − M) 24, 49, 49
49    SM = M
50    DO 52 J = 1, N
51    EWT (J) = TWT (J) / SM
52    EDT (J) = TDT (J) / SM
53    PRINT 54, (TWT (J), J = 1, N)
54    FORMAT (8F15.2)
55    PRINT 54, (TDT (J), J = 1, N)
56    PRINT 54, (EWT (J), J = 1, N)
57    PRINT 54, (EDT (J), J = 1, N)
58    GO TO 3
59    END
60    FUNCTION EXPVAR (X)
61    COMMON N1, M1,
62    N1 = N1 * M1
63    R = N1
64    R = R / 1.0E10
65    EXPVAR = − X * LOGF(R)
66    RETURN
67    END
```

Figure 7-1 (continued)

are generated for all N processes by the exponential variate subroutine. Idle times are then computed for each process according to the equations given by 5-52 in statements 12-15, while total idle time is calculated by statement 16. The total process times for all N processes are accumulated by statements 17-20, and waiting time for each process is set equal to zero in statement 21 according to Eqs. 5-51. Statement 22 is a PRINT statement.

The arrival of a second order is indicated by statement 24 by the generation of an arrival time AT. A set of N new process times is generated by statements 25-27. Statement 28 indicates that the total number of orders should be incremented by one. The sign tests that are called for in blocks 9-24 of Figure 5-5 for a particular order, the total time that the order spends at each process, and the total idle time for each process are all condensed into FORTRAN statements 29-43. Total process times are then computed by statements 44-46. Statement 47 is a PRINT statement.

If I is greater than or equal to M in statement 48, then expected waiting time and expected idle time are computed for each process, and total waiting time, total idle time, expected waiting time, and expected idle time are printed out. On the other hand, if I is less than M, we return to statement 24.

In order to facilitate a comparison of FORTRAN with two of the special purpose languages, this simple program has also been written in GPSS II and GASP. These programs appear at the end of the sections of this chapter, which treat GPSS II and GASP, respectively.

GPSS II (BY R. EFRON AND G. GORDON)*

Recent years have seen the development of several general purpose digital computer programs aimed at simplifying the task of carrying out simulation studies [1]. Among these is a program called the General Purpose Systems Simulator (GPSS) [11, 15]. Substantial experience accumulated in the use of this program has led to a number of suggested improvements and the present article describes a second version of the program, called the General Purpose Systems Simulator II (GPSS II) [12, 13].

GPSS II is consistent with the original GPSS program in the sense that it employs the same principles and that all functions performed by the earlier program can also be performed by GPSS II. Although this paper does not assume prior knowledge of GPSS, before describing the new program some insight may be gained by giving a summary of the major improvements incorporated. In brief, these improvements are:

Greater ability to sense the current state of the system, and to implement decisions based upon that state. "Variable statements" permit FORTRAN-like algebraic computations upon system variables. These capabilities provide

---

* This section on GPSS II has been reprinted in its entirety from an article by R. Efron and G. Gordon, entitled "A General Purpose Digital Simulation and Examples of its Applications," which appeared in the *IBM Systems Journal*, Vol. 3, No. 1, 1964. Permission to reprint this article was obtained directly from the International Business Machines Corporation.

much improved control over the flow of transactions in response to the current state of the system.

The ability to associate a greater amount of information with each transaction in the form of eight parameters.

The introduction of an indirect specification feature which permits a transaction to specify from its parameters the characteristics of the block being entered, rather than requiring these characteristics to be fixed for an entire simulation. This adds flexibility and makes it possible to reduce the size of certain types of models.

The generalization of GPSS functions to permit a wider variety of arguments and a greater number of data points for inserting data descriptive of the system.

An optional assembly feature which simplifies the description of the block diagram by furnishing the block numbers from symbolic names, and which enables the program to set up and call in "block macros." These macros are user-defined segments of a block diagram which can be used repetitively within a model, with the block characteristics varied as desired.

The ability to go into FAP subroutines prepared by the user.

Expanded output statistics and error information.

Generally faster execution.

Block Diagram Language

In GPSS II, the structure of the system being simulated is described in the form of a block diagram drawn with a fixed set of predefined *block types*. Each block type represents a specific action that is characteristic of some basic operation that can occur in a system. Connections between the blocks of the diagram indicate the sequence of actions that occur in the system. Where there is a choice of actions, more than one connection is made from a block to indicate the choice.

Moving through the system being simulated are certain basic units that depend upon the nature of the system. For example, a communication system is concerned with the movement of messages, a traffic system with vehicles or a data processing system with data records, and so on. These units are identified with entities called transactions. The sequence of actions occurring in the system in real time is reflected in the movement of transactions from block to block in simulated clock time.

Action Times

Clock time is represented by an integral number, with the interval of real time corresponding to a unit change of clock time chosen by the program user. The program computes an *action time* for each transaction entering a block to represent the time taken by the system action simulated by the block. The transaction remains at the block for this interval of simulated time before attempting to proceed. The action time may be a fixed interval (including zero), a random variable, or it can be made to depend upon conditions in the system in various ways. An action time is defined by giving a *mean* and *modifier* for the block. If the modifier is zero, the action time is a constant equal to the mean. If the modifier is a number ($\leq$ mean), the action time is a random variable chosen from the range, mean $\pm$ modifier, with equal probabilities given to each number in the range.

It is possible to introduce into the simulation, a number of *functions* which are tables of numbers relating an input variable x to an output variable y. Any number (>1) of pairs of values (x,y) can be used in a table defining a function. The table can be interpreted in the continuous mode by assuming linear variation between the points, thereby approximating any desired function with straight line segments. In the discrete mode, the table defines a step function.

By specifying the modifier at a block to be a function, the output of the function controls the block time. There are several modes of operating the functions, depending upon the choice of the input variable for the function. If a random number mode is selected, for example, the input is a random variable with uniform distribution between 0 and 1 so that the output is a random variable with a distribution controlled by the function. Other modes of operating functions are described later.

Associated with the system being simulated, there are certain physical or control elements that operate on the units represented by transactions and direct their flow through the system. Three types of system entities are defined in GPSS to represent such elements. Two, called *facilities* and *storages*, are characteristic of the physical equipment of the system. A third, called *logic switches*, is characteristic of the control elements of the system.

System Entities

A facility is defined as any piece of equipment that can be engaged by a single transaction at a time. A storage is defined as any piece of equipment that can be occupied by many transactions at a time up to some predetermined limit. A logic switch is a two-level indicator that can be used to record the state of some system condition that is instrumental in deciding when or how operations are executed. A number of systems' entities of each type may be employed, and they are identified by num-

Table 7-1

GPSS II Entity	System Entity
Facility	Card punch
Storage	Memory
Logic switch	Sense switch
Facility	Toll booth
Storage	Road
Logic switch	Traffic light

ber. Some examples of how the systems' entities might be interpreted are shown in Table 7-1.

These definitions of the system entities are descriptive and are not meant to determine literally the manner in which system elements are translated into simulation entities. Certain control decisions that depend specifically upon the state of equipment represented by facilities or storages can be made directly without the need to employ a logic switch. On the other hand, facilities and storages may be introduced in the simulation not to represent identifiable items of equipment but to control the flow of transaction by the restrictions implied in their definitions. For example, if a segment of a system can only be entered by a limited number of units, entry to the part of the block diagram representing this segment can be made contingent upon transactions being able to enter a storage with a capacity set to this limit.

Similarly, the interpretation of transactions as representing physical units moving through the system should not be interpreted too literally. Transactions may be introduced to help control the system rather than to represent the basic units handled by the system. In the systems of Table 7-1, for example, the logic switches might be controlled by transactions whose movements from block to block represent changes in system environment rather than the movement of some physical element.

Choice of Paths

Each block is given a number to identify it, and the connections between blocks are made by specifying at each block the number of the next block or blocks to which a transaction is to go. Provision is made for making a choice by specifying two next blocks, referred to as next blocks A and B. The method to be used for choosing between alternatives is indicated by a *selection factor*, which can be set to indicate one of several modes. If there is no choice, the successor is next block A. A random choice can be made by setting the selection factor S to a decimal fraction. The probability of going to next block A is then 1-S and to the next block B is S. A conditional mode, indicated by setting S = BOTH, sends a transaction to next block A if this move is possible and to next block B if it is not. A random selection can also be made over any number of blocks by a selection mode called PICK. The choice can then be any block in the range of numbers A through B (B > A), with equal probability being given to each. Similarly, a mode called ALL makes a conditional choice over the range of blocks from numbers A through B by trying A first, A + 1 next, and so on.

Creation, Delay, and Removal

Each block type is represented by a particular symbol and it is also given a name which is usually an imperative verb descriptive of the block action. Figure 7-2 shows the symbols and names of a number of the block types concerned with creating, delaying, and removing transactions. Transactions are created and entered into the simulation by a block type called ORIGINATE, with the action time controlling the interval between successive creations. The TERMINATE block removes the transactions from the simulation. An ADVANCE block is used to represent any action that takes time and therefore delays the transaction but does not involve any equipment. It is also used as a buffer in which to keep transactions while waiting for equipment to become available or for some condition in the system to change.

Figure 7-3 illustrates a number of blocks concerned with the use of equipment by transactions. The number of the item of equipment employed by the block is indicated in the flag attached to the symbol.

ORIGINATE   ADVANCE   TERMINATE

Figure 7-2.

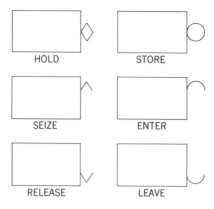

Figure 7-3.

Use of Equipment

A HOLD block allows a transaction to engage a facility for as long as the transaction remains in the block. The SEIZE block similarly allows a transaction to engage a facility, but control of the facility is not given up by the transaction until some time later when it enters a RELEASE block. In a similar manner, the STORE block allows a transaction to occupy space in a storage while it is in the block, an ENTER block allows a transaction to occupy space only, and a LEAVE block allows space to be vacated.

Gathering Statistics

When the conditions for advancing a transaction are not satisfied, several transactions may be kept waiting at a block. Such transactions are kept in order by the program and allowed to move on by a first-in, first-out rule. No information about the queue of transactions is gathered, however, unless the queue forms a QUEUE block, shown in Figure 7-4, which is expressly designed to measure the average and maximum queue lengths and, if required, the distribution of time spent on the queue.

It is also desirable to measure the length of time taken by transactions to move through the system or parts of the system, and this can be done with the MARK and TABULATE blocks which are also shown in Figure 7-4. Each of these block types notes the time a transaction arrives at the block. Also, the TABULATE block enters in a table

Figure 7-4.

the difference between the times of arrival at the MARK and TABU-LATE blocks. In addition to working in conjunction with a MARK block to derive transit times of transactions, a TABULATE block may be used by itself to tabulate a wide variety of different quantities, as described later.

Data Processing Example

To illustrate the features of the program that have been described so far, consider the following example of simulating the flow of messages in a real-time data processing system. A computer receives messages from a terminal, locates corresponding records on a disk file, and uses these records to process the messages. It will be assumed that there are three disk files, each with an independently operated arm, but with all three files sharing a single channel for sending records into the computer. In this example, each message is a transaction, and the unit of time chosen is one millisecond. Action times, where used, are for simple rectangular distributions. In Figure 7-5, block 1 shows a mean of 50 and a modifier of 25 as indicated in the center of the block. The numbers

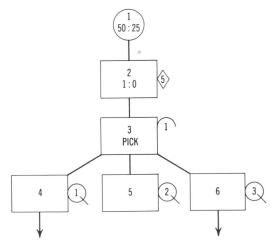

Figure 7-5. Enter message.

appearing at the top of the blocks are the block numbers. At the bottom of some of the blocks, a selection factor is indicated.

Receiving Messages

Figure 7-5 shows first the section of the block diagram concerned with entering messages into the system. Block number 1 is an ORIGINATE block that creates the transactions and sends them to a HOLD block using facility number 5 that represents the central processing unit of the computer. The time at this block, 1 millisecond, represents the time taken to read the message into the computer. A storage, number 1, is defined to represent the computer memory. The capacity of this storage is set to control the number of messages that can be held in the computer at one time. Messages occupy space by moving into an ENTER block. The ENTER block uses a random selection mode PICK to send transactions to one of three queues with equal probability. Here they wait for the availability of one of the disk files. Since the block diagram for each stream of transactions is identical from this point on, except that differently numbered disk files are used, only one stream is illustrated.

Reading the Disk File

The disk file can only search for one record at a time. It is, therefore, defined as a facility. The transactions in the QUEUE block are waiting for the disk file to become available. When this happens, the transaction at the head of the queue moves into the SEIZE block and so takes over control of the disk file (Figure 7-6). The time at the SEIZE block represents the time

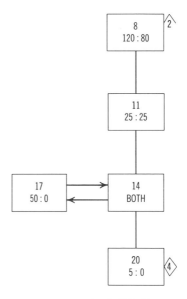

Figure 7-6. Read disk file.

taken to position the arm over the correct track of the disk. When the transaction emerges from the SEIZE block, the arm is correctly positioned. It must now wait for the record to come under the head of the arm. The disk revolution time is assumed to be 50 milliseconds, so the waiting time can be anything from 0 to 50 units. The transaction is, therefore, sent to an ADVANCE block with a mean and modifier both equal to 25.

One more condition must be satisfied before the record can be read. The channel, which is being shared by all three disk files, must be available at the time the record comes under the head. To test for this condition, the transaction passes into an ADVANCE block with zero time and a selection factor of BOTH. The channel is represented by facility number 4, and if it is available, the transaction passes into a HOLD block to use the channel. If the channel is not free, the conditional selection mode at the ADVANCE block sends the transaction to another ADVANCE block where it waits for a period of 50 milliseconds and returns to try for the channel again when the record next comes under the head. If necessary, it keeps retrying in this manner until it does get onto the channel.

When the transaction has passed through the HOLD block representing the channels, the record has been read and the disk file is

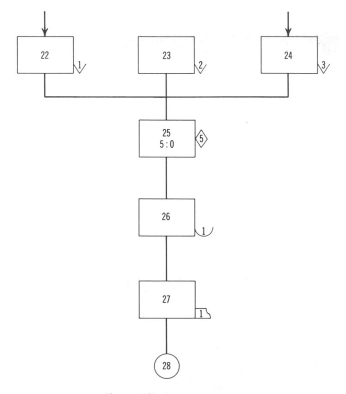

Figure 7-7. Process message.

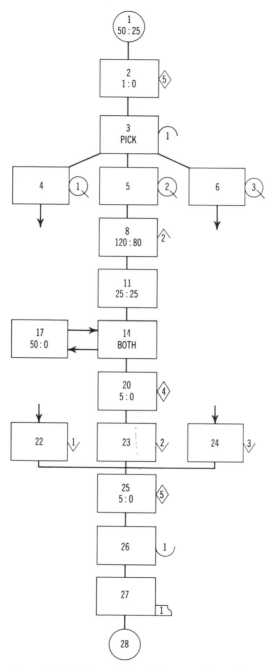

Figure 7-8. Simple real-time, data processing system.

released by moving the transaction to a RELEASE block (Figure 7-7). The transaction moves into a HOLD block, using facility number 5 to represent the processing being carried out by the computer. When processing of the record at the HOLD block is complete, the transaction goes to a LEAVE block to give up the computer memory space and then goes to a TERMINATE block to be removed from the simulation. The complete block diagram is illustrated in Figure 7-8.

Transaction Properties

As described so far, transactions have no particular identity. Each is treated by a block in the same manner as any other. In fact, transactions have two attributes—*priority* and *parameters*, which influence the way they are processed by blocks.

Each transaction has a priority assigned to it. There are eight priority levels, 0 being the lowest level, which is the level set at the time of creating the transaction. At any point in the block diagram, the priority can be reset up or down by a PRIORITY block illustrated in Figure 7-9. Where there is competition between transactions to occupy a block or take over equipment, the service rule established by the program is to advance transactions in order of priority and first-in, first-out within a priority class.

Parameters are integral positive numbers that can be attached to a transaction. Up to eight parameters can be placed on any one transaction. They are placed there by an ASSIGN block (Figure 7-9), which can use as a source for the parameter any function or any of the system variables that are described later. An ASSIGN block can either add to, subtract from, or replace a parameter.

The meaning of the parameters is determined by the program user and depends upon the use to be made of the parameter. The most important use of parameters is through a program feature, called *indirect addressing*, that is associated with blocks. When a block is defined normally (directly) a set of numbers must be given to deter-

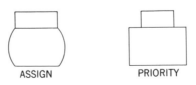

ASSIGN   PRIORITY

Figure 7-9.

mine such factors as the mean, modifier, equipment number, and the next blocks. With indirect addressing, one or more of these numbers can be left unspecified at the time of defining the block. Instead, the program can be instructed to take for this number a parameter that has been assigned to the transaction entering the block. In this way, the manner in which the block processes the transaction depends upon the transaction itself.

Indirect Addressing

Indirect addressing is indicated by placing an asterisk followed by a parameter number in a field defining the block. For example, *3 in the equipment number field of a HOLD block makes that block use the value of parameter number 3 as the facility number. Such an indirectly defined HOLD block entered by a transaction with the number 15 in parameter 3 would act exactly as a HOLD block in which the facility was specified directly as being 15. This is illustrated in Figure 7-10. Indirect addressing increases the ability of the program to represent systems. It can also substantially decrease the size of the block diagram representing the system by making it unnecessary to duplicate segments of the diagram which are functionally equivalent but differ in specific values.

Example of Indirect Addressing

As an example, Figure 7-11 shows the same system described before but in this case making use of priority, parameters, and indirect

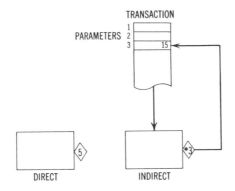

Figure 7-10. Indirect addressing.

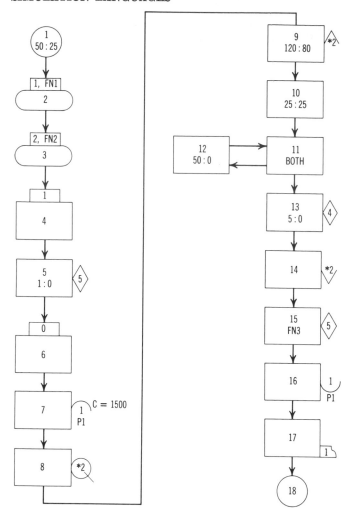

Figure 7-11. Data processing system using indirect addressing.

addresses. The transactions leaving the ORIGINATE block are sent through two ASSIGN blocks. The first block places in parameter number 1 a number representing the message length which is derived from a continuous function, number 1, operating in a random number mode. The second ASSIGN block sets parameter number 2 to be a number 1, 2, or 3 derived from a discrete function, number 2, operating in a random number mode, which represents the disk file to be searched.

The proportion of transactions sent to each of the disk files can be controlled with this function by choosing the values of x at which it is defined; in this case, the probabilities of going to the three disks are equal.

To illustrate the use of priority, the system is arranged to give priority for the use of the central processing unit to new messages arriving in the system. This is done by sending the transactions to a PRIORITY block that sets the level of priority to 1 just prior to the HOLD block representing the process of reading messages into the computer and then resetting the priority to zero when the message has been read in. Now, with indirect addressing, it is no longer necessary to draw a separate segment of the block diagram for each of the transaction streams. Instead, a single QUEUE and a single SEIZE block are used with the queue number and the facility number specified indirectly by parameter number 2. The remainder of the block diagram is the same as before except that the RELEASE block that gives up the disk file is also indirectly addressed on parameter number 2.

Further Uses of Parameters

Two other uses of parameters are illustrated in this example. Functions can operate in a *parameter mode*, in which case they take as the input variable a parameter of the transaction calling for the function. At block number 15 of Figure 7-11, this feature is used to make the processing time depend upon the message length as indicated by parameter number 1. It is also possible to allow a parameter to control the amount of space the transaction occupies in a storage. This feature is used at block numbers 7 and 16 of Figure 7-11, to make the space occupied by the transaction equal to the number of characters in the message.

Program Input

Having drawn the complete block diagram, as shown in Figure 7-11, one card is punched for each block, and this set of cards, together with some control and definition cards, forms the input to the program. The cards are read by the program and used to set up the simulation model, execute the simulation for a specified length of time, and print out results in a single program run. Figure 7-12 shows a listing of the cards that need to be punched for the block diagram of Figure 7-11. There is an assembly option in the program that allows block numbers to be given symbolically and also assigns sequential

LOC	NAME	X	Y	Z	SEL	NBA	NBB	MEAN	MOD	REMARKS
*										
*										MESSAGES FROM A TERMINAL ARE READ INTO A
*										COMPUTER. A SEARCH IS MADE ON ONE OF THREE
*										DISK FILES FOR A RECORD WHICH IS THEN PROCESSED.
*										THE SYSTEM HAS THREE INDEPENDENT DISK FILES
*										WHICH SHARE A COMMON CHANNEL. TIME UNIT
*										IS 1 MILLISEC.
	ORIGINATE							50	25	
	ASSIGN	1	FN1							
	ASSIGN	2	FN2							
	PRIORITY	1								
	HOLD	5						1		
	PRIORITY	0								
	ENTER	1	P1							
	QUEUE	*2								
	SEIZE	*2						120	80	
	ADVANCE							25	25	
TRY	ADVANCE				BOTH	GO	WAIT			
WAIT	ADVANCE					TRY		50		
GO	HOLD	4						5		
	RELEASE	*2								
	HOLD	5								FN3
	LEAVE	1	P1							
	TABULATE	1								
	TERMINATE	R						COUNT TO END OF SIMULATION		
*										
*	FUNCTION							FOR ASSIGNING MESSAGE LENGTH. RANDOM MODE		
*										
1	FUNCTION	RN1	C5							
0	5	0.2	6	0.4	9	0.6	19	0.8	24	1.0 25
*										
*	FUNCTION							FOR ASSIGNING DISK NUMBER. RANDOM MODE		
*										
2	FUNCTION	RN1	D3							
.333	1	0.667	2	1.0	3					
*										
*	FUNCTION							TO DETERMINE PROCESSING TIME. PARAMETER MODE		
*										
3	FUNCTION	P1	C2							
0	0	25	10							
*										
*	CARD TO DEFINE CAPACITY OF STORE									
*										
1	CAPACITY	1500								
*										
*	CARD TO ESTABLISH TABULATION INTERVALS									
*										
1	TABLE	M1	0	250	25			TABULATES TIME IN SYSTEM		
*										
*	CARD TO CONTROL LENGTH OF RUN									
*										
	START	1000						RUN UNTIL 1000 TRANS. TERMINATE		
*										
	END							PLACED AT END OF ALL PROBLEMS BEING RUN		

Figure 7-12. Listing of problem input.

CLOCK TIME REL 52758 ABS 52758

BLK	TRANS, TOTAL	BLK	TRANS, TOTAL	BLK	TRANS, TOTAL	BLK	TRANS, TOTAL	BLK	TRANS, TOTAL
1	0,1074	2	0,1074	3	0,1074	4	0,1074	5	0,1074
6	0,1074	7	0,1074	8	71,1074	9	2,1003	10	1,1001
11	0,1071	12	0, 71	13	0,1000	14	0,1000	15	0,1000
16	0,1000	17	0,1000	18	0,1000				

FACILITY NR	AVERAGE UTILIZATION	NUMBER ENTRIES	AVERAGE TIME/TRANS	TRANS	$TRANS
1	0.9769	336	153.39	65,S	0
2	0.9616	333	152.35	32,S	0
3	0.9987	334	157.75	36,S	0
4	0.0948	1000	5.00	0	0
5	0.1213	2074	3.08	0	0

STORAGE NR	CAPACITY	AVERAGE CONTENTS	AVERAGE UTILIZATION	NUMBER ENTRIES	AVERAGE TIME/TRANS	CURRENT CONTENTS
1	1500	606.06	0.4040	15227	2099.87	984

QUEUE NR	MAXIMUM CONTENTS	AVERAGE CONTENTS	TOTAL ENTRIES	ZERO ENTRIES	PERCENT ZEROS	AVERAGE TIME/TRANS	TABLE NUMBER	CURRENT CONTENTS
1	32	14.52	364	7	1.9	2105.22	0	28
2	14	3.76	343	17	5.0	577.94	0	10
3	37	21.19	367	1	0.3	3045.78	0	33

Figure 7-13. Results of simulation run.

TABLE NUMBER 1

ENTRIES IN TABLE 1000		MEAN ARGUMENT 2089,295	STANDARD DEVIATION 1555.665		NON-WEIGHTED	
UPPER LIMIT	OBSERVED FREQUENCY	PERCENT OF TOTAL	CUMULATIVE PERCENTAGE	CUMULATIVE REMAINDER	MULTIPLE OF MEAN	DEVIATION FROM MEAN
0	0	0.00	0.0	100.0	0.000	-1.343
250	57	5.70	5.7	94.3	0.120	-1.182
500	134	13.40	19.1	80.9	0.239	-1.022
750	105	10.50	29.6	70.4	0.359	-0.861
1000	47	4.70	34.3	65.7	0.479	-0.700
1250	68	6.80	41.1	58.9	0.598	-0.540
1500	60	6.00	47.1	52.9	0.718	-0.379
1750	21	2.10	49.2	50.8	0.838	-0.218
2000	37	3.70	52.9	47.1	0.957	-0.057
2250	26	2.60	55.5	44.5	1.077	0.103
2500	46	4.60	60.1	39.9	1.197	0.264
2750	41	4.10	64.2	35.8	1.316	0.425
3000	59	5.90	70.1	29.9	1.436	0.585
3250	54	5.40	75.5	24.5	1.556	0.746
3500	27	2.70	78.2	21.8	1.675	0.907
3750	26	2.60	80.8	19.2	1.795	1.068
4000	41	4.10	84.9	15.1	1.915	1.228
4250	31	3.10	88.0	12.0	2.034	1.389
4500	50	5.00	93.0	7.0	2.154	1.550
4750	16	1.60	94.6	5.4	2.273	1.710
5000	18	1.80	96.4	3.6	2.393	1.871
5250	13	1.30	97.7	2.3	2.513	2.032
5500	5	0.50	98.2	1.8	2.632	2.192
5750	7	0.70	98.9	1.1	2.752	2.353
OVERFLOW	11	1.10	100.0	0.0		

Figure 7-13. (Continued).

block numbers automatically. This option has been employed in Figure 7-12. After assembly of the cards shown in Figure 7-12, the block numbers are assigned as shown in Figure 7-11. The assembly program also allows the user to define macros consisting of sets of blocks describing some segment of a system which is to be used repeatedly. Once defined, the macro is given a name and thereafter can be called by that name. Any number of the fields defining the blocks in the macro can be left unspecified at the time of definition—instead they are supplied at the time of calling the macro.

Program Output

The results of a run in which 1000 messages were processed are shown in Figure 7-13. Information is given about the number of times each block is entered, the utilization made of the facilities and storages, the size of the queues, and the tabulation of the transit times through the system. In this case, because the transit time is measured from the time of creation, it is not necessary to use a MARK block.

Controlling Transaction Flow

Some of the block types, illustrated in Figure 7-14, are concerned with the use of logic switches and the control of transaction flow. One block type, called LOGIC, allows a transaction to either set, reset, or invert a logic switch. Another block type, called GATE, is able to test the status of a logic switch, facility, or storage. The program allows a transaction into this block only if the condition being tested is satisfied. Also shown in Figure 7-14 is a LOOP block which decrements a specified parameter and sends the transaction one way or the other, according to

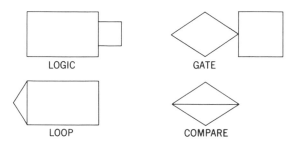

LOGIC

GATE

LOOP

COMPARE

Figure 7-14.

whether the result is zero or not (the COMPARE block is discussed later).

Simple Polling System

To show how these blocks are used in controlling the flow of transactions, suppose that in the previous example there are several terminals sending messages to the computer and a simple polling system is set up whereby each terminal in turn gets access to the computer for a fixed length of time. If, for example, there are three terminals, each represented by an ORIGINATE block, the entry of messages into the system would be controlled as shown in Figure 7-15. One logic switch is associated with each terminal, and transactions leaving the ORIGINATE blocks are checked by a GATE block looking for the switch to be set. Transactions can enter the computer only when the switch is set.

In a small closed loop there is a single transaction cycling around that opens and closes each logic switch in turn. This is done by making parameter number 1 of this control transaction represent the number of the terminal to be checked. At the beginning of a cycle, this parameter is set to 3, and it is then used at a LOGIC block to set one of the switches by indirect addressing. The switch remains set for a fixed length of time T and is then reset when the control transaction moves to a second LOGIC block. The LOOP block decrements the parameter by 1 and

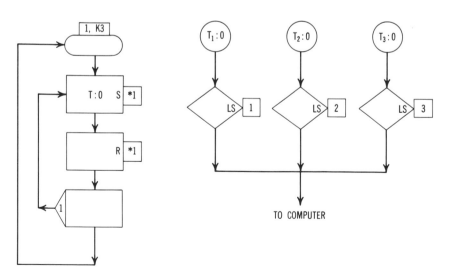

Figure 7-15. Polling terminals with equal times.

sends the transaction to the next switch unless the parameter has been reduced to zero, in which case it restarts the cycle. In this way, the three logic switches are each opened, in turn, for a fixed interval T, thereby giving each terminal in sequence access to the computer.

System Variables

The control of transaction flow in the examples described so far has depended upon the state of facilities, storages, and logic switches. In addition, the program can make use of various items of data known collectively as *system variables*. These are numbers that describe the state of the system, and they can be referenced by the program through the use of symbols. For example, the number of transactions at block 20 is represented by W20, the contents of storage 15 by S15, the length of queue number 5 by Q5, and so on. In addition to system properties, reference to an absolute number, such as 6, can be made by using the symbols K6. It is also possible to form combinations of system variables using simple mathematical operators to form what are called *variable statements*. For example, variable statement V1 might be defined as V1 — S6 -| Q5/K2. This provides a system variable V1 whose value is the contents of storage number 6, plus half the contents of queue number 5.

More Advanced Polling System

To illustrate how system variables are used, suppose in the previous example concerned with polling terminals that the system is arranged to skip a terminal if no messages are waiting at that terminal. The loop controlling the polling would then look as shown in Figure 7-16. A COMPARE block has been added to check whether a terminal is empty or not. This block type operates like the GATE block, but the condition tested can be a comparison between any two system variables. References to system variables can be made indirectly. Here the COMPARE block is used to check whether the number of transactions at the block indicated by parameter number 1 of the control transaction is zero. This parameter represents the number of the terminal to be checked next in the polling sequence. If this number is zero, there are no messages waiting at that terminal, and the control transaction does not enter the COMPARE block. Instead, it is diverted directly to the LOOP block to step on to the next terminal. If there are messages waiting, the control transaction passes through the COMPARE block and switches a logic switch in the manner described before.

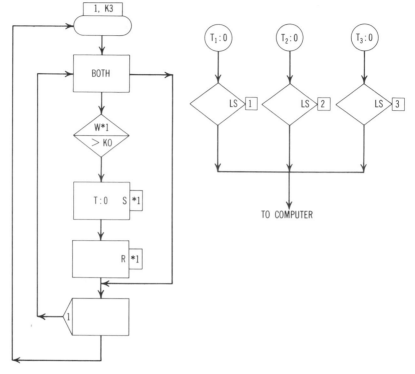

Figure 7-16. Polling terminals, skipping empty terminals.

Systems variables greatly enhance the logical ability of the program. They also extend the ability to derive statistical data about the performance of the system, since any system variable can be tabulated by a TABULATE block to derive a statistical distribution or it can be printed out to give a chronological record. In addition, any system variable may be used as the input variable of a function. The random number, clock, storage, and parameter modes of operating functions are examples of system variables used for this purpose.

Some Other Block Types

Brief descriptions are given of some of the other block types. The INTERRUPT block (Figure 7-17) represents a higher-level use of the facility by a transaction. A transaction is admitted to the block only if the facility it is to interrupt is not already interrupted by another transaction. The facility remains interrupted until the transaction

INTERRUPT   PREEMT   RETURN

Figure 7-17.

exits from the INTERRUPT block. If another transaction is using the facility at the first level of usage, that transaction is suspended in its progress through the block diagram until the interrupt concludes. The suspension is not unconditional, but the various special conditions can be ignored by the user, since the program maintains all the necessary records and automatically takes the proper action in every case. The PREEMPT block also represents a higher-level use of a facility by a transaction but differs from the INTERRUPT block in that a separate block, the RETURN block, is used to signal the conclusion of the interrupt.

The SPLIT, MATCH, ASSEMBLE, and SAVEX blocks are shown in Figure 7-18. The SPLIT block creates a duplicate of each transaction that enters the block. The transactions thus created are said to be members of an *assembly set*. Further creation of transactions by splitting adds members to the set. Since the duplicate transaction may be synchronized with the original, the SPLIT block is useful in representing simultaneous events in a system. The MATCH blocks, used in pairs, synchronize the progress of two transactions of an assembly set. The transactions do not join but continue to advance independently through the block diagram. An ASSEMBLE block joins a specified number of transactions from an assembly set into a single transaction. The final merging of independently manufactured parts is frequently represented by an ASSEMBLE block. The SAVEX block permits the

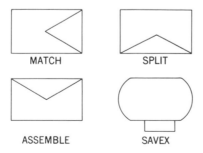

MATCH   SPLIT

ASSEMBLE   SAVEX

Figure 7-18.

user to gather and print information from the block diagram and to transmit information from one transaction to another. Entry to a SAVEX block causes storage of the value of a specified system variable in certain memory locations—referred to as SAVEX locations.

Not all the block types and features of the GPSS II program have been described, but it is hoped that enough information has been given to illustrate the principles of the program and its operation.*

GPSS II: EXAMPLE PROBLEM†

To further illustrate the GPSS II simulation language the single-channel, multiprocess model which was programmed in FORTRAN (Figure 7-1) at the beginning of this chapter has also been written in GPSS II. The flow chart for this model appears in Figure 7-19 and the GPSS II statements are in Figure 7-20. Figures 7-21 through 7-24 contain the output reports generated by a GPSS II run consisting of 1000 order arrivals. The program assumes that our system consists of a series of 5 service stations (processes). The service times for each of these five service stations have negative exponential probability distributions with expected values equal to 10 minutes. Order arrival times are assumed to follow a negative exponential distribution also but with expected arrival time equal to 15 minutes.

It is not possible to generate exponential variates directly with GPSS II. Instead it is necessary to read into the computer a set of five parameter cards (Figure 7-20) containing 24 discrete points on a cumulative negative exponential distribution function with expected value equal to 1. This set of parameter cards is called FUNCTION 1 (FN1). Negative exponential variates with a given expected value can be generated by specifying the expected value which is required and calling FN1.

The first block in our GPSS program (block 10) is an ORIGINATE block. (See Figures 7-19 and 7-20.) The purpose of this block is to create transactions, which in our case means to generate production orders. Furthermore, block 10 indicates that 1000 such orders should be generated and that the time interval between orders has a proba-

---

* This concludes the text of the article by R. Efron and G. Gordon, loc. cit.

† We are indebted to Geoffrey Gordon of the Advanced Systems Development Division of International Business Machines Corporation for providing us with a GPSS II program for our single-channel multiprocess model, as well as the results of a sample run of the program on an IBM 7094.

Single-String Multiple Station Model

GPSS Diagram   Explanation

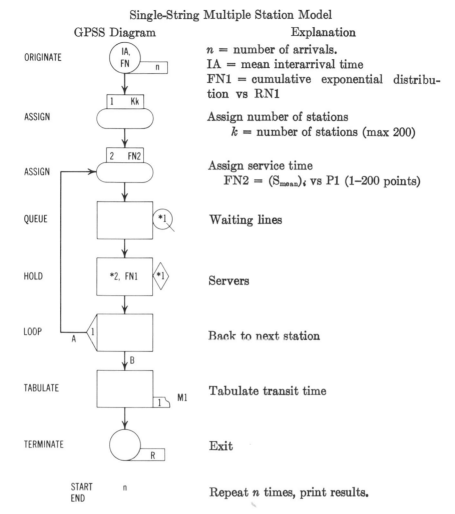

ORIGINATE — n = number of arrivals.
IA = mean interarrival time
FN1 = cumulative exponential distribution vs RN1

ASSIGN — Assign number of stations
k = number of stations (max 200)

ASSIGN — Assign service time
FN2 = (S_{mean}); vs P1 (1–200 points)

QUEUE — Waiting lines

HOLD — Servers

LOOP — Back to next station

TABULATE — Tabulate transit time

TERMINATE — Exit

START n Repeat n times, print results.
END

Figure 7-19. A GPSS flow chart for a simulation model of a multiprocess firm.

bility distribution given by FN1 (negative exponential) with expected value equal to 15 minutes.

The second and third blocks in our program (blocks 20 and 30) are ASSIGN blocks. In block 20 the constant 5 is assigned to parameter 1, indicating that there are five service stations in our system. Block 30 assigns FUNCTION 2 (FN2) to parameter 2. The purpose of FUNC-

```
LOC   NAME      X     Y     Z     SEL   NBA   NBB   MEAN  MOD   REMARKS
 *    JOB       SIMULATION OF 5 STATION PRODUCTION SYSTEM
 *              UNITS ARRIVE AT FIRST OF FIVE STATIONS. INTER-ARRIVAL
 *              TIME AT FIRST STATION HAS NEGATIVE EXPONENTIAL
 *              DISTRIBUTION WITH MEAN EQUAL TO 15. UNITS ARE
 *              PROCESSED SEQUENTIALLY THROUGH THE FIVE
 *              STATIONS. SERVICE TIME FOR ALL STATIONS HAS
 *              NEGATIVE EXPONENTIAL DISTRIBUTION WITH MEAN
 *              EQUAL TO 10. TIME UNIT IS 1 MINUTE.

 *    FUNCTION TO DETERMINING ARRIVAL TIME AT FIRST STATION. RANDOM MODE

 1    FUNCTION  RN1   C24                 CUMULATIVE  EXP.  DIST. VS    RN1
 0    0    .1   .104  .2    .222  .3    .355  .4    .509  .5    .69
 .6   .915 .7   1.2   .75   1.38  .8    1.6   .84   1.83  .88   2.12
 .9   2.3  .92  2.52  .94   2.81  .95   2.99  .96   3.2   .97   3.5
 .98  3.9  .99  4.6   .995  5.3   .998  6.2   .999  7.0   .9997 8.0

 *    FUNCTION TO DETERMINE SERVICE MEAN TIME. PARAMETER MODE

 2    FUNCTION  P1    D5                  SERVICE MEAN TIME VS P1
 1    10   2    10    3     10    4     10    5     10

 10   ORIGINATE              1000              20          15    FN1
 20   ASSIGN    1            K5                30
 30   ASSIGN    2            FN2               40
 40   QUEUE     *1                             50
 50   HOLD      *1                             60          *2    FN1
 60   LOOP      1                              30    70
 70   TABULATE  6                              80
 80   TERMINATE R

 *    STATISTICAL TABLES

 *    TABULATION INTERVALS FOR DISTRIBUTION OF TIME IN QUEUES

 1    QTABLE    1     0     10    20    TABULATES TIME IN QUEUE =1
 2    QTABLE    2     0     10    20    TABULATES TIME IN QUEUE =2
 3    QTABLE    3     0     10    20    TABULATES TIME IN QUEUE =3
 4    QTABLE    4     0     10    20    TABULATES TIME IN QUEUE =4
 5    QTABLE    5     0     10    20    TABULATES TIME IN QUEUE =5

 *    TABULATION INTERVALS FOR DISTRIBUTION OF TIME IN SYSTEM

 6    TABLE     M1    0     10    20    TABULATES TIME IN SYSTEM

      START     1000              RUN UNTIL 1000 TRANS. TERMINATE
```

Figure 7-20. A GPSS II program for a simulation model of a multi-process firm.

TION 2 is to indicate that the expected service time for each of the five service stations in the system is 10 minutes.

Block 40 is a QUEUE block with an indirect specification *1, which means that statistics should be maintained for five queues. (Parameter 1 sets the number of queues at 5.) Block 40, in conjunction with the specified TABULATION INTERVALS found in section 4 of Figure 7-20, causes five QUEUE TABLES to be tabulated at the end of the simulation run with upper class limit equal to zero, class interval equal to 10, and total number of classes equal to 20. (The five QUEUE TABLES are printed out in Figures 7-21 through 7-24.)

The fifth block is a HOLD block which records the usage of a facility by a transaction that enters the block. In our case "the usage of a facility" is equivalent to the service time at each process in our sys-

CLOCK TIME REL   14597   ABS   14597

TRANS COUNTS	BLOCK	TRANS,TOTAL	BLOCK	TRANS,TOTAL	BLOCK	TRANS,TOTAL	BLOCK	TRANS,TOTAL	BLOCK	TRANS,TOTAL
	10	0, 1000	20	0, 1000	30	0, 1000	40	0, 5000	50	0, 5000
	60	0, 5000	70	0, 1000	80	0, 1000				

FACILITY NR	AVERAGE UTILIZATION	NUMBER ENTRIES	AVERAGE TIME/TRANS	TRANS	$TRANS
1	.6679	1000	9.75	0	0
2	.6657	1000	9.72	0	0
3	.6510	1000	9.50	0	0
4	.6320	1000	9.23	0	0
5	.6353	1000	9.27	0	0

QUEUE NR	MAXIMUM CONTENTS	AVERAGE CONTENTS	TOTAL ENTRIES	ZERO ENTRIES	PER CENT ZEROS	AVERAGE TIME/TRANS	TABLE NUMBER	CURRENT CONTENTS
1	16	1.26	1000	341	34.1	18.44	1	0
2	18	1.84	1000	324	32.4	26.86	2	0
3	11	1.24	1000	353	35.8	18.10	3	0
4	12	1.06	1000	374	37.4	15.40	4	0
5	10	1.11	1000	356	35.6	16.18	5	0

TABLE NUMBER 1

ENTRIES IN TABLE 1000   MEAN ARGUMENT 18.442   STANDARD DEVIATION 26.423   NON-WEIGHTED

UPPER LIMIT	OBSERVED FREQUENCY	PER CENT OF TOTAL	CUMULATIVE PERCENTAGE	CUMULATIVE REMAINDER	MULTIPLE OF MEAN	DEVIATION FROM MEAN
0	341	34.10	34.1	65.9	.000	-.698
10	192	19.20	53.3	46.7	.542	-.319
20	160	16.00	69.3	30.7	1.084	-.059
30	88	8.80	78.1	21.9	1.627	.437
40	74	7.40	85.5	14.5	2.169	.816
50	50	5.00	90.5	9.5	2.711	1.194
60	27	2.70	93.2	6.8	3.253	1.573
70	14	1.40	94.6	5.4	3.796	1.951
80	16	1.60	96.2	3.8	4.338	2.330
90	6	.60	96.8	3.2	4.880	2.708
100	7	.70	97.5	2.5	5.422	3.087
110	7	.70	98.2	1.8	5.965	3.465
120	1	.10	98.3	1.7	6.507	3.844
130	5	.50	98.8	1.2	7.049	4.222
140	9	.90	99.7	.3	7.591	4.601
150	3	.30	100.0	.0	8.134	4.979

REMAINING FREQUENCIES ARE ALL ZERO

Figure 7-21. GPSS II output report.

TABLE NUMBER   2
ENTRIES IN TABLE   1000

		MEAN ARGUMENT 26.862	STANDARD DEVIATION 37.974		NON-WEIGHTED	
UPPER LIMIT	OBSERVED FREQUENCY	PER CENT OF TOTAL	CUMULATIVE PERCENTAGE	CUMULATIVE REMAINDER	MULTIPLE OF MEAN	DEVIATION FROM MEAN
0	324	32.40	32.4	67.6	.000	-.707
10	180	18.00	50.4	49.6	.372	-.444
20	114	11.40	61.8	38.2	.745	-.181
30	80	8.00	69.8	30.2	1.117	-.083
40	59	5.90	75.7	24.3	1.489	.346
50	49	4.90	80.6	19.4	1.861	.609
60	42	4.20	84.8	15.2	2.234	.873
70	32	3.20	88.0	12.0	2.606	1.136
80	25	2.50	90.5	9.5	2.978	1.399
90	20	2.00	92.5	7.5	3.350	1.663
100	10	1.00	93.5	6.5	3.723	1.926
110	11	1.10	94.6	5.4	4.095	2.189
120	6	.60	95.2	4.8	4.467	2.453
130	11	1.10	96.3	3.7	4.840	2.716
140	8	.80	97.1	2.9	5.212	2.979
150	8	.80	97.9	2.1	5.584	3.243
160	11	1.10	99.0	1.0	5.956	3.506
170	6	.60	99.6	.4	6.329	3.769
180	1	.10	99.7	.3	6.701	4.033
OVERFLOW	3	.30	100.0	.0		

Figure 7-22. GPSS II output report.

TABLE NUMBER 3

ENTRIES IN TABLE 1000 MEAN ARGUMENT 18.098 STANDARD DEVIATION 24.742 NON-WEIGHTED

UPPER LIMIT	OBSERVED FREQUENCY	PER CENT OF TOTAL	CUMULATIVE PERCENTAGE	CUMULATIVE REMAINDER	MULTIPLE OF MEAN	DEVIATION FROM MEAN
0	358	35.80	35.8	64.2	.000	-.731
10	190	19.00	54.8	45.2	.553	-.327
20	139	13.90	68.7	31.3	1.105	.077
30	85	8.50	77.2	22.8	1.658	.481
40	71	7.10	84.3	15.7	2.210	.885
50	45	4.50	88.8	11.2	2.763	1.289
60	35	3.50	92.3	7.7	3.315	1.694
70	28	2.80	95.1	4.9	3.868	2.098
80	13	1.30	96.4	3.6	4.420	2.502
90	16	1.60	98.0	2.0	4.973	2.906
100	7	.70	98.7	1.3	5.525	3.310
110	5	.50	99.2	.8	6.078	3.714
120	4	.40	99.6	.4	6.631	4.119
130	2	.20	99.8	.2	7.183	4.523
140	1	.10	99.9	.1	7.736	4.927
150	1	.10	100.0	.0	8.288	5.331

Figure 7-22. (Continued).

TABLE NUMBER   4

ENTRIES IN TABLE   MEAN ARGUMENT   STANDARD DEVIATION   NON-WEIGHTED
     1000   15.404   22.088

UPPER LIMIT	OBSERVED FREQUENCY	PER CENT OF TOTAL	CUMULATIVE PERCENTAGE	CUMULATIVE REMAINDER	MULTIPLE OF MEAN	DEVIATION FROM MEAN
0	374	37.40	37.4	62.6	.000	-.697
10	220	22.00	59.4	40.6	.649	-.245
20	116	11.60	71.0	29.0	1.298	.208
30	114	11.40	82.4	17.6	1.948	.661
40	62	6.20	88.6	11.4	2.597	1.114
50	40	4.00	92.6	7.4	3.246	1.566
60	17	1.70	94.3	5.7	3.895	2.019
70	20	2.00	96.3	3.7	4.544	2.472
80	16	1.60	97.9	2.1	5.193	2.924
90	4	.40	98.3	1.7	5.843	3.377
100	4	.40	98.7	1.3	6.492	3.830
110	5	.50	99.2	.8	7.141	4.283
120	5	.50	99.7	.3	7.790	4.735
130	3	.30	100.0	.0	8.439	5.188

REMAINING FREQUENCIES ARE ALL ZERO

TABLE NUMBER   5

ENTRIES IN TABLE   MEAN ARGUMENT   STANDARD DEVIATION   NON-WEIGHTED
     1000   16.177   21.498

UPPER LIMIT	OBSERVED FREQUENCY	PER CENT OF TOTAL	CUMULATIVE PERCENTAGE	CUMULATIVE REMAINDER	MULTIPLE OF MEAN	DEVIATION FROM MEAN
0	356	35.60	35.6	64.4	.000	-.752
10	196	19.60	55.2	44.8	.618	-.287
20	149	14.90	70.1	29.9	1.236	.178
30	100	10.00	80.1	19.9	1.854	.643
40	68	6.80	86.9	13.1	2.473	1.108
50	49	4.90	91.8	8.2	3.091	1.573
60	30	3.00	94.8	5.2	3.709	2.038
70	26	2.60	97.4	2.6	4.327	2.504
80	12	1.20	98.6	1.4	4.945	2.969
90	6	.60	99.2	.8	5.563	3.434
100	1	.10	99.3	.7	6.182	3.899
110	2	.20	99.5	.5	6.800	4.364
120	2	.20	99.7	.3	7.418	4.829
130	1	.10	99.8	.2	8.036	5.295
140	2	.20	100.0	.0	8.654	5.760

REMAINING FREQUENCIES ARE ALL ZERO

Figure 7-23. GPSS II output report.

TABLE NUMBER   6

ENTRIES IN TABLE   1000   MEAN ARGUMENT 142.451   STANDARD DEVIATION 67.332   NON-WEIGHTED

UPPER LIMIT	OBSERVED FREQUENCY	PER CENT OF TOTAL	CUMULATIVE PERCENTAGE	CUMULATIVE REMAINDER	MULTIPLE OF MEAN	DEVIATION FROM MEAN
0	0	.00	.0	100.0	.000	-2.116
10	0	.00	.0	100.0	.070	-1.967
20	0	.00	.0	100.0	.140	-1.819
30	2	.20	.2	99.8	.211	-1.670
40	13	1.30	1.5	98.5	.281	-1.522
50	23	2.30	3.8	96.2	.351	-1.373
60	30	3.00	6.8	93.2	.421	-1.225
70	46	4.60	11.4	88.6	.491	-1.076
80	62	6.20	17.6	82.4	.562	-.928
90	78	7.80	25.4	74.6	.632	-.779
100	62	6.20	31.6	68.4	.702	-.630
110	55	5.50	37.1	62.9	.772	-.482
120	64	6.40	43.5	56.5	.842	-.333
130	68	6.80	50.3	49.7	.913	-.185
140	50	5.00	55.3	44.7	.983	-.036
150	59	5.90	61.2	38.8	1.053	.112
160	53	5.30	66.5	33.5	1.123	.261
170	51	5.10	71.6	28.4	1.193	.409
180	33	3.30	74.9	25.1	1.264	.558
OVERFLOW	251	25.10	100.0	.0		

Figure 7-24. GPSS II output report.

tem. The indirect specification *1 indicates that there are five processes in our system, and indirect specification *2 denotes the fact that the expected service time for each of our five processes is 10 minutes according to FN2. The holding time (service time) has an exponential distribution given by FN1. Given the discrete values of FN1 and the expected service times for each of the 5 processes, the computer can then generate exponential service times for each process.

Block 60 is a LOOP block which controls the number of times a transaction passes through blocks 30 through 60. The number of times that a transaction passes through blocks 30 through 60 is determined by parameter 1, which indicates that there are 5 processes in the system and, hence, a transaction should go through the loop 5 times.

The seventh block is a TABULATE block. The purpose of this block is to generate TABLE NUMBER 6, which tabulates the total time required for an order to travel through the entire system. (See Figure 7-24.)

The final block in our program is a TERMINATE block. This block is used to represent the completion of the path of flow in our system. The TERMINATE block will cause the simulation run to cease after 1000 orders have been generated. Figures 7-21 through 7-24 contain the output reports for our sample run.

SIMSCRIPT (BY B. DIMSDALE AND H. M. MARKOWITZ)*

The production of a digital simulator program, or of any program for that matter, involves two steps: creating the model, then writing the program. Fundamentally, the writing of the program is a technical detail which must of necessity wait upon the creation of the model. Nevertheless, the nature of the machinery available for producing simulation programs is bound to exercise an influence on the nature of the model. This is true because effective modeling requires abstraction of the essence of the system under investigation, the direction taken in the abstraction being determined by the goals of the investigation. For complex systems it is very often not clear which of many possible abstractions is most valid for the purposes at hand.

---

* This section has been reproduced in full by permission of the International Business Machines Corporation from an article by B. Dimsdale and H. M. Markowitz, "A Description of the SIMSCRIPT Language," *IBM Systems Journal*, III, No. 1 (1964), 57–67. The SIMSCRIPT compiler may be obtained by writing for SHARE Distribution Number, 3031, RSSIMS, Program Distribution Center, P. O. Box 790, White Plains, N.Y.

The choice in this case is naturally made of the one which is easiest to handle even, perhaps, if it appears slightly less desirable than another one which will clearly lead to great difficulties in programming. At this point, it is worth remarking that the normal course of a simulation is not described by modeling, programming, end of process but rather by modeling, testing, modeling, testing, etc., until an adequate model is developed. It seems a natural conclusion that the less restraint placed upon the modeler by the nature of his tools and their ease of use, the more rapidly this process will converge on the average, this phenomenon being the more pronounced for the more complex systems. From this it follows that the nature of the programming language should facilitate program debugging, modification, and repetitive testing. Storage capacity should not be wasted, reports of simulation results should be easy to arrange and use, and not too much time should be necessary to test models.

SIMSCRIPT Universe

The SIMSCRIPT language [25] is based upon a description of systems involving concepts denoted by entity, attribute, set, state, and event. In this language, these terms have been assigned the following meanings. Briefly, an *entity* is a class of objects described by a fixed collection of parameters called *attributes*. Individual members of an entity class have specific numerical values assigned to their parameters. *Sets* are collections of individual entities having certain common properties. The *state* of the model at any given instant is completely described by the current list of individual entities, their attributes, and set memberships. The dynamics of the system are represented by changes of state; that is, addition or deletion of individuals, change of attribute values, set memberships, or some combination of these. These changes take place instantaneously at discrete points in simulated time and are called *events*. The time at which an event is to occur is most frequently prescribed by SIMSCRIPT programming as current time plus some increment. The occurrence of the event is caused automatically by the SIMSCRIPT system at the prescribed time. That is to say, changes of state take place automatically and instantaneously (with reference to simulated time) at successive discrete points in time. At the conclusion of any event, simulation time is automatically increased to the time of the next event.

In order to indicate the nature of SIMSCRIPT programming, it is necessary to discuss some of the subcategories of the concepts mentioned above. As a matter of convenience, both with regard to conserving computer storage space and ease of programming, entities have been separated into two categories, permanent and temporary. *Permanent* entities are known in advance to be present during the entire simulation. *Temporary* entities are of known form, but individuals, in general, appear and disappear during the simulation. There is a special kind of temporary entity called an *event notice* which is used to schedule future events, that is, changes of state. The distinction is made because event notices, as distinguished from other temporary entities, affect the automatic timing operations.

Sets may have 0, 1, or 2 subscripts specifying the number of entities with which the set is associated, that is, owner entities. That is to say, an unsubscripted set belongs to the system, a singly subscripted set belongs to one entity class, a doubly subscripted set belongs to a pair of entity classes. The members of the set may be ordered as FIFO, LIFO, or ranked on some attribute, high or low.

Events are of two kinds, endogenous and exogenous. *Endogenous* events are those internally generated by the system itself; *exogenous* are those imposed upon the system from the external world. Simulations consisting only of endogenous events (aside from initialization and requests for reports of a kind which do not influence the simulation) are called *closed* simulations elsewhere, all others being called *open*.

It is worth noting at this point that continuous processes are apparently, but only apparently, excluded. The difficulty with continuous processes is not contained in the SIMSCRIPT view of the universe but rather in the fact that arithmetic processes performed by digital computers are finite. The resolution of the difficulty lies in the use of well-known numerical methods for solving differential equations. This point will be dealt with at some length later.

SIMSCRIPT Programming

The examples which follow will serve to indicate some of the features of SIMSCRIPT programming. Consider a small neighborhood market assumed to have one checkout stand and a fixed number of carts, customers arriving according to a predetermined schedule, each with a shopping list. Also, the customer is assumed to have certain personal characteristics: the length of time he is willing to wait for a cart and the length of time he is willing to wait in the checkout line. At the time the customer enters the simulation, his first act is to look for a cart. If he finds one, he immediately proceeds to shop, for a length of time determined by his shopping list plus a random increment. Once he finishes shopping, he moves on to the checkout stand. If the stand is not in use, he immediately checks out, this process taking an amount of time determined by the number of items plus a random number. When he is checked out, his cart is returned for further use, and he leaves. If, on arrival at the store, no cart is available, he waits in a FIFO queue until one does become available, in which case he proceeds to shop as before, unless his maximum waiting time is exhausted, in which case he leaves without shopping. If, on arrival at the checkout, the stand is in use, a similar process takes place. It is assumed, in the event he leaves without checking out, that his cart is returned for further use. The information desired is of three kinds:

1. Number of customers completely processed and the associated quantities of merchandise.

2. Number of customers lost by cart shortage and their merchandise statistics.

3. Number of customers lost at checkout and their merchandise statistics.

In this model there is only one temporary entity, aside from event notices, customers whose name is SHOPR, names being limited to five letters. A SHOPR has ten attributes: CANS, DAIRY, FROST, DELI, FRUIT, MEAT, and several other items as shown in Figure 7-25. Each of these attributes is used to contain the number of items of the various categories of merchandise on the shopping list. Provision is made to allow random generation of any of these numbers to account for impulse buying. Three more attributes are CRTWT, CKWAT, and WAIT. The first two contain maximum waiting times for carts and for checkout. The last is used to contain the time at which waiting begins in either case. In addition to these thirteen attributes, there are SCRTQ and SCKQ. These are defined in order to be used by the SIMSCRIPT system in handling queues. They contain the names of the successors to this shopper in the cart and checkout queues, respectively, and are used only by the SIMSCRIPT system. For any sensible limitation on number of items and length of waiting time, SIMSCRIPT memory organization allows this information to be packed into an eight-word IBM 7090/94 record. (The SIMSCRIPT system was programmed for this equipment.)

There are two event notices. One is called SHOP and comes into being when a SHOPR begins shopping. It schedules the end of shopping procedure. It has one attribute, WHO, which is used to cross-reference the record of a SHOPR. The other event notice is called CKOUT and comes into being when a SHOPR begins checking out. It schedules the end of checkout procedure. It has one attribute, PAYER, which is used to cross-reference the record of a SHOPR.

The definition form reproduced in Figure 7-25 shows how the above

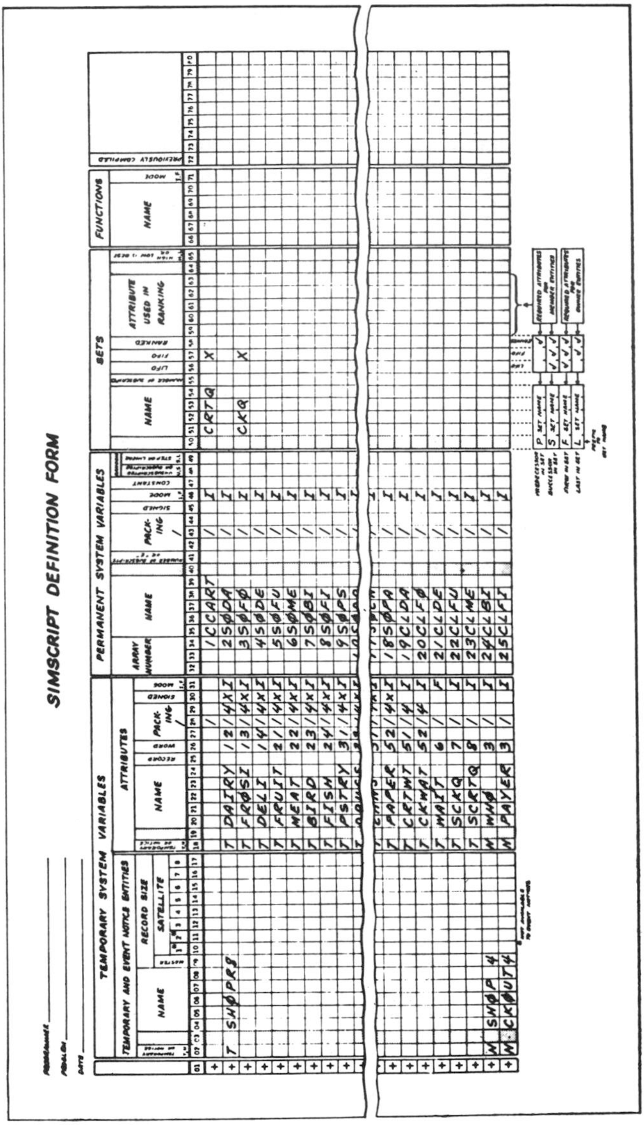
SIMSCRIPT DEFINITION FORM
PROGRAMMER
PROBLEM
DATE
TEMPORARY SYSTEM VARIABLES
TEMPORARY AND EVENT NOTICE ENTITIES
NAME
RECORD SIZE
SATELLITE
ATTRIBUTES
NAME
PACK-ING
MODE
PERMANENT SYSTEM VARIABLES
ARRAY NUMBER
NAME
PACK-ING
SIGNED
MODE
CONSTANT
SETS
NAME
LIFO
FIFO
RANKED
ATTRIBUTE USED IN RANKING
FUNCTIONS
NAME
MODE
PREVIOUSLY COMPILED
T SHOPRS
M SHOP 4
M CKOUT 4
T DAIRY 1 2/4 X I
T FROSI 1 3/4 X I
T DELI 1 4/4 X I
T FRUIT 2 1/4 X I
T MEAT 2 2/4 X I
T BIRD 2 3/4 X I
T FISH 2 4/4 X I
T PSTRY 3 1/4 X I
T PAPER 5 2/4 X I
T CRTWT 5 1/4 I
T CKWAT 5 2/4 I
T WAIT 6 / F
T SCKQ 7 / I
T SCRTQ 8 / I
M WHO 3 / I
M PAYER 3 / I
1 CCART / I
2 SODA / I
3 SOFO / I
4 SODE / I
5 SOFU / I
6 SOME / I
7 SOBI / I
8 SOFI / I
9 SOPS / I
18 SOPA / I
19 CLDA / I
20 CLFO / I
21 CLDE / I
22 CLFU / I
23 CLME / I
24 CLBI / I
25 CLFI / I
CRTQ X
CKQ X
P SET NAME
S SET NAME
F SET NAME
L SET NAME
REQUIRED ATTRIBUTES FOR MEMBER ENTITIES
REQUIRED ATTRIBUTES FOR OWNER ENTITIES

Figure 7-25.

information is formally assembled. In a large measure, the form explains itself. It may be worth noting, however, that entity records may have from 1 to 72 words, consisting of a master record and as many as 8 satellites. Each may have 1, 2, 4, or 8 words, each word being capable of storing 1, 2, 3, or 4 items of information. These can be signed or unsigned, floating or integer, with floating items being restricted to either a half or whole word. In this example, permanent system variables are used to provide storage for the number of carts currently available (CCART) or for various statistical quantities and other incidental information.

The endogenous event SHOP is described in detail to demonstrate SIMSCRIPT statements and events sequencing. The career of the customer begins with an exogenous event CUST, which creates a SHOPR and loads his record appropriately. The same event creates an event notice SHOP and schedules it. The event exhibited below takes place on schedule.

```
        STORE WHO (SHOP) IN PRSN
        DESTROY SHOP
        IF (CKWT)EQ(0), GO TO 660
        LET CCK = CCK + 1
        FILE PRSN IN CKQ
        STORE TIME IN WAIT (PRSN)
        GO TO 760
   660  STORE 1 IN CKWT
        CREATE CKOUT
        CALL CHEKT
        STORE PRSN IN PAYER  (CKOUT)
        CAUSE CKOUT AT TIME + CT
   760  RETURN
```

The first instruction retrieves the pointer to the SHOPR and stores it in temporary storage called PRSN. The second instruction is used here to return to dynamic storage the space used for the SHOP event notice record, just as a CREATE statement removes from dynamic storage the space for the record being created. The third statement investigates availability of the check stand. If not available, the next statement files the pointer in its appropriate place in the queue and adjusts the queue count. FILE (and REMOVE) involve dynamic storage allocation again. Present time is filed for later computation of the time spent by the SHOPR in the queue, and this part of the process ends. If the check stand is available, it is made busy. An event notice CKOUT is created in order to schedule the end of checkout event. A subroutine CHEKT is used to compute the amount of checkout time. The pointer for the SHOPR is stored, and the CAUSE statement schedules the end of checkout event at current time plus a time computed in the subroutine. To underline a point about sequencing, note that this event creates and schedules a next event. Obviously it could have created and scheduled any number of events.

The above routine illustrates all the SIMSCRIPT "entity operations" except CANCEL, REMOVE, and REMOVE FIRST. CANCEL deletes an event from the schedule and may be followed by destruction of the event notice or by a new CAUSE if the event is to be rescheduled. REMOVE and REMOVE FIRST are set operations of obvious intent. Among the most noteworthy of the remaining SIMSCRIPT statements are the decision commands which may be modified by control phases. For example, the statement

FIND FIRST, FOR EACH PRSON OF CKQ
WITH (CKWAT(PRSN)LE(12), AND (CANS(PRSN))
EQ(0), AND (FRUIT(PRSN))GE(6), OR (BIRD
(PRSN)) LS(2) AND (DRUG(PRSN))GR(3), IF NONE,
GO TO 50

has the following effect, if CKQ is a ranked queue: it goes through the members of the queue one by one, seeking the first member who meets at least one of the two conditions:

1. The maximum he will wait in the check stand queue is less than or equal to twelve minutes; he is buying no cans; he is buying six or more fruit items.

2. He is buying less than two poultry items; he is buying more than three drug items.

If such a member is found, the pointer to his record is stored in PRSN, and the program continues with the next statement.

Another pair of commands of great power are ACCUMULATE, COMPUTE. For example, COMPUTE A1, A2, A3, A4, A5, A6 = MEAN, SUM, SUM-SQUARES, MEAN-SQUARE, VARIANCE, STD-DEV OF CANS (PRSN), FOR EACH PRSN OF CKQ, which is self-explanatory.

Up to this point, no mention has been made of the report generator. The first step required in producing a report is to assign a name to it, whence it may be called as a subroutine. The format is specified on a report generator layout form, as in Figure 7-26. The name appears in the first line. The form indicates structure of the line, asterisks (*) representing variables to be inserted. The content line specifies which varia-

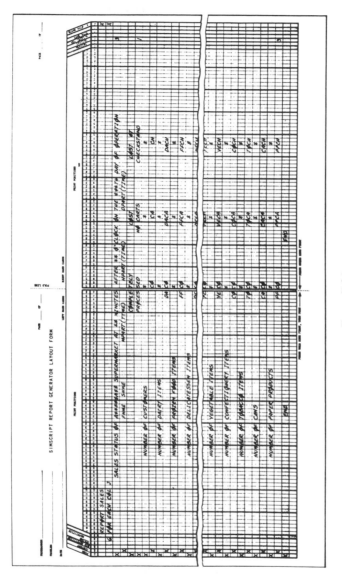

Figure 7-26.

bles are in fact to be inserted. The repetition specifications have to do with printing arrays. Thus in the example, the command CALL PROFIT provides for a report as indicated, including an array whose contents may be specified by the user (at execute time). Figure 7-27 shows a report produced by this model. Obviously, it is extremely simple to insert special reports for tracing and snapshots. This means, of course, that debugging both the program and the model in the source language is no problem.

The model discussed above is useful only as an illustrative device to introduce SIMSCRIPT concepts. Another supermarket model includes the entrance of the customer as an endogenous event, and the number of check stands as automatically controlled by the volume of business on hand, within limits. A larger variety of statistics is gathered concerning queues at the check stands and cart usage. In particular, a report is made showing the number of carts in use as a function of time. An entry appears in this table for each change in the number, opposite the time at which the change occurs. The programming of the report is

	COM-PLETELY PROC-ESSED	LOST NO CARTS	LOST AT CHECK-STAND
NUMBER OF CUSTOMERS	387	52	93
NUMBER OF DAIRY ITEMS	729	204	312
NUMBER OF FROZEN FOOD ITEMS	587	62	51
NUMBER OF DELICATESSEN ITEMS	79	102	93
NUMBER OF FRUIT ITEMS	487	62	153
NUMBER OF MEAT ITEMS	78	109	36
NUMBER OF POULTRY ITEMS	983	326	487
NUMBER OF FISH ITEMS	158	62	39
NUMBER OF PASTRY ITEMS	79	0	3
NUMBER OF DRUG ITEMS	426	39	158
NUMBER OF HARDWARE ITEMS	627	128	79
NUMBER OF LIQUOR ITEMS	36	72	58
NUMBER OF PERIODICALS	196	212	108
NUMBER OF VEGETABLE ITEMS	47	63	22
NUMBER OF CONFECTIONARY ITEMS	8	12	15
NUMBER OF TOBACCO ITEMS	386	72	204
NUMBER OF CANS	119	33	47
NUMBER OF PAPER PRODUCTS	59	27	93

Figure 7-27. Sales status of XYZ supermarket at 18 minutes after 11 o'clock on the 7th day of operation.

quite simple. An array of proper size is provided, and entries are made in successive positions in that array. With the assistance of a counter, this report is CALLed when the array is full or when the simulation ends.

Continuous Models

Returning to the question of continuous models, suppose now that a model involves a set of differential equations as well as a discrete structure. For the moment also suppose that the simplest possible integration technique is adequate. That is to say, given the values of the variables at a point t in time, the values of those variables at a time $t + \Delta t$ is obtained by increasing the values of the variables in proportion to their slopes at time t, the factor of proportionality being Δt. (This is the kind of model to which the DYNAMO [8] system addresses itself and the integration technique used there.) The SIMSCRIPT technique for dealing with this situation is as follows:

1. The exogenous event which begins the simulation also creates an event notice (perhaps called STEP) and CAUSEs it (that is, schedules it) at TIME + DT, DT being fed in at execute time. It also computes and stores initial slopes.

2. The event routine (STEP) goes to a subroutine to compute updated values of the variables and their slopes, and again CAUSEs STEP at TIME + DT.

The effect of this is to cause a single step to take place every DT in time. If values of x are required for times other than those arising in the integration, a simple interpolation suffices. Output of tables of functions against time can be obtained by the device indicated above for arriving at a chart of cart usage against time.

There are problems inherent in this approach to continuous models which imply the necessity of a more flexible arrangement. The most obvious of these problems is that sufficient accuracy with this kind of integration formula may require an extremely small time interval, hence an inordinate amount of computer time; it is quite possible, in fact, that no time interval exists which provides a specified accuracy of solution. Resolution of such a difficulty may require introduction of a higher order, that is, more precise integration method. This is, in fact, the reason for subroutinizing the integration process in (2) above. It is a simple matter once arranged this way to replace the integration subroutine.

Another case involves models in which a continuous process may be characterized by a set of parameters that eliminates the need for integration. For example, the motion of a satellite may be described by differential equations of motion and the flight path computed by integration. For certain purposes it may also be described by certain sets of equations, the equation of the ellipse among others, so that position for any specified time, or vice versa, can be computed directly. In a case such as project Mercury, where the requirement may be to find time of arrival at some dozen positions around the earth, this would have the effect of replacing thousands of events involving integration by a dozen events involving evaluation of some formulas.

All of these problems, in addition to problems which arise when there are discontinuities in the solutions or their derivatives, such as those introduced in the various phases of a missile launch, are quite easily handled in the SIMSCRIPT language. This is not to say that the associated mathematical problems are easy. The difficulties associated with these problems are simply not resolvable by programming techniques. However, once they have been resolved by other means, SIMSCRIPT makes it easy to program the result.

Processing and Performance Characteristics

Once the definition and report generator forms are completed, event routines are written, an events list is made up, and cards are punched from all this preparatory to translation. SIMSCRIPT translation then takes place on a 7090/94 under the control of the FORTRAN II monitor. This translation produces a FORTRAN input tape. Wherever it finds SIMSCRIPT type errors, it incorporates devices into the FORTRAN program to force diagnostics—it also prints SIMSCRIPT diagnostics on line. Examples of such errors are improper punctuation, missing parentheses, and certain misspellings.

The next process is compilation of the FORTRAN program into machine language, under control of the FORTRAN II monitor. This, of course, leads to standard FORTRAN output. It may well be noted that all options available in FORTRAN are also available in SIMSCRIPT; that is, the input deck to the SIMSCRIPT translator may be entirely in SIMSCRIPT or a mixed SIMSCRIPT-binary deck. The user also has the option of requesting, through control cards, a translation and compile only or a translation-compile-execute run. In the latter case, an input data deck must also be provided. The first few cards of the data deck must be of a specified form expected by the housekeeping section of the program as provided by the SIMSCRIPT translator.

The function of these cards is to allow initialization of all permanent system variables; in particular, this allows the user to specify array size at execute time rather than compile time.

Corrections can conveniently be made either at the SIMSCRIPT or machine language level. SIMSCRIPT compilation is arranged in conjunction with segmentation of the SIMSCRIPT deck in such a manner that only those segments which have been changed need to be recompiled. For example, each event routine and each subroutine is a segment, as is the deck of definition cards produced from the definition forms, so that if one event routine is changed, only that routine needs to be recompiled and so forth. Since binary corrections are made in a binary deck produced by the FORTRAN compiler, they are made in the customary manner.

In some cases, it may be desirable to let the computer analyze the results of previous runs (to determine the value of policy parameters for a next run) and then make this next run immediately without getting off the machine. To accomplish this, the calendar may be cleared of coming events, as described elsewhere [16], then time reset with the statement.

$$LET \ TIME = 0.0$$

In large programs which require more than one core-load and in "games" in which human participants interact with computer runs, the RECORD and RESTORE statements are useful. The statement

RECORD MEMORY ON TAPE J.
RESTORE TO 30

puts a complete snapshot of core and registers on the specified tape. When a RESTORE FROM TAPE K statement is executed with tape K positioned at the start of the previously RECORDed file, then the machine will be set up as it was when the RECORD statement was executed, except that control is first given to statement 30. The FORTRAN chain feature is also available.

Some 25 SIMSCRIPT programs in the areas of logistics, manufacturing, medicine, and computer systems were examined. It turns out that for most of these simulations, execution time is in the neighborhood of 10,000 events per minute. This assumes that event routines are of "reasonable size" (which is usually the case), that the logic is not unusually complex with respect to loop structure, and that there are not too many long set searches. It is to be noted in this connection that complex simulations do not normally owe their complexity to the existence of such conditions but rather to the existence of a larger variety of events of normal size.

The statistics for compilation time show that SIMSCRIPT compilation normally takes about one-third as long as the subsequent FORTRAN compilation. It should be remarked here that if the simulation program were written directly in FORTRAN, the time for compilation of the program would probably be larger than the time for the double compilation required for SIMSCRIPT. The reason for this is that the timing and initialization routines, among others, are provided in binary form. The SIMSCRIPT compiler only retouches them to fit the specific problem at hand, a process which takes very little time, particularly as compared with the FORTRAN compilation of complete routines of this complexity.

As for utilization of storage space, dynamic storage allocation obviously provides substantial advantages with regard to both utilization of available space and speed of execution, since it obviates any necessity for reshuffling storage and wastes no storage capacity on nonexistent entities or set members.

Space is also conserved by the flexibility provided for structuring entity records and by the fact that dimensions are not specified until execute time.

The storage requirements of the SIMSCRIPT control routines during execution are as follows: two thousand cells are required during initialization and are then returned to the pool for temporary entities; another two thousand cells are required for the other SIMSCRIPT chores, such as control of the dynamic storage allocation process, the exogenous events buffer, random number generator, etc.

Enough teaching experience has been accumulated to state that most persons in this field with no other programming experience can be taught SIMSCRIPT in from 30 to 40 hours of instruction, which includes writing one or two small sample programs.

Those who have learned SIMSCRIPT say that it has helped to structure their view of the system to be simulated. That is, the manner in which SIMSCRIPT looks at a system to be simulated is in itself an aid to model building.

In a trivial sense, SIMSCRIPT can accomplish anything the computer can accomplish since it can do anything FORTRAN and FAP can do. In practice, FORTRAN and FAP code is rarely used. It is significant to note that, to date, no programmable simulation problem has been proposed to the authors which has not been amenable, in rather straightforward fashion, to SIMSCRIPT treatment.*

---

* This concludes the text of the article by B. Dimsdale and H. M. Markowitz, loc. cit.

GASP [22, 23]

GASP, developed by Philip J. Kiviat while he was with United States Steel Corporation, represents a completely different concept in simulation languages than that offered by GPSS II and SIMSCRIPT because it is written in FORTRAN and can therefore be recompiled using any FORTRAN compiling system available to a particular analyst. (A version of GASP has also been written in FORTRAN IV.) GASP is a FORTRAN-compiled set of 23 subroutine programs and function subprograms (and a small FAP subroutine for pseudorandom number generation) linked and organized by a main program known as the GASP EXECUTIVE. The principal advantages offered by GASP are its machine-independence and its modular characteristics, which make it quite easy to expand and alter simulation programs to suit the needs of any given system. "As the entire GASP program is written in FORTRAN, the transference of a model from one machine to another is limited only by the existence of a FORTRAN translator plus any concessions that must be made to computer memory limitations" [23, p. 3].

Once the components, variables, parameters, and functional relationships for the system under study have been specified, then a small set of special symbols and GASP-oriented flowcharting conventions can be used to write flow charts describing the behavior of the system. Flow charts written with these GASP conventions are easily transcribed into machine-translatable FORTRAN statements. Four different concepts are embodied in GASP flow charts: operations, decisions, transfers, and control.

Most of the important procedures involved in simulating a given system on a computer are accomplished by a set of programming instructions called GASP-FORTRAN macroinstructions. Among the more important GASP macroinstructions are included [23, pp. 4-6]:

1. *Time Movement and Control Instructions*
    a. Selection of next imminent event to occur in time.
    b. Scheduling of an event to occur sometime in the future.
    c. Cancellation of an event that was previously scheduled.
    d. Control of start and end of a simulation run.
    e. Provision of variables whose values represent current simulated time in minutes, hours, days, and weeks.
2. *File Maintenance Instructions*
    a. Filing of items (elements) in queues or waiting lines.

  b. Removal of items from queues according to specified priority rules.

  c. Evaluation of certain attributes of queues or the sum or product of some attribute of all the items currently in the queue.

 3. *Data Generation Instructions*

  a. Generation of random samples from uniform, normal, Erlang, Poisson, and log-normal distributions.

  b. Generation of random samples from discrete probability functions.

  c. Generation of random samples from regression equations.

 4. *Input-Output Instructions*

  a. Standard initialization routine for setting parameter values, for setting certain simulation control values, and for sequential running of the simulation model with different data bases.

  b. Computation of the mean, the variance, the maximum, and minimum of simulation-generated data.

  c. Computation of a frequency count (histogram) for simulation-generated data.

  d. Standard automatic reporting at the end of a simulation run of a listing of all the information produced by the output statements above plus informative statistics on all queues used by the model.

 5. *Other Instructions*

  a. Automatic monitoring of program variables and conditions for error detection and debugging.

  b. Selective tracing of program flow.

  c. Programmed dumping of all system variables.

GASP views the real world as though it consisted of the following basic components.

 1. Elements
 2. Attributes
 3. Events
 4. Decision Rules
 5. Processes
 6. States
 7. Values

Items that exist in the real world such as people, machines, job-orders, computers, etc. are called *elements*. Elements are classified as either "permanent" or "temporary," depending on the nature of their use in the system under consideration. Numerically valued *attributes* are used to describe elements. The specification of the attributes of a permanent element is equivalent to naming a FORTRAN variable with one to three subscripts. Elements interact with other elements through *events*. Events are GASP subroutines written by the user which cause some kind of change to one or more elements.

The events and their effects upon system elements take place over time through the media of logical *decision rules* and *physical processes*. These rules and processes depend on the *state* of the system in time, that is, on the particular *values* of the element attributes and on various logical and physical parameters that characterize the system. As the model progresses through time, certain events generate data that represents changes in the system resulting from the particular data characterization and logical structure of the model. After a period of simulated time the simulation is terminated, and the data examined to evaluate the performance of the model [23, p. 4].

As we have previously indicated GASP is essentially a set of subprograms connected via a main program called the GASP EXECUTIVE.

. . . The GASP EXECUTIVE assumes responsibility for assuring that all events happen in correct time order so that temporal order of the model is retained. This is done by a GASP process known as scheduling; for example: In a machine shop a job has just been loaded onto a machine (event 1), it is known that processing of the job will be completed in 10 minutes at which time it can be removed from the machine (event 2). When event 1 occurs the machine is loaded and event 2 is scheduled to occur in 10 minutes.

As each event occurs the simulation time is set to the time of the occurrence of the event, which time GASP calls TNOW. Thus at the start of a simulation run, TNOW = 0.00; as the simulation goes on TNOW may be 30.45 minutes. Assume that event 1 has just occurred; then schedule event 2 at TNOW + 10.00 minutes. If TNOW was 30.45, then when the simulated time reaches 40.45 minutes, event 2 will occur and TNOW becomes 40.45 [22, p. 11].

Although we have repeatedly pointed out that subroutines play a somewhat more dominant role in GASP than they do in GPSS II and SIMSCRIPT, for the purpose of comparison it is necessary to emphasize that the following GASP data generation subroutines are analogous to those found in GPSS II and SIMSCRIPT. These include subroutines for generating random samples from uniform, normal, Erlang, Poisson, and log-normal distributions; discrete probability functions; and regression equations. The generation of random samples from regression equations represents a unique feature of GASP that is not available with other simulation languages.

With the advent of GPSS II and SIMSCRIPT, the value of GASP as a simulation language for large-scale computers such as the IBM

7090/94 was substantially reduced. However, its principal value lies in its ability to serve the needs of those users who have access to only medium or small-scale computers. For example, GASP is the only simulation language that is available for the IBM 1620 and the Control Data G-20. GASP has also been written for use on the IBM 7040/44, IBM 7070/74, CDC 1604, and Burroughs B-5000. All that is actually required to run GASP simulation programs is a computer which has a FORTRAN compiler available. Needless to say, a large number of computers fall into this category.

The fact that GASP is written in a general purpose language such as FORTRAN is both an advantage and a disadvantage. Since FORTRAN is a universal scientific programming language, the programmer is not likely to find it necessary to learn a new language or obtain a compiler which is not readily available for his particular computer. Furthermore, GASP subroutines are easily modified by the programmer to suit the needs of the particular system being simulated. However, by using FORTRAN we encounter the usual problems of input and output formatting, time consuming compilation runs, and lengthy debugging procedures.

Although debugging and error detection are usually tedious processes with FORTRAN, GASP provides three very powerful automatic error detection and debugging features. These include automatic monitoring of program variables and conditions for error detection and debugging, selective tracing of program flow, and programmed dumping of all system variables.

Next we turn to the actual simulation procedure followed by the GASP language with regard to initial values, data generation, time flow, and output. Although the initial conditions or starting values for a simulation run are usually somewhat arbitrary, they may exert considerable influence on the final results of a simulation run. GASP, therefore, offers the programmer three alternative ways of obtaining a suitable set of starting conditions for a simulation run. First, if the analyst has previously decided on the initial values for a particular simulation run, then the subroutine DATAIN can be programmed to read these values into the computer in the form of constants. Second, it is possible to start a simulation run with some arbitrary set of initial values and let the system run for some predetermined initialization period using the condition of the system at the end of this time interval to determine the starting conditions for the actual simulation run. Third, "trace" events can be entered as input data, which, together with other output statements programmed by the analyst in the MONITR subroutine, will print out event data and other pertinent statistics to assist in monitoring for starting conditions during a trial run of the system.

Having previously described the rather extensive data generation capabilities of GASP in some degree of detail, we now turn to the time flow mechanism used by GASP. Like SIMSCRIPT, GASP utilizes a variable time increment time flow mechanism.

GASP models and flow charts are constructed with the use of the event-scheduling principle. Each event is considered a separate program; each event description is therefore a separate flow chart. By proper scheduling of events the GASP executive executes the subprograms so that the simulation model reproduces the behavior of the real system in time [22, p. 11].

It is possible to obtain a wide variety of output reports with GASP including the mean, the variance, the maximum, the minimum, and a histogram for simulation-generated data, as well as informative statistics on all queues used by the system.

Most of the applications of GASP have been related to the steel industry, since GASP was developed by the Applied Research Laboratory of the United States Steel Corporation. Some of the simulation projects which have used the GASP simulation language include [23, p. 8]:

1. Simulation of an open-hearth steelmaking shop.
2. Simulation of new techniques in steelmaking.
3. Simulation of a steel plate heat-treating and annealing shop.
4. Simulation of the capacity of a railroad track section.
5. Simulation of the transportation system in a steel mill.

To illustrate the GASP simulation language we shall now develop a GASP program for our single-channel, multiprocess model described by the flow chart in Figure 5-5 of Chapter 5.* This is the same model that was formulated as a FORTRAN program in Figure 7-1. The particular version of GASP that is presented here was written for the IBM 7044 computer and assumes the existence of a FORTRAN IV compiler.

Arrival times are assumed to have a negative exponential distribution with expected value equal to 0.2222. The model consists of four processes or service stations (N = 4). The service time at each station has an exponential distribution with expected value equal to 0.2000.

---

* We are indebted to Philip J. Kiviat of the Rand Corporation for providing us with a GASP program for our multiprocess model, as well as the results of a sample run of the program on an IBM 7044. The GASP program took about two hours to write and computer running time was approximately 1100 simulated jobs per computer minute.

(1) A SINGLE CHANNEL, MULTI-STAGE MODEL
(2) 1   2   1   1   0   0   100   10   0.00   500.0
(3) QUEUE
(4)   0.0   1   1
(5) 0.2222   0.01   0.3333   1.0   POISSON ARRIVALS 1/LAMBDA
(6) 0.2000   0.01   0.2000   1.0   EXPONENTIAL SERVICE 1/MU

Figure 7-28. Input data for GASP program.

A first in-first out (FIFO) queue discipline is assumed, and the maximum queue length is 100.

Figure 7-28 contains a set of input cards which are read by the GASP DATAIN subroutine. The first card is a *title* card. The second is a *control* card. The third card indicates that the *queue discipline* is FIFO. The fourth card is an *initialization* card. Cards five and six are *parameter* cards which contain the expected value and minimum and maximum values for arrival times and service time, respectively. The number of processes N is also read in by DATAIN. Figures 7-29 through 7-33 contain the five subroutines that must be written by the user for our multi-process model, and Figure 7-34 contains a listing of the output generated by the GASP simulation run. In order to reduce the amount of space required to list each of the five GASP subroutines we have omitted all of the COMMON and DIMENSION statements. Needless to say these statements must be included if we expect to write operative programs with GASP.

The first subroutine (Figure 7-29) is called *SUBROUTINE EVENTS*. This subroutine merely contains a computed GO TO statement and CALL statements for subroutines EARRIV, ESERVC, and

```
        SUBROUTINE EVENTS
        GO TO (1, 2, 3), JEVENT
    1   CALL EARRIV
        RETURN
    2   CALL ESERVC
        RETURN
    3   CALL ESTFRE
        RETURN
        END
```

Figure 7-29. GASP subroutine events.

ESTFRE. Subroutine EVENTS is essentially a branching mechanism to transfer from the GASP EXECUTIVE to our program. The RETURN statements cause the control of the program to be transferred back to the EXECUTIVE.

The subroutine *EARRIV* (Figure 7-30) generates the arrival of a new order. It begins with a CALL SCHDL statement consisting of three arguments—scheduled time, an event code, and an auxiliary code. At time TNOW + ERLANG (1) the GASP EXECUTIVE will cause event number one (the arrival of a new order) to occur. ERLANG (1) is a library subroutine that generates stochastic variates with an exponential distribution with known parameters given by card 5 of the input data in Figure 7-28. The zero (i.e., the third argument in the subroutine) indicates that an auxiliary code is not required here. The second statement of the subroutine EARRIV is a CALL FILEM statement. This instruction puts the new order in a file of outstanding orders and records the arrival time. This order is then sent directly (JEVENT = 2, JUMP = 3) to the first process (JEQD = 1) of our system.

The next subroutine (Figure 7-31), *ESERVC*, simulates the movement of orders from one process or service station to another. The first statement is an IF statement, where JEQD is the number of the process (JEQD = 1, 2, 3, 4) at which the order has just arrived, and JSS ( ) denotes the status of process JEQD. If JSS(JEQD) is equal to 1, then process JEQD is occupied and control is transferred to statement 1. Statement 1 is a CALL FILEM statement, which files the order in the waiting line of orders waiting to be processed at process JEQD. Next an unflagged control (JUMP = 2) is used to indicate that no output is required at this point and that the next event should be selected from the list of events waiting to be scheduled. If JSS(JEQD) does not equal 1, then process JEQD is idle, and the order arrival

```
SUBROUTINE EARRIV
CALL SCHDL (TNOW + ERLANG (1), 1, 0)
CALL FILEM (TNOW, 0, 0, QUEUE, N + 1)
JEVENT = 2
JUMP = 3
JEQD = 1
RETURN
END
```

Figure 7-30. GASP subroutine EARRIV.

```
       SUBROUTINE ESERVC
       IF (JSS (JEQD). EQ. 1) GO TO 1
       SERVICE = ERLANG (2)
       CALL SCHDL (TNOW + SERVCE, 2, JEQD + 1)
       CALL SCHDL (TNOW + SERVCE, 3, JEQD)
       JSS (JEQD) = 1
       JUMP = 1
       RETURN
  1    CALL FILEM (TNOW, 0, 0, QUEUE, JEQD)
       JUMP = 2
       RETURN
       END
```

Figure 7-31. GASP subroutine ESERVC.

is scheduled at the next process (JEQD + 1) at time (TNOW + SERVCE), that is, immediately after service has been completed at process JEQD. ERLANG (2) generates an exponential variate with parameters given by input card 6 of Figure 7-28. The "2" contained in the argument of the first CALL SCHDL statement indicates that event 2 is to occur; that is, the order must be moved from one process to the next. The next CALL SCHDL statement indicates that process JEQD will become idle at time (TNOW + SERVCE), where the "3" denotes event number 3. Event 3 causes a process to become free. Process JEQD then becomes the process number of the next process, and JSS(JEQD) is set equal to 1 indicating that the next process is now occupied. The statement (JUMP = 1) indicates that output is required and the next event will be selected from the list of events waiting to be scheduled.

The subroutine *ESTFRE* (Figure 7-32) simulates the event that a process becomes idle. The variable TIME is initially set equal to zero. The IF statement checks whether the number of orders in the waiting line for process JEQD is equal to zero. If there are no orders waiting to be processed, we go to statement 1, which sets the status of process JEQD equal to zero, indicating that it is idle. The statement JUMP = 1 indicates that output is required and that the next event should be selected from the list of unscheduled events. But if the number of orders in the waiting line is not equal to zero, the CALL FETCHM statement will remove one of the orders in waiting line JEQD and record the time (TIME) of the removal. The first CALL SCHDL statement indicates that the order will move to process (JEQD + 1) at time

```
      SUBROUTINE ESTFRE
      TIME = 0.0
      IF (NQ (QUEUE, JEQD). EQ. 0) GO TO 1
      CALL FETCHM (TIME, X, Y, QUEUE, JEQD)
      SERVCE = ERLANG (2)
      CALL SCHDL (TNOW + SERVCE, 2, JEQD + 1)
      CALL SCHDL (TNOW + SERVCE, 3, JEQD)
      GO TO 2
  1   JSS (JEQD) = 0
  2   JUMP = 1
      RETURN
      END
```

Figure 7-32. GASP subroutine ESTFRE.

(TNOW + SERVCE). The second CALL SCHDL statement sets the time for removing the order from process JEQD at time (TNOW + SERVCE).

The final subroutine (Figure 7-33) of our GASP program is an *OUTPUT* subroutine that enables us to print-out the data which has been generated and collected during the simulation run. This subroutine begins with a GO TO statement. Statement 1 is an error halt. Statement 2 is a CALL COLECT statement for computing the idle time statistics for the second four rows of our output in the GASP SUMMARY REPORT (Figure 7-34). Statement 3 causes the waiting


```
      SUBROUTINE OUTPUT
      GO TO (1, 2, 3), JEVENT
  1   CALL ERROR (1)
  2   CALL COLECT (TNOW − TIDLE (JEQD), N + JEQD)
      RETURN
  3   IF (TIME. GT. 0) CALL COLECT (TNOW − TIME, JEQD)
  4   IF (JSS (JEQD). EQ. 0) TIDLE (JEQD) = TNOW
      IF (JEQD. NE. N) RETURN
      CALL FETCHM (TIME, X, Y, QUEUE, N + 1)
      CALL COLECT (TNOW − TIME, 2 * N + 1)
      RETURN
      END
```

Figure 7-33. Subroutine OUTPUT.

** GASP SUMMARY REPORT **
** GENERATED DATA **

CODE	MEAN	STD. DEV.	MIN.	MAX.	OBS.
1	2.29	1.92	0.00	7.82	2118
2	1.34	1.24	0.00	5.57	1997
3	2.18	2.16	0.00	9.11	2063
4	2.10	1.53	0.00	6.97	2103
5	0.22	0.22	0.00	1.26	178
6	0.22	0.19	0.00	0.97	298
7	0.21	0.21	0.00	1.04	230
8	0.23	0.21	0.00	0.98	174
9	7.99	4.39	0.43	18.61	2276

Figure 7-34. Output from GASP program run.

time statistics (the first four rows of our output) of the GASP SUM-
MARY REPORT to be computed. Finally, the statements beginning
with statement 4 generate the total time statistic (row nine of our
output) for the GASP SUMMARY REPORT.

At the end of the GASP run the GASP EXECUTIVE will print out
a GASP SUMMARY REPORT consisting of the mean, standard deviation, maximum, minimum, and number of observations for the waiting
time for each process (rows 1 to 4), the idle time for each process (rows
5 to 8), and the total time for an order to pass through all four processes
(row 9). With GASP it is also possible to print out a histogram of
waiting times, idle times and total times, as well as detailed information
on each of the four waiting lines.

DYNAMO

DYNAMO is a special-purpose simulation language created by
Phyllis Fox and Alexander L. Pugh at the Massachusetts Institute of
Technology [28] for the purpose of simulating certain types of dynamic
information-feedback systems that can be described in terms of a set of
finite difference equations. For the most part DYNAMO has been used
to simulate large-scale economic systems which have been formulated
as econometric models, but there is no reason why this compiler could
not be applied to other biological, physical, and social systems. In
general, it can be argued that DYNAMO is more applicable to the

kinds of systems described in Chapter 6 of this book rather than those found in Chapter 5. Although it is certainly possible to simulate waiting line and scheduling problems with DYNAMO, it would be very costly in terms of programming time to do so.

In contrast with GPSS, SIMSCRIPT, and SIMPAC, DYNAMO utilizes notation that is closer to FORTRAN. A special set of flow chart symbols and figures have been developed by Jay Forrester [8] for writing flow charts for economic and industrial systems that are to be converted into DYNAMO simulation programs. DYNAMO makes use of two different types of instructions (equations and directions) to obtain step-by-step (recursive) numerical solutions to the set of difference equations describing the system under study. The basic components of the DYNAMO language are almost identical to those found in FORTRAN because they include:

1. Variables
2. Constants
3. Subscripts
4. Equations
5. Functions

However, in DYNAMO variables are further subdivided into levels, auxiliaries, rates, supplementary variables, boxcar trains, and initial values. DYNAMO equations are classified as either levels, ratios, or boxcars. Among the special functions or subroutines which are available with DYNAMO are included:

1. Exponential
2. Logarithmic
3. Square root
4. Trigonometric
5. Uniform variates
6. Normal variates
7. Third-order delays
8. Step functions
9. Ramp functions
10. Samplers
11. Maximum and minimum functions
12. Limiting functions
13. Switch functions
14. Table functions
15. Summing functions

DYNAMO will operate on any IBM 709 or 7090 with at least one data channel and three tape drives. A DYNAMO run consists of the following six phases.

1. The *input phase* reads the cards describing the model specifications, and generates tables in preparation of later phases.

2. The *generation phase* transforms the model specifications into computer instructions.

3. The *running phase* computes the values of the model variables, thereby generating data for printing and plotting.

4. The *printing phase* tabulates the data in the form requested on PRINT cards.

5. The *plotting phase* plots the data in accordance with the PLOT card requests.

6. The *rerun phase* modifies constants in preparation for rerunning a model by the running phase [28, p. 44].

DYNAMO programs consist of the following steps.

1. Formulation of a mathematical model of the system under study in DYNAMO notation.
2. Specification of the initial values of the system.
3. Provision of input data.
4. Assignment of values to constants in the model.
5. Specification of variables to be printed or plotted.
6. Identification of the model.
7. Specification of the required length of a simulation run.

The state of the system at the beginning of the simulation run is specified by the initial values or starting conditions included in the DYNAMO equations. Then the computer determines the values of the endogenous variables of the system at the end of each time interval. Since DYNAMO is a fixed-time-increment simulation language, each time interval is of equal length. Time can be advanced over as many time intervals as are required by the investigator. The values of the variables of the model of the system can either be printed in graphical or tabular form at the end of each iteration. Both the printout procedure and the length of the simulation run are communicated to the computer by means of a set of direction instructions.

Although space does not permit a detailed description of the DYNAMO language, the reader may be able to gain some insight into the rudiments of DYNAMO by reference to the following example program. (For a complete treatment of DYNAMO the reader should consult the *DYNAMO User's Manual* [28] by Alexander Pugh.) The example program contained in Figure 7-35 is a DYNAMO version of Cobweb Model 1, which was described previously in Figure 6-1. The numbers found on the right-hand side of Figure 7-35 are strictly for expository purposes and should not be considered as part of the program.

The DYNAMO equations for the Cobweb Model are listed as Eqs. 7-4 through 7-12. Equations 7-4 through 7-6 are subroutines for generating

RUN	1966TN	(7-1)
NOTE	COBWEB MODEL I	(7-2)
NOTE	NOTE	(7-3)
34A	U. K. = (1) NORMRN (0.0, 1.0)	(7-4)
34A	V. K. = (1) NORMRN (0.0, 1.0)	(7-5)
34A	W.K. = (1) NORMRN (0.0, 1.0)	(7-6)
37B	P = BOXLIN (2, 1.0)	(7-7)
12A	DP.K = (D) (P*2.K)	(7-8)
8A	S.K. = A + DP.K + V.K	(7-9)
7A	D.K. = S.K − W.K	(7-10)
24A	X.K = (1/B) (A − C − DP.K + U.K + W.K − V.K)	(7-11)
56A	P * 1.K = MAX (X.K, 0.0)	(7-12)
NOTE		(7-13)
NOTE	INITIAL CONDITIONS	(7-14)
NOTE	NOTE	(7-15)
C	P* = 0/25	(7-16)
NOTE		(7-17)
NOTE		(7-18)
NOTE	CONSTANTS	(7-19)
C	A = 100	(7-20)
C	B = 2	(7-21)
C	C = 50	(7-22)
C	D = 3	(7-23)
NOTE		(7-24)
PRINT	1) S/2) D/3) P * 1	(7-25)
PLOT	S = S, D = D, P * 1 = P	(7-26)
SPEC	DT = 1.0/LENGTH = 50/PRTPER = 2/PLTPER = 1	(7-27)

Figure 7-35. A DYNAMO listing of Cobweb Model 1.

values for the stochastic variates U, V, and W, which are assumed to have expected values equal to 0.0 and standard deviations equal to 1.0. The letter K is a subscript that is analogous to T in Figure 6-1. K denotes the present time period. The symbol 34A denotes the type of DYNAMO equations found in Eqs. 7-4 through 7-6. It is necessary to specify the exact type of all equations by a similar coding procedure as is implied by the left-hand columns of the DYNAMO listing. Equation 7-7 is a "boxcar" function used to permit the storage and later use of historical data. In this example P_T is stored in the memory location denoted by the variable P * 1.K, and P_{T-1} is stored in the location denoted by P * 2.K. After each iteration is completed the value stored in location P * 1.K is shifted into P * 2.K, and the number zero is stored in P * 1.K. Equations 7-8 and 7-9 correspond to the supply equation in Figure 6-1. Equation 7-10 is the equilibrium condition for the model, and Eq. 7-11 is the price equation. Equation 7-12 is a subroutine for checking negative prices. If the price falls below zero, Eq. 7-12 automatically sets price equal to zero. The initial conditions and constants for the model are given by Eqs. 7-16 and 7-20 through 7-23, respectively. The starting price is assumed to be 25, and A, B, C, and D are given by

$$A = 100$$
$$B = 2$$
$$C = 50$$
$$D = 3.$$

Equation 7-25 contains a print instruction indicating that variables S, D, and P * 1 should be tabulated. Equation 7-26 indicates that these same three variables should be plotted graphically. Finally, Eq. 7-27 specifies the length of each time interval (one year), the total number of time intervals to be simulated (50), the frequency with which the output variables should be tabulated (every other year), and the frequency with which the output variables should be plotted (every year).*

We stated at the outset that DYNAMO has achieved its widespread use in the simulation of econometric models of economic systems. By far the most widely publicized application of DYNAMO is "Industrial Dynamics" [8], the work of Jay Forrester at The Massachusetts Institute of Technology in which he uses DYNAMO to simulate the behavior of complex industrial systems. Other important applications of DYNAMO include Nord's [26] study of interaction between a company's capacity acquisition policy and the growth rate of new products, Packer's [27] study of research acquisition in corporate growth, Holland and Gillespie's [17] simulation of the Indian economy, and Yance's [35] simulation of the shoe, leather, hide sequence.

OTHER SIMULATION LANGUAGES

In the preceding pages we have described in some detail four of the leading general purpose simulation languages that are in use today—

---

* We are indebted to Gary McKay and Jerry Yurow of the Civilian Industrial Technology Program in Textiles (U.S. Dept. of Commerce) in Washington, D.C. for a number of helpful suggestions regarding our DYNAMO program and the discussion of the DYNAMO simulation language in general.

GPSS II, SIMSCRIPT, GASP, and DYNAMO. In addition to these languages, we are aware of the existence of at least seven other simulation languages:

1. SIMPAC [29]
2. SIMULATE [18]
3. GSP [32, 33]
4. ESP [34]
5. CSL [4]
6. MONTECODE [21]
7. CLP [5]

In the following paragraphs we shall briefly describe each of these. The reader should consult the indicated reference if he wishes to obtain more detailed information on these languages.

SIMPAC

SIMPAC is a simulation language developed in conjunction with the "Mark I Business System Project" [19] at the System Development Corporation by M. R. Lackner and J. Kagdis. Models formulated in SIMPAC consist of four basic components—activities, transactions, queues, and operational resources. SIMPAC is a fixed time increment language written for the IBM 7090 and uses standard flow chart symbols. Although SIMPAC is characterized by a fairly flexible range of output reports, it is a somewhat more difficult language to learn than GPSS, GASP, and DYNAMO. In terms of applications SIMPAC was developed to handle waiting line and scheduling problems of a similar nature to those problems which have been treated by GPSS, SIMSCRIPT, and GASP. SIMPAC has been widely used within the System Development Corporation, but its applications outside of this organization have not been widely publicized.

SIMULATE

Program SIMULATE is a simulation language developed by Charles C. Holt and others at the Social Systems Research Institute at the University of Wisconsin in connection with the "Brookings–SSRC Quarterly Econometric Model of the United States." The objective of program SIMULATE is to determine those parameters that are critical in terms of stability and the instrument (decision) variables that are of maximum effectiveness in improving stability for large-scale econometric models. This program begins by analyzing an econometric model in terms of recursive blocks of equations and then proceeds to solve any linear systems contained in the model by matrix inversion and the nonlinear systems by iterative methods. Program

SIMULATE has been successfully applied to the Klein-Goldberger econometric model of the United States and the 40-equation Klein Quarterly model. This language was written in FORTRAN for the CDC 1604. It is also available in FORTRAN IV and is compatible with the IBM 7094, as well as the IBM 360 series.

GSP

One of the pioneering works on simulation languages was done by Dr. K. D. Tocher and his colleagues at the United Steel Companies Ltd. in England in 1960 [33]. Tocher's simulation language is called the General Simulation Program (GSP) [32]. Although many of the desirable features of GSP (e.g., the event-time flow mechanism) have been incorporated into simulation languages written in the United States, GSP itself has met with only limited usage outside of the United Kingdom and Western Europe. The primary reason for this is that it was written in a symbolic language for the Ferranti Pegasus Computer and the Elliot 503. Neither of these computers have had widespread distribution in the United States. For this reason it is difficult to make many definitive statements concerning the relative merits of GSP versus GPSS, SIMSCRIPT, GASP, and DYNAMO. However, in general GSP is particularly oriented toward systems found in manufacturing plants for such words as "plant," "machine," "collection of machines," "state of the plant," etc. play an integral part in this simulation language.

ESP

This language is one of three direct descendants of GSP that have been written by computer users in the United Kingdom. Two unique features distinguish ESP from other simulation languages. First, it consists of a set of ALGOL procedures, and, second, it uses a set of sophisticated sorting routines and dynamic storage allocation to permit multiple occurrences of any event with independent sets of parameters. ESP is available on the Elliot 503 and 803 computers.

CSL

A second descendant of GSP has been developed by IBM United Kingdom Ltd. and ESSO Petroleum Company Ltd. This language is called Control and Simulation Language (CSL). Although CSL was developed independently, it possesses a number of features that are similar to those found in SIMSCRIPT. For example, CSL statements must first be compiled into FORTRAN statements before compilation into IBM 7090 machine language takes place. Furthermore, there is a similarity in the components of CSL and the components of SIM-SCRIPT as is evidenced by the following list of CSL terminological conventions: sets, entities, arithmetic expressions, statement labels, and cell names. Like SIMSCRIPT, CSL is oriented towards industrial scheduling and waiting line systems.

MONTECODE

MONTECODE is a variable time increment simulation language written for the Ferranti Pegasus I Computer. It is alleged to be easier to learn than GSP, but for large-scale simulations the program running time of GSP is superior [21]. Like GSP, ESP, and CSL, MONTE-CODE was designed for simulating industrial scheduling problems.

CLP

CLP is a language developed by R. W. Conway, W. L. Maxwell, and others at Cornell University for use by engineering students. "As a vehicle to introduce the concepts of simulation and list processing, and as a means of implementing the relatively small problems that are characteristic of student investigations it has been most successful" [5]. CLP has been written for the Control Data 1604 and the Burroughs 220.

COMPARISON OF SIMULATION LANGUAGES

In view of the large number of simulation languages which now exist, a detailed comparison of the various languages is beyond the scope of this book. However, we shall mention three excellent papers which have attempted to compare simulation languages. The paper by Krasnow and Merikallio [24] contains a comprehensive comparison of SIMSCRIPT, CSL, GPSS, SIMPAC, and DYNAMO. Teichroew and Lubin [31] have analyzed SIMSCRIPT, CLP, CSL, GASP, GPSS, and SOL. (SOL is based on ALGOL.) In addition, Teichroew and Lubin have provided an exhaustive bibliography on simulation languages. GPSS, SIMSCRIPT, and SIMPAC have also been treated in a paper by Young [36]. Tocher's paper entitled, "Review of Simulation Languages," [33] is probably the most recent publication in this area.

REFERENCES AND BIBLIOGRAPHY

1. Blake, K., and Gordon, G. "Systems Simulation with Digital Computers," *IBM Systems Journal*, III No. 1 (1964), 14–20.

2. Boyd, D. F., and Krasnow, H. S. "Economic Evaluation of Management Information Systems," *IBM Systems Journal*, **II**, No. 2 (1963).

3. Boyd, D. F., Krasnow, H. S., and Petit, A. C. R. "Simulation of an Integrated Steel Mill," *IBM Systems Journal*, **III**, No. 1 (1964), 51–56.

4. Buxton, J. N., and Laski, J. G. "Control and Simulation Language," *The Computer Journal*, **V** (1962).

5. Conway, R. W., Delfausse, J. J., Maxwell, W. L., and Walker, W. E. "CLP— The Cornell List Processor," *Communications of the ACM*, **VIII** (April 1965).

6. Conway, R. W., Johnson, B. M., and Maxwell, W. L. "Some Problems of Digital Systems Simulation," *Management Science* (October 1959).

7. Efron, R., and Gordon, G. "A General Purpose Digital Simulator and Examples of its Application: Part I—Description of the Simulator," *IBM Systems Journal*, **III**, No. 1 (1964), 22–34.

8. Forrester, Jay W. *Industrial Dynamics.* New York: The M.I.T. Press and John Wiley and Sons, 1961.

9. Gainen, Leon, and Voosen, B. J. *The Heath Sm-80 Repair Simulation Analysis Model; Peculiar Test Equipment*, The RAND Corporation, RM-3459 (March 1963).

10. Geisler, M. A., and Markowitz, H. M. "A Brief Review of SIMSCRIPT as a Simulating Technique," The RAND Corporation, RM-3778-PR (Aug. 1963).

11. *General Purpose Systems Simulator*, Program Library, Reference 7090-CS-05X, International Business Machines Corporation.

12. *General Purpose Simulator II*, Program Library, Reference 7090-CS-13X, International Business Machines Corporation.

13. *General Purpose Systems Simulator II, Reference Manual*, International Business Machines Corporation.

14. Gordon, G. "A General Purpose Systems Simulation Program," *Proceedings of the Eastern Joint Computer Conference*, Washington, D.C., Dec. 12–14, 1961. New York: The Macmillan Co., 1961.

15. Gordon, G. "A General Purpose Systems Simulator," *IBM Systems Journal*, **I** (1962).

16. Hausner, B., and Markowitz, H. M. "Technical Appendix on the SIMSCRIPT Simulation Programming Language," The RAND Corporation, RM-3813-PR (Aug. 1963).

17. Holland, Edward P., and Gillespie, Robert W. *Experiments on a Simulated Underdeveloped Economy: Development Plans and Balance of Payments Policies.* Cambridge: The M.I.T. Press, 1963.

18. Holt, Charles C.; Shirey, Robert W.; Steward, Donald V.; Midler, Joseph L.; and Stroud, Arthur. "Program SIMULATE, a User's and Programmer's Manual," Social Systems Research Institute, University of Wisconsin, May 1964 (Mimeographed).

19. *Introduction to Management Control Systems*, TM-708/100/00, Systems Development Corporation, Santa Monica, California.

20. Karr, Herbert, W. "A Quick Look at SIMSCRIPT," The RAND Corporation, P-2658 (Oct. 1962).

21. Kelly, D. H., and Buxton, J. N. "Montecode—An Interpretive Program for Monte-Carlo Simulations," *The Computer Journal*, **V** (1962).

22. Kiviat, Philip J. "GASP—A General Activity Simulation Program," Project No. 90. 17-019(2), Applied Research Laboratory, United States Steel, Monroeville, Pennsylvania, July 8, 1963.

23. Kiviat, Philip J., and Colker, Alan. "GASP—A General Activity Simulation Program," The RAND Corporation, P-2864 (Feb. 1964).

24. Krasnow, Howard S., and Merikallio, Reino A. "The Past, Present, and Future of General Simulation Languages," *Management Science,* **XI.** (Nov. 1964), 236–267.

25. Markowitz, H. M., Hausner, Bernard, and Karr, H. W. *SIMSCRIPT: A Simulation Programming Language,* The RAND Corporation, RM-3310 (Nov. 1962).

26. Nord, Ole C. *Growth of a New Product: Effects of Capacity—Acquisition Policies.* Cambridge: The M.I.T. Press, 1963.

27. Packer, David W. *Resource Acquisition in Corporate Growth.* Cambridge: The M.I.T. Press, 1964.

28. Pugh, Alexander L. *DYNAMO User's Manual.* Cambridge, Mass.: The M.I.T. Press, 1963.

29. *SIMPAC User's Manual,* TM 602/00/00, Systems Development Corporation, Santa Monica, California, April 15, 1962.

30. SIMSCRIPT Compiler Program: SHARE Distribution Number, 3031, RSSIMS, Program Distribution Center, P. O. Box 790, White Plains, N.Y.

31. Teichroew, Daniel, and Lubin, John F. "Computer Simulation: Discussion of the Technique and Comparison of Languages," Working Paper No. 20, Graduate School of Business, Stanford University, Stanford, California, August 26, 1964.

32. Tocher, K. D., and Hopkins, D. A. "Handbook of the General Simulation Program MK. II," Report No. 118/ORD 10/TECH, United Steel Companies, Ltd., Sheffield, England, June 22, 1964.

33. Tocher, K. D. "Review of Simulation Languages," *Operational Research Quarterly,* **XVI** (June 1965).

34. Williams, J. W. J. "The Elliott Simulator Package," *The Computer Journal,* **VI** (Jan. 1964), 328–331.

35. Yance, J. V. "A Model of Price Flexibility," *American Economic Review,* **L** (June 1960), 401–418.

36. Young, Karen. "A User's Experience with Three Simulation Languages (GPSS, SIMSCRIPT, and SIMPAC)," System Development Corp., TM-1755/000/00 (1963).

Chapter 8 | The Problem of Verification

INTRODUCTION

In discussing procedures and techniques used in designing and carrying out simulation experiments with business and economic systems, we have on several occasions referred to the problem of verifying the results of simulation studies, but have said very little about how to go about "verifying" a simulation model. In part, our reason for avoiding the subject of verification is that the problem of verifying simulation models remains today perhaps the most elusive of all the unresolved problems associated with computer simulation techniques. The question of verification of simulation models is in reality no different from the question of verification when applied to any type of hypothesis or model, whether it be expressed as a verbal model, a physical model, a mathematical equation, or a computer program.

To verify or validate any kind of model means to prove the model to be true. But to prove that a model is "true" implies (1) that we have established a set of criteria for differentiating between those models which are "true" and those which are not "true" and (2) that we have the ability to readily apply these criteria to any given model. Yet the concept of "truth" has successfully eluded philosophers and theologians since the history of mankind. To decide upon a particular set of criteria that must be satisfied before we can have "truth" suggests that we must choose a subset of rules (truth rules) from an infinite set of rules handed down by philosophers, theologians, and metaphysicians. When placed in this perspective, the problem of verification is completely overwhelming because it may well be argued that man is incapable of recognizing "truth" at all, even if "truth" exists.

However, Reichenbach does admit the possibility that persons can agree on a concept of verification for a certain limited class of statements and the possibility of *indirect* verification of other statements.

Sentences can be verified in various ways. The simplest form of verification is through direct observation; but only a narrow group of sentences is thus verifiable, such as "it rains," or Peter is taller than Paul." If an observation sentence refers to the past, we regard verification as possible even if there was no observer; for instance, the sentence "it snowed on Manhatten Island on November 28, A.D. 4" is verifiable and thus meaningful because there might have been an observer. Other sentences cannot be directly verified. That there was a time when dinosaurs inhabited the earth and no human race existed, or that matter consists of atoms, can only be indirectly verified by the help of inductive inferences based on direct observations. Such sentences are meaningful because they admit of an indirect verification. The rules for this kind of verification are given by the calculus of probability. The sentence thus verified is uttered in the sense of a posit. If it concerns the future, it may be used as a guide for actions. The sign system constructed on this definition of meaning is so devised that it can be employed as an instrument of prediction—that is its function for the sign user. If it serves this purpose, it is called knowledge [23, pp. 257–258].

In the following section we explore four major methodological positions concerning the problem of verification in economics. (The relevance of this digression to the subject at hand should be obvious to the reader.) However, we shall make no attempt to take sides with any particular one of these positions, leaving the question of which position is more "suitable" for the reader to decide himself.

FOUR METHODOLOGICAL POSITIONS ON VERIFICATION

Synthetic Apriorism

Synthetic apriorism holds that economic theory (or for that matter any kind of theory) is merely a system of logical deductions from a series of synthetic premises of unquestionable truth, "not themselves open to empirical verification or general appeal to objective experience" [1, p. 612] [23, p. 39]. Immanuel Kant (1724–1804), who believed that such premises exist, is credited with coining the term *synthetic a priori*. Kant's alleged proof of the existence of a synthetic a priori has been succinctly summarized by Reichenbach.

Geometrical propositons . . . are derivable by strict logical deduction from the axioms. But these axioms themselves are not so derivable—they cannot be derivable because every derivation of synthetic conclusions has to start with synthetic premises. The truth of the axioms must therefore be established by other means than logic; they must be synthetic a priori. Once the axioms are known to be true for physical objects, the applicability of the theorems to these objects is then guaranteed by logic, since the truth of the axioms is transferred by logical derivation to the theorems. Conversely, if one is convinced that geometrical theorems apply to physical reality, one admits belief in the truth of the axioms and therefore in a synthetic a priori. Even those persons who would not like to commit themselves openly to a synthetic a priori indicate through their behavior that they believe in it: they do not hesitate to apply the results of geometry to practical measurements. This argument, Kant maintains, proves the existence of the synthetic a priori [23, p. 41].

The classical argument for synthetic apriorism in economic theory, albeit an extreme form, from which most discussions of methodology in economics begin is the argument outlined by Lionel Robbins in *An Essay on the Nature and Significance of Economic Science* [24]. The following passage summarizes Robbins' views on synthetic apriorism in economic theory.

The propositions of economic theory, like all scientific theory, are obviously deductions from a series of postulates . . . These are not postulates the existence of whose counterpart in reality admits of extensive dispute once their nature is fully realized. We do not need controlled experiments to establish their validity: they are so much the stuff of our everyday experience that they have only to be stated to be recognized as obvious. Indeed, the danger is that they may be thought to be so obvious that nothing significant can be derived from their further examination [24, pp. 78–80].*

Although Robbins' eloquent passages must indeed be reassuring to those economists who believe in the existence of a synthetic a priori, other analysts may be somewhat bewildered by the prospects of attempting to find a set of postulates of economics that are "not themselves open to empirical verification" [1, p. 612]. In other words, Robbins has reduced the problem of verification in economics to the problem of searching for a synthetic a priori. But Reichenbach denies the very existence of a synthetic a priori.

Scientific philosophy . . . refuses to accept any knowledge of the physical world as absolutely certain. Neither the individual occurrences, nor the laws controlling them, can be stated with certainty. The principles of logic and mathematics represent the only domain in which certainty is attainable; but these principles are analytic and empty. Certainty is inseparable from emptiness: there is no synthetic a priori [23, p. 304].

Ultraempiricism

At the opposite end of the methodological spectrum in economics, in complete opposition to synthetic apriorism, is ultraempiricism. Reichenbach has defined empiricism as follows.

* Reprinted in [19].

The philosophers of the second type regard empirical science, and not mathematics, as the ideal form of knowledge; they insist that sense observation is the primary source and the ultimate judge of knowledge, and that it is self-deception to believe the human mind to have direct access to any kind of truth other than that of empty logical relations. This type of philosophy is called empiricism [23, pp. 73–74].

However, ultraempiricism refuses to admit any postulates or assumptions in economics that cannot be independently verified. This extreme form of logical positivism asks that we begin with facts, not assumptions [1, pp. 612–613].

Unquestionably, the leading proponent of ultraempiricism as a means of verification in economics is T. W. Hutchison. In his work entitled *The Significance and Basic Postulates of Economic Theory*, Hutchison "seems at times to suggest that all economics should be purged of all tautologies and that the completion of this task would leave little standing" [1, pp. 612–613].

Propositions of pure theory, by themselves, have no prognostic value or "causal significance" [18, p. 162].

The advocacy of the psychological method of "a priori facts" involves a confusion of the obscure conceptions of "introspection" and the "a priori" [18, p. 163].

However, Blaug suggests that throughout the history of economic thought some economists have been willing to compromise on these two extreme points of view—synthetic apriorism and ultraempiricism.

But even an a priorist may agree that predicted results deduced from assumptions, if not the fundamental assumptions themselves, should be subject to empirical testing. And few ultra-empiricists, no matter how much they insist that all scientifically meaningful statements must be conceivably falsifiable by observation, go so far as to deny any role whatever to tautology in scientific theorizing. The controversy is over matters of emphasis, and economists since the days of J. S. Mill have always occupied the middle ground between extreme a priorism and empiricism [1, pp. 612–613].

Positive Economics

Milton Friedman in his article entitled "The Methodology of Positive Economics," *Essays in Positive Economics* [13], argues that critics of economic theory have missed the point by their preoccupation with the validity of the assumptions of economic models. According to Friedman the validity of an economic model depends not on the validity of the assumptions on which the model rests but rather on the ability of the model to predict the behavior of the endogenous variables that are treated by the model.

Although the notion that conformity to observed behavior is a desirable check on the validity of an economic model is indeed an appealing methodological position, Friedman has by no means escaped criticism for maintaining such a position. "Friedman's position is unassailable until it is realized that he is insisting on empirical testing of predictions as the sole criterion of validity; he seems to be saying that it makes no difference whatever to what extent the assumptions falsify reality" [1, pp. 612–613].

Multistage Verification

The three preceding methodological positions suggest yet a fourth possible approach to the problem of verification—an approach which may be particularly well suited to the verification of computer simulation experiments on business and economic systems. This approach to verification of simulation models is in reality a three-stage procedure incorporating the methodology of synthetic a priority, ultraempiricism, and positive economics. Multistage verification is essentially an eclectic approach to the problem of verification which says that each of the aforementioned methodological positions is a necessary procedure for validating simulation experiments but that neither of them is a sufficient procedure for solving the problem of verification.

The first stage of this procedure calls for the formulation of a set of postulates or hypotheses describing the behavior of the system of interest. To be sure these are not just any postulates because what is required in stage one is a diligent search for Kant's "synthetic a priori" and Robbins' basic postulates using all possible information at our disposal.

But having arrived at a set of basic postulates on which to build our simulation model, we are not willing to assume, like Robbins, that these postulates are of such a nature as to require no further validation. (In fact, we do not expect to ever find any such postulates.) Instead we merely submit these postulates as tentative hypotheses about the behavior of a system. Whenever possible we will insist on applying Karl R. Popper's [22] criterion of falsifiability to our postulates. According to Popper a postulate or model is scientifically meaningful if and only if it is possible to refute the postulate by empirical observation.

In other words, the second stage of our multistage verification procedure calls for an attempt on the part of the analyst to "verify" the postulates on which the model is based, subject to the limitations of existing statistical tests such as the t-test, F-test, chi-square test, distribution-free tests, etc. Although we cannot solve the philosophical problem of "What does it mean to verify a postulate?" we can apply the "best" possible statistical tests available to us to these postulates.

The third stage of this verification procedure consists of testing the model's ability to predict the behavior of the system under study. However, it should be noted that accuracy in prediction is *not* the sole criterion for validation in our multistage procedure, for this procedure attaches equal weight to the validity of the assumptions of the model and the predictive capabilities of the model. In the remaining sections of this chapter we will elaborate on several procedures for testing the degree of conformity to observed behavior of data generated by a computer simulation model.

VERIFICATION OF EXPLANATORY AND NORMATIVE MODELS

Before turning to a direct treatment of the verification of results of computer simulation experiments, it is important to differentiate between the different uses which may be made of simulation models, namely explanatory analysis and normative analysis. Although the form of models used in each of these two types of analysis may be identical, the motivation underlying them is quite different.

When we use a computer simulation model for *explanatory* or *positive* analysis, we are concerned primarily with explaining how some particular system behaves. Conclusions or predictions implied by data generated by such a model must be subjected to direct empirical observation for either verification or refutation. Historical and/or predictive verification lend support to the model as a whole. Refutation implies that one or more assumptions underlying the model inadequately explain the behavior of the actual system [19, p. 134].

On the other hand, the purpose of simulation models used for *normative* or *prescriptive* purposes is to recommend to someone (or group of individuals) a policy or course of action that is expected to accommodate one or more of that person's (or group's) objectives concerning the behavior of the system. If the policy is implemented this in itself may provide a means of testing the validity of the computer simulation model of the system.

However, it may also happen that, because of the continual impact of factors disregarded in the analysis, or because of the all-pervasive effect of the action implemented, no opportunity remains for observing the effect of not taking the recommended action or of taking some alternative action. In such cases, the recommendation is as good as the postulates from which it is correctly derived, but the analysis need not be less worthwhile for that reason [19, p. 134].

HISTORICAL VERIFICATION

In order to test the degree to which data generated by computer simulation models conform to observed data, two alternative approaches are available—historical verification and verification by forecasting. In this section we are concerned with the problem of historical verification.

Several approaches to historical verification have been suggested by operations researchers and economists who have acquired considerable experience in the design of simulation experiments. Among them is the one outlined by Orcutt et al.

Given what is thought to be a reasonable model of [a system], it could be used to generate both micro- and aggregative cross-sectional and time-series data. The statistical techniques used in estimating parameters of the model could then be applied to data generated by the model to see if such application would again lead us to essentially the same model. If they did we would be reassured. If they did not we would know that our estimation procedures produce significantly biased results and we would be given some leads as to how to improve upon the situation [21, pp. 388–389].

Clarkson, referring to his experiences with simulating investment portfolio selection procedures, has taken aim on an even more difficult problem of historical verification.

In the case of . . . simulation models the model as a whole can be subjected to statistical tests by matching the time series generated by the model against the actual time series of the variables under consideration. In this way a measure of "goodness of fit" can be obtained and the model as a whole can be confirmed on its ability to predict the time series. The problem of testing the mechanism employed by the model is not so simple because there is no clear way of either testing the functional form of the equations or the estimates of the parameters [6, p. 34].

Concerning the problem of historical verification of large-scale econometric simulation models, such as the *Brookings–SSRC Quarterly Econometric Model of the United States* [10], Charles C. Holt has suggested the following verification procedure in an article entitled "Validation and Application of Macroeconomic Models Using Computer Simulation" [10].

The first question to explore is how well the model fits known data. Usually the model is estimated from historical data and the use of the same set of data to test the model would appear somewhat questionable. However, two important points can be explored. First, if the model was estimated as a set of individual equations or alternatively as subsets of equations, then it may be a significant test to solve the equations as a simultaneous system. It is quite possible for the individual equations, or subsystems of equations, to fit reasonably well, but when all of the equations are solved jointly the errors may accumulate and a bad fit be obtained. Second, the parameter estimates usually are made on the basis of "forecasting" one time period ahead. Since many applications of the model will require forecasts for a time horizon of several or even many time periods, it is important to test whether the model is capable of giving reasonably good forecasts over longer forecast spans. After the unknown endogenous variables for one time period have been solved, time is advanced one time period and then the unknown endogenous variables for the following period are solved, and so on. As this process is repeated we would anticipate that the calculated values would gradually suffer from accumulating errors and the forecast performance gradually worsen. This is a severe test even when the model has the advantage of being tested against the data which was used in its estimation. Should the model fall down badly on either of these two tests, there is clear indication that further work is needed before any great confidence can be placed in the model.

Of course, no model is expected to fit the data exactly, the question is whether the residual errors are sufficiently small to be tolerable and sufficiently unsystematic to be treated as random. For complex nonlinear systems we have no adequate statistical theory to provide criteria for judgment, but we can at least compute and examine the errors.

The fit and the forecasting ability of the model is likely to be considerably better for some variables than others, and this suggests that it may be fruitful to run tests on portions of the model in order to isolate the sources of the difficulty. Reformation of portions of the model is likely to be indicated at this point [10].

GOODNESS OF FIT

One of the most serious problems that arises in attempting to fit data generated by computer simulation experiments to actual time series data is the question of "goodness of fit."* Cohen and Cyert have outlined the nature of the problem and have suggested three general procedures for solving the problem.

The likelihood of a process model incorrectly describing the world is high, because it makes some strong assertions about the nature of the world. There

---

* See [11] for a discussion of standard statistical tests for goodness of fit.

are various degrees by which any model can fail to describe the world, however, so it is meaningful to say that some models are more adequate descriptions of reality than others. Some criteria must be devised to indicate when the time paths generated by a process model agree sufficiently with the observed time paths so that the agreement cannot be attributed to mere coincidence. Tests must be devised for the "goodness of fit" of process models with the real world. The problem of model validation becomes even more difficult if available data about the "actual" behavior of the world is itself subject to error.

Although the final details have not yet been adequately developed, there appear to be at least three possible ways in which the validation problem for process models can be approached. First, distribution-free statistical methods can be used to test whether the actual and the generated time series display similar timing and amplitude characteristics. Second, simple regressions of the generated series as functions of the actual series can be computed, and then we can test whether the resulting regression equations have intercepts which are not significantly different from zero and slopes which are not significantly different from unity. Third, we could perform a factor analysis on the set of generated time paths and a second factor analysis on the set of observed time paths, and we can test whether the two groups of factor loadings are significantly different from each other [8].

FORECASTING

It is our position that the ultimate test of a computer simulation model is the degree of accuracy with which the model predicts the behavior of the actual system (which is being simulated) in the future. Furthermore, we would argue that the possibility that computer simulation models may be able to predict the future constitutes the major source of justification for the use of computer simulation as a tool of analysis. This is not to say that all computer simulation models are capable of yielding accurate forecasts about the future. In fact, at the present time the number of computer simulation studies that can claim even a modicum of success in predicting the behavior of some economic system are meager indeed. However, we do not feel that the limited success achieved thus far by computer simulation models in terms of forecasting ability reflects some fundamental underlying deficiency in the technique itself. Rather, we strongly suspect the principal difficulty stems from the limited experience that has been accumulated by researchers using this technique. There is also the further limitation imposed by the speed and memory capacity of existing computer hardware. However, we remain optimistic on both of these points, conjecturing that these are short-run problems that man is capable of dealing with in due time.

We view computer simulation methods as a form of the scientific method, and like Reichenbach we take the position that the scientific method represents a "functional concept of knowledge, which regards knowledge as an instrument of prediction" [23, p. 252]. Yet we do not consider either computer simulation techniques or the scientific method as means of achieving complete certainty in forecasting because the foundation on which they both rest is probability theory not "truth."

The concept of posit is the key to the understanding of predictive knowledge. A statement about the future cannot be uttered with the claim that it is true; we can always imagine that the contrary will happen, and we have no guarantee that future experience will not present to us as real what is imagination today. This very fact is the rock on which every rationalist interpretation of knowledge has been wrecked. A prediction of future experiences can be uttered only in the sense of a trial; we take its possible falsehood into account, and if the prediction turns out to be wrong, we are ready for another trial. The method of trial and error is the only existing instrument of prediction. A predictive statement is a posit; instead of knowing its truth we know only its rating, which is measured in terms of probability [23, p. 241].

REFERENCES AND BIBLIOGRAPHY

1. Blaug, M. *Economic Theory in Retrospect.* Homewood, Illinois: Richard D. Irwin, 1962.
2. Bonini, Charles P. *Simulation of Information and Decision Systems in the Firm.* Englewood Cliffs: Prentice-Hall, 1963.
3. Carnap, R. "Testability and Meaning," *Philosophy of Science,* III (1936), 425.
4. Churchman, C. West. "An Analysis of the Concept of Simulation," *Symposium on Simulation Models.* Edited by Austin C. Hoggatt and Frederick E. Balderston. Cincinnati: South-Western Publishing Co., 1963.
5. Churchman, C. West, Ackoff, Russell L., and Arnoff, E. Leonard. *Introduction to Operations Research.* New York: John Wiley and Sons, 1957.
6. Clarkson, Goeffrey, P. E. *Portfolio Selection: A Simulation of Trust Investment.* Englewood Cliffs, N.J.: Prentice-Hall, 1962.
7. Cohen, K. J. *Computer Models of the Shoe, Leather, Hide Sequence.* Englewood Cliffs: Prentice-Hall, 1960.
8. Cohen, Kalman J., and Cyert, Richard M. "Computer Models in Dynamic Economics," *The Quarterly Journal of Economics,* LXXV (Feb. 1961), 112–127.
9. Cyert, Richard M., and March, James G. *A Behavioral Theory of the Firm,* Englewood Cliffs: Prentice-Hall, 1963.
10. Duesenberry, James S., Fromm, Gary, Klein, Lawrence R., and Kuh, Edwin (editors). *The Brookings-SSRC Quarterly Econometric Model of the United States.* Chicago: Rand McNally and North-Holland Press, 1965.
11. Fisher, R. A. *Statistical Methods for Research Workers.* London: Oliver and Boyd, 1944.

12. Forrester, Jay W. *Industrial Dynamics.* New York: The M.I.T. Press and John Wiley and Sons, 1961.
13. Friedman, Milton. *Essays in Positive Economics.* Chicago: University of Chicago Press, 1953.
14. Hempel, G. C., and Oppenheim, Paul. "A Definition of Degree of Confirmation," *Philosophy of Science,* IXI (1945), 98–115.
15. Holland, Edward P., and Gillespie, Robert W. *Experiments on a Simulated Underdeveloped Economy: Development Plans and Balance of Payments Policies.* Cambridge: The M.I.T. Press, 1963.
16. Holt, Charles C.; Shirey, Robert W.; Steward, Donald V.; Midler, Joseph L.; and Stroud, Arthur. "Program SIMULATE, a User's and Programmer's Manual," Social Systems Research Institute, University of Wisconsin, May 1964 (Mimeographed).
17. Hood, William C., and Koopmans, Tjalling C. (editors). *Studies in Econometric Method.* Cowles Commission Monograph 14. New York: John Wiley and Sons, 1953.
18. Hutchison, T. W. *The Significance and Basic Postulates of Economic Theory.* London: Macmillan and Co., 1938.
19. Koopmans, Tjalling C. *Three Essays on the State of Economic Science.* New York: McGraw-Hill Book Co., 1957.
20. Madansky, Albert. "The Fitting of Straight Lines When Both Variables are Subject to Error," *Journal of the American Statistical Association,* LIV (1959), 173–205.
21. Orcutt, Guy H., Greenberger, Martin, Korbel, John, and Rivlin, Alice M. *Microanalysis of Socioeconomic Systems: A Simulation Study.* New York: Harper and Brothers, 1961.
22. Popper, Karl R. *The Logic of Scientific Discovery.* New York: Basic Books, 1959.
23. Reichenbach, Hans. *The Rise of Scientific Philosophy.* Berkeley: University of California Press, 1951.
24. Robbins, Lionel. *An Essay on the Nature and Significance of Economic Science.* London: Macmillan, 1935.
25. Rosenblueth, Arturo, and Wiener, Norbert. "The Role of Models in Science," *Philosophy of Science* XII, No. 4 (Oct., 1945), 316–321.
26. Sargan, J. P. "The Estimation of Economic Relationships Using Instrumental Variables," *Econometrica,* XXVI (1958) 393–415.

Chapter 9 | Design of
Simulation Experiments*

INTRODUCTION

The reader who hopes to find in the pages of this chapter a thorough classification of simulation experimental design situations together with a step-by-step design procedure to be followed in each category is going to be disappointed. Entire books have been written on the subject of experimental design [16, 21, 25, 26, 31, 41, 50, 66, 75]. Any attempt to condense the material in these books into a single chapter is bound to confuse the reader and may mislead him.

If such is the case, why should the authors bother with a chapter on experimental design? Why not just provide references to the various books on the subject? The answer again lies in the amount and complexity of the material available on experimental design. The research worker interested in designing a simulation experiment who goes directly to existing literature may find himself spending entirely too much time wading through large amounts of material containing unfamiliar terms. Even so, his efforts may go unrewarded because only a limited amount of the existing literature is explicitly directed toward the design of computer simulation experiments.

It is our hope therefore that this chapter will strike a happy medium between the attempt to do too much and the attempt to do too little. Our aim is to provide the background which will enable the reader to consult existing literature on design of experiments with incisiveness. In the discussion of specific techniques emphasis will be given to a description of the basic nature of the techniques and the situations or problems in which they can be usefully applied rather than to a description of how to do it yourself. Emphasis will also be given to definitions

---

* This chapter is based in part on a paper by Donald S. Burdick and Thomas H. Naylor entitled, "Design of Computer Simulation Experiments for Industrial Systems," *Communications of the ACM* (1966).

of terms commonly encountered in the literature on experimental design. Armed with this basic information, the reader should be able to recognize the situations in which an existing technique would be helpful to him and to consult the references for how-to-do-it-yourself directions—all with a minimum of wasted effort.

EXPERIMENTAL DESIGN TERMINOLOGY

The two most important terms in the language of experimental design are *factor* and *response*. Both terms refer to variables. Whether a variable in a particular experiment is a factor or a response depends upon the role played by the variable in the experiment in question. To illustrate the difference between a factor and a response, suppose we have two variables, X and Y. If our experiment is designed to answer the question how does a change in X affect Y, then X is a factor and Y is a response. Sometimes, particularly in regression models, response variables are called dependent variables and factors are called independent variables. In an experiment upon a computer simulation model a response must of necessity be an endogenous (output) variable, whereas a factor will normally be a parameter or an exogenous (input) variable or some property of its probability distribution.

For example, a computer model of a single-channel, multiprocess waiting line model for a firm [17] could have as factors: $E(AT)$, expected arrival time; $Var(AT)$, variance of arrival time; $E(ST_j)$, expected process time of the jth process, $j = 1, 2, \ldots , N$; $Var(ST_j)$, variance of process time for the jth process, $j = 1, 2, \ldots , N$. The responses could be waiting times and/or idle times for individual arrivals or processes or for averages over orders and/or processes.

For another example, suppose the experiment involves a production process utilizing machines and operators. The factors might be operators, machines, lighting, general noise level, positioning of individuals, day of the week, or weather conditions. Responses could be measures of quantity or quality of output.

A large percentage of the terms and concepts in the theory of experimental design results from classification of the factors in the experiment by the following dichotomous questions:

1. Is the factor in question controlled or not?
2. Are the values (levels) of the factor observed or not?
3. Is the effect of the factor a subject for study or is the factor included merely to increase the precision of the experiment?

4. Are the levels of the factor quantitative or qualitative?
5. Is the factor fixed or random?

A factor is *controlled* if its levels are purposefully selected by the experimenter. For example, in the production experiment mentioned above, the experimenter may select which operator to use with which machine or which day of the week. The operator, machine, and day of week factors are therefore controlled factors. On the other hand, weather conditions and general noise level are factors which might affect the output but which would not be subject to control by the experimenter (at least not in the particular experiment under discussion).

In most experiments there will be a number of factors which are *controllable* but which are not *controlled*. If, for example, the experimenter in the production experiment selects the day of the week by some random or arbitrary process, rather than purposefully, the day of week factor would not be controlled. Similarly, the positioning factor and possibly the lighting factor are controllable factors which might be uncontrolled in the given experiment.

A factor is *observed* if its levels are observed or measured and recorded as part of the data. More often than not the observed factors consist of just the controlled factors in a particular experiment, but there are frequent exceptions. It is unwise to control a factor without observing it, but an uncontrolled factor may often be observed. For example, in the production experiment the weather conditions, although uncontrolled, can be observed. Observations on uncontrolled factors are often called *concomitant observations*. In the analysis of data concomitant observations should be treated differently from observations on controlled factors. The *analysis of covariance* is a technique of data analysis which utilizes concomitant observations. Although concomitant observations are useful, in the real world it is never possible to observe *all* the factors which might affect a given response.

The distinction between factors which are of basic interest and those which are included to increase precision is an important distinction, for it serves to emphasize the fact that for almost all experiments the factors of basic interest are not the only ones to significantly affect the outcome. In the literature controlled factors which are included to increase precision are often called block factors and their levels are called blocks. In computer simulation experiments one never has uncontrolled or unobserved factors. The role which uncontrolled and unobserved factors play in the real world is played in a computer simulation model by the random character of exogenous variables.

The effects or variations in response which these factors cause in the real world have been incorporated in the computer simulation model in the form of experimental errors or random deviations. Once we have a model, the factors are determined, and it is not possible in an experiment on the model to identify additional factors as sources of variation.

It is, of course, possible in the process of model building to consider the inclusion of factors which are not of basic interest in order to improve the validity or precision of the model. An obvious extension of the blocking concept to computer simulation experiments is the use of a common sequence of pseudorandom numbers with repeated computer runs on a particular model.

This procedure . . . sharpens the contrast between [computer runs] by reducing residual variation. Differences can be detected, their statistical significance tested, and their economic significance assessed with much smaller sample sizes than would otherwise be required [23, p. 53].

A factor is *quantitative* if its levels are numbers which are expected to have a meaningful relationship with the responses. Otherwise a factor is *qualitative*. In the production experiment machines, operators, and day of the week are all qualitative factors. On the other hand, weather conditions in the form of temperature and/or humidity would be a quantitative factor. Similarly, lighting measured on a quantitative brightness scale and noise level measured on some suitable quantitative scale would be quantitative factors. In the simulation experiment on the single-channel, multi-process waiting line model for a firm the factors $E(AT)$, $Var(AT)$, $E(ST_j)$, and $Var(ST_j)$ (which are parameters for the probability distributions of AT and ST_j) are all quantitative factors. The type of probability distribution (e.g., exponential or log-normal) would be a qualitative factor. If part of the input to a simulation model consists of a decision rule and if several decision rules are under consideration, the "decision rule" could be a qualitative factor.

It is, of course, possible to assign numbers to the levels of a qualitative factor. In the production experiment the operators or the machines might be numbered 1, 2, 3, etc. However, we would not expect a meaningful relationship (in mathematical terms a continuous functional relationship) between the response and the numbers assigned to the levels of a qualitative factor. For example, we should no doubt be astonished if the output was very nearly equal to the machine number divided by the square root of the operator number.

It is also possible to treat a quantitative factor as a qualitative factor by disregarding the numerical properties of its levels. For example, the lighting factor could be considered a qualitative factor with the two levels, "bright" and "dim." The treatment of a quantitative factor as a qualitative one involves the discarding of information, which should never be done without good reason.

When an experimenter is investigating the effect of a factor on a response, he will be interested in drawing inferences with respect to a certain range or population of levels for the factor. If all the levels of interest of a particular factor are included in the experiment, that factor is said to be *fixed*. If, however, the levels of a factor that are actually included in the experiment constitute a random (or representative) sample from the population of levels in which the experimenter is interested, then the factor is said to be *random*.

In the production experiment the experimenter may desire to draw inferences about the population of operators presently employed by a particular firm. If the experimenter utilizes all the operators in the population, the operator factor is fixed. On the other hand, if practical considerations require that the experiment utilize a random sample of the operators employed by the firm, then the operator factor is random.

A random factor may be regarded as a fixed factor if the inferences drawn from the data are restricted to the levels of the factor which are actually included in the experiment. The notion of random factors permits inferences of a probabilistic nature to be made about factor levels which do not actually appear in the experiment. The techniques for accomplishing these inferences do not require that the factor be quantitative. In fact, for quantitative factors much more powerful techniques (curve fitting and regression analysis) are available. Therefore, it is generally inadvisable to treat a quantitative factor as random for the purpose of drawing inferences about levels of the factor not included in the experiment. Discussions of this concept can be found in Chapter 10 of the book by Hicks [41] and in the paper by Eisenhart [30].

BASIC IDEAS IN THE ANALYSIS OF VARIANCE

In a well-designed experiment consideration must be given to methods of analyzing the data once it is obtained. Most of the classical experimental design techniques described in the literature are used in the expectation that the data will be analyzed by one or both of the following two methods: analysis of variance and regression analysis.

The analysis of variance including multiple comparison and ranking procedures is a collection of techniques for data analysis which are appropriate when qualitative factors are present, although quantitative factors are not excluded. (Remember that a quantitative factor can always be regarded as a qualitative factor if the experimenter desires it.) Regression analysis is a collection of techniques for data analysis which utilizes the numerical properties of the levels of quantitative factors. From a mathematical point of view the distinction between regression and the analysis of variance is somewhat artificial. For example, an analysis of variance can be performed as a regression analysis using dummy variables which can assume only the values zero or one. A treatment of the relationship between regression and the analysis of variance can be found in the book by Graybill [39].

The great bulk of the experimental design techniques described in the literature have the analysis of variance as the intended method of data analysis. Therefore, in keeping with our purpose to provide a guide to presently existing techniques, it behooves us to describe a few basic ideas of the analysis of variance.

As an illustration let us consider the production experiment with operators and machines as factors. Suppose there are six operators and six machines. In other words the operator and machine factors have six levels each. A basic experimental design calls for collection of data from each of the six operators in combination with each of the six machines. This basic design is called the factorial design for two factors. It is customary to present this design in a two-way table as in Figure 9-1.

Each one of the thirty-six cells or boxes in Figure 9-1 corresponding to the thirty-six combinations of operators with machines represents a

Operator	Machine					
	A	B	C	D	E	F
1						
2						
3						
4						
5						
6						

Figure 9-1. Layout for a two-factor factorial design.

population of possible observations. For example, if daily production is the response variable, we might imagine a population of daily production data for all days during which machine D might conceivably be operated by operator 2. Of course, the actual experimental data will contain only a sample (e.g., four days' data) from this population.

If we are interested in investigating the effects of the factors on the response, a logical first question to ask is, "Do the factors have any effect at all on the response?" The statement that the factors have no effect is a statement about the thirty-six populations in the experiment. It says that these thirty-six populations are all the same. We can therefore rephrase our logical first question to, "Do the (thirty-six) populations of our experiment differ, or are they all the same?"

We still may not have the question we really want to ask of the data. There are many ways in which populations can vary, and we usually are not interested in all of these ways. The population mean is an aspect of populations in which we are most likely to be interested. A more suitable question might be, "Do the means of the (thirty-six) populations of our experiment differ, or are they all the same?" The analysis of variance is a tool for answering this question.

To answer questions about means of populations one can and usually does look at means of random samples from these populations. However, one can not conclude that population means differ simply by noting that the corresponding sample means differ. The random character of sample means makes it virtually certain that two sample means will differ even when the corresponding population means are the same. In order to infer that population means differ we must first measure the magnitude of random fluctuations. Such a measurement is obtained from the variation between observations in the same sample or cell (the within-cell variance). Using a measurement of the magnitude of random fluctuations, we can set reasonable limits for the variation between cell means (the between-cell variance). If the population means are in fact equal, then these limits will seldom be exceeded by the sample means of the cells. Therefore, if our data shows that these limits are exceeded, we can infer that the population means are probably different. This type of inference, established by comparing between-cell variance to within-cell variance, is the essence of the analysis of variance.

Of course, it is not enough to state that the factors in toto affect the response. We are very much interested in identifying and measuring the effects individual factors have on the response. For example, suppose the population means for all the cells in any one column are the same, but the population means differ from column to column. In the production experiment if columns represent machines as in Figure 9-1, this would mean that different operators using the same machine would have the same output, but that different machines have different outputs. In this case we would say that the machine factor affects (i.e., causes variation in) the response, but the operator factor does not.

In order to separate the effects due to the two factors it is customary to consider row and column means. In our example a row mean would be the average output for a particular operator (row) using all six machines (columns). A column mean would be the average output for a particular machine and all six operators.

We have reached a point from which it would be difficult to continue without introducing some notation. Let $\bar{X}_{ij}$ denote the average output of operator number i using machine number j. Let $\bar{X}_{i.}$ denote the average output of operator i using all six machines (the ith row mean), and let $\bar{X}_{.j}$ denote the average output of machine j for all six operators (the jth column mean). We can also denote the average for all thirty-six cells by $\bar{X}_{..}$. The quantity $\bar{X}_{..}$ is called the grand mean.

A *main effect* for a particular row (or column) is defined to be the deviation of the corresponding row (or column) mean from the grand mean. Thus, the main effect for operator i is $\bar{X}_{i.} - \bar{X}_{..}$ and the main effect for machine j is $\bar{X}_{.j} - \bar{X}_{..}$. Suppose as suggested above, that for any one machine the average output for each of the six operators is the same. If the means are the same for the six operators using any one machine, they will be the same for the six operators when averaged over machines. Therefore, we will have $\bar{X}_{1.} = \bar{X}_{2.} = \bar{X}_{3.} = \bar{X}_{4.} = \bar{X}_{5.} = \bar{X}_{6.}$. Since all row means are equal, they will also be equal to their average $\bar{X}_{..}$, the grand mean, and therefore $\bar{X}_{i.} - \bar{X}_{..} = 0$ for each i. In other words, the row main effects are all zero. On the other hand, if output varies from machine to machine, the averages over operators will also and the column means will differ. Since the column means differ, they can not all be equal to their average, the grand mean, so some column main effects must be nonzero. Thus, by looking at main effects, we can obtain information regarding the relative importance of the factors.

If the main effects told the whole story, then each cell mean could be represented as the sum of the grand mean, a row main effect, and a column main effect [i.e., $\bar{X}_{ij} = \bar{X}_{..} + (\bar{X}_{i.} - \bar{X}_{..}) + (\bar{X}_{.j} - \bar{X}_{..})$]. The fact that this is not true in general can be simply illustrated. Suppose in the production experiment that even-numbered operators have above average output when using even-numbered machines but below average output when using odd-numbered machines, whereas odd-numbered operators have above average output using odd-numbered machines but below average output using even-numbered machines. (This example is admittedly artificial and unrealistic, but it serves well to illustrate the point in question.) Each operator will have above average output for half the machines and below average output for the other half. Therefore, the output averaged over machines will be the same for each operator, and the row main effects will be zero. Similarly, each machine will have above average output for half the operators and below average output for the other half, which implies that the column main effects are also zero. If the equation $\overline{X}_{ij} = \overline{X}_{..} + (\overline{X}_{i.} - \overline{X}_{..}) + (\overline{X}_{.j} - \overline{X}_{..})$ held in general, then each cell mean would have to be equal to the grand mean whenever all main effects are zero. In the example just discussed, however, some cell means are above the grand mean and others are below it even though all main effects are zero.

The difference between a cell mean and the value predicted from the grand mean and the main effects, given by $\overline{X}_{ij} - \overline{X}_{..} - (\overline{X}_{i.} - \overline{X}_{..}) - (\overline{X}_{.j} - \overline{X}_{..}) = \overline{X}_{ij} - \overline{X}_{i.} - \overline{X}_{.j} + \overline{X}_{..}$, is called an *interaction effect*. It is also customary to speak of a *two-factor interaction between the machine and operator factors*. This terminology is redundant in an experiment involving only two factors. However, in experiments with more than two factors interactions involving three or more factors can occur, and two-factor interactions can occur between any pair of factors in the experiment.

In the absence of interaction the equation $\overline{X}_{ij} = \overline{X}_{..} + (\overline{X}_{i.} - \overline{X}_{..}) + (\overline{X}_{.j} - \overline{X}_{..})$ will hold. If the average output for operator i is 3 units above the overall average, and if the average output for machine j is 2 units below the overall average, then, in the absence of interaction, we can predict that the average output for operator i using machine j will be $3 - 2 = 1$ unit above the overall average. In other words, the performance of operator i *in combination with* machine j can be predicted from a measurement (i.e., main effect) on operator i only and a measurement on machine j only. Thus, the absence of interaction implies that a certain kind of independence exists between the factors. When this independence fails [as it did in the above example, since an average operator in combination with an average machine could produce an above (or below) average result], then interaction will be present.

The absence of interaction implies even more than independence of the factors. It implies that the effects of the factors are additive. In other words the average output for operator i in combination with machine j is the *sum* of an overall average, an effect for operator i, and an effect for machine j. If, instead, the average output were the *product* of an overall average, an effect for operator i, and an effect for machine j, then interaction would be present even though the factors retain their independence.

An interaction which is caused by nonadditivity of independent factors can often be removed by a suitable transformation of the data. For example, if effects are multiplicative when output data are used, then additivity can be restored by using logarithms of outputs as the mode of expression for the data. Further reading on additivity and the use of transformations can be found in the books by Cox [25] and Winer [75].

Many experimenters habitually conclude that the presence of interaction implies that the factors are not independent without giving any consideration to the possibility of independent but non-additive factors. This practice is inadvisable and should be avoided.

Let us next consider a three-factor experiment. Suppose in our production example that day of week is included as a factor with five levels (Monday, Tuesday, Wednesday, Thursday, Friday). Our basic layout is now three dimensional instead of two dimensional, but we might represent it as a series of two dimensional layouts as in Figure 9-2.

Let us define $\overline{X}_{ijk}$ to be the average output for the ith operator using the jth machine on the kth day of the week. We define $\overline{X}_{ij.}$ to be the output for operator i using machine j averaged over the days of the week. We define $\overline{X}_{i..}$ to be the output for operator i averaged over machines and days of the week. In a similar manner we can define $\overline{X}_{i.k}$, $\overline{X}_{.jk}$, and $\overline{X}_{.j.}$, $\overline{X}_{..k}$. Finally, $\overline{X}_{...}$ is defined to be the overall average output for operators, machines, and days of the week. The main effect for operator i is $\overline{X}_{i..} - \overline{X}_{...}$ and similarly for machine j and

Operators	Machines				
	Monday	Tuesday	Wednesday	Thursday	Friday
	A B C D E F	A B C D E F	A B C D E F	A B C D E F	A B C D E F
1					
2					
3					
4					
5					
6					

Figure 9-2. Layout for a three-factor factorial design.

day k. The interaction effect for operator i and machine j is $\overline{X}_{ij.} - \overline{X}_{i..} - \overline{X}_{.j.} + \overline{X}_{...}$ and similarly for the ik and jk combinations.

We might now ask whether the cell average $\overline{X}_{ijk}$ could be expressed as a sum of main effects, two-factor interaction effects, and the overall average. The answer again is no. The difference $\overline{X}_{ijk} - (\overline{X}_{ij.} - \overline{X}_{i..} - \overline{X}_{.j.} + \overline{X}_{...}) - (\overline{X}_{i.k} - \overline{X}_{i..} - \overline{X}_{..k} + \overline{X}_{...}) - (\overline{X}_{.jk} - \overline{X}_{.j.} - \overline{X}_{..k} + \overline{X}_{...}) - (\overline{X}_{i..} - \overline{X}_{...}) - (\overline{X}_{.j.} - \overline{X}_{...}) - (\overline{X}_{..k} - \overline{X}_{...}) - \overline{X}_{...} = \overline{X}_{ijk} - \overline{X}_{ij.} - \overline{X}_{i.k} - \overline{X}_{.jk} + \overline{X}_{i..} + \overline{X}_{.j.} + \overline{X}_{..k} - \overline{X}_{...}$ is defined to be the three-factor interaction effect for operator i, machine j, and day k.

From our consideration of the three-factor example it should be clear that four-factor and higher-order interactions can be defined in a strictly analogous manner (although the algebra becomes increasingly complex). The interpretation of higher-order interactions is somewhat more difficult, but it remains true that the absence of interaction implies both additivity and independence (of a sort).

Before moving on to design problems, we shall give a brief description of spectral analysis, an increasingly important method for analyzing data from computer simulation experiments. Spectral analysis [6] is a statistical technique which is widely used in the physical sciences to analyze time-dependent physical processes. There are at least two reasons why one may want to consider spectral analysis as a technique for analyzing data generated by computer simulation models. First, data generated by computer simulation experiments are usually highly autocorrelated [47]. Yet classical statistical theory of the design of experiments (analysis of variance) is based on the assumption that component observations or experimental outcomes are independently distributed. In simulation experiments involving autocorrelated data classical statistical theory must be replaced by a sampling theory such as spectral analysis in which "the probabilities of component outcomes in a series depend on other outcomes at other time points in the series" [47]. Second, as one becomes more sophisticated in the analysis of computer simulation data, he may become interested in analyzing more than expected values and variances. "When one studies a stochastic process, he is interested in the average level of activity, deviations from this level, and how long these deviations last, once they occur" [32]. Spectral analysis provides us with this kind of information. "Spectral analysis studies the salient time properties of a process and presents them in an easily interpretable fashion for descriptive and comparative purposes" [32].

Fishman and Kiviat [32] have written an excellent survey article on the use of spectral analysis in analyzing data generated by computer simulation models. The book by Blackman and Tukey [6] and the papers by Jenkins [46] and Parzen [64] are recommended to those readers who are interested in obtaining the basic elements of spectral analysis. Tukey [72] has also written an article in which spectral analysis and the analysis of variance are compared in detail.

BASIC DESIGN PROBLEMS AND TECHNIQUES FOR SOLVING THEM

In this section we describe five problems which arise in the design of experiments and identify some of the techniques which have been developed to solve them. The five experimental design problems include: (1) the problem of validity; (2) the problem of stochastic convergence; (3) the problem of size; (4) the problem of motive; and (5) the many response problem. We shall consider each of them in turn.

1. The Problem of Validity

In the area of validity there is a sharp distinction between the type of problems encountered in real world experimentation and the type encountered in experimenting with computer simulation models. In the real world the problem of validity usually takes the form of ensuring that the assumptions used to derive techniques of data analysis, such as the analysis of variance, are met so that conclusions based on these techniques will be valid. The conclusions and inferences depend on both statistical assumptions, such as the assumption that the data are generated by a random process with a normal probability distribution, and extrastatistical assumptions, such as the assumption that effects in the response are really caused by the stated factors rather than by some other hidden factors which are associated with the stated factors.

The fulfillment of both statistical and extrastatistical assumptions is greatly aided by the process of randomization. The process of randomization involves the random assignment of factor combinations to experimental units. An experimental unit is in effect a selection of levels for all factors which are uncontrollable in the experiment. The selection of an experimental unit usually requires the specification of when, where, and under what conditions (other than levels of the controlled factors) a particular observation is to be made. When the required number of experimental units has been selected, the factor levels are assigned to the units at random. A discussion of the purposes and procedures of randomization can be found in Cox [25].

For computer simulation experiments the problem of validity is quite different. Normally, a computer simulation model will automatically satisfy the assumptions required for the data analysis. The effects of all uncontrolled factors are absorbed in the random character of input (exogenous) variables. Randomization, therefore, is unnecessary as a design technique in computer simulation experiments.

Of course, one rarely gets something for nothing. Problems of validation are the price we pay for freedom from the problems of validity for which randomization techniques are appropriate. In computer simulation experiments the problem of validity is the problem of ensuring that the computer model we are using is a valid model of the real world, so that conclusions and inferences obtained from experiments on the model can be applied to the real world.

2. The Problem of Stochastic Convergence

Most experiments are intended to yield information about population quantities or averages such as average waiting time per order in the single-channel, multiprocess waiting line model or average output for a particular operator using a particular machine on Tuesdays in the production experiment. As estimates of population averages the sample averages we compute from several runs on a computer or from several days data for a particular operator using a particular machine on Tuesdays will be subject to random fluctuations and will not be exactly equal to the population averages. However, the larger the sample (i.e., the more runs or daily outputs we observe), the greater the probability that the sample averages will be very close to the population averages. The convergence of sample averages for increasing sample size is called *stochastic convergence.*

The problem of stochastic convergence is that it is slow. A measure of the amount of random fluctuation inherent in a chance quantity is its standard deviation. If σ is the standard deviation of a single observation, then the standard deviation of the average of n observations is $\sigma/\sqrt{n}$. Thus, in order to halve the random error one must quadruple the sample size n; to decrease the random error by a factor of ten, one must increase the sample size by a factor of one hundred. It can easily happen that a reasonably small random error requires an unreasonably large sample size.

The notion of sample size in computer simulation experiments is more complex than the concept of sample size in real world experiments. With computer simulation sample size may be increased in three different ways [35]. First, the total length of the simulation run may be increased from, say one month of simulated time to two months of simulated time. Second, runs of a given length may be replicated by using different sets of pseudorandom numbers. Third, since a "digital simulation operates in a discrete fashion, given the duration of events and actions as an integral multiple of some minimum time-unit," [24] an alternate way of increasing sample size is to reduce the minimum time-unit from, say one minute to one second.

Determining sample means and variances with one of the above methods to increase sample size and reduce variance is by no means a trivial problem. The article by Gafarian and Ancker [35] evaluates the properties of mean value estimates obtained by each of the three aforementioned methods. Fishman and Kiviat [32] have also examined the problem of simulation run length and the determination of sample means and variances. Geisler [36] has calculated sample sizes, measured in number of simulated time periods, required to estimate certain parameters of inventory models with specified statistical precision and confidence.

Because of the slowness of stochastic convergence we are led to seek methods other than increasing sample size to reduce random error. In real world experiments error reduction techniques commonly involve including factors such as blocks or concomitant variables which are not of basic interest to the experimenter. As was stated previously, the random assignment of experimental units (combinations of levels of controlled factors) ensures that the effects of the uncontrolled factors will make a random contribution to the observed treatment effects. If some of these factors, instead of being uncontrolled and unobserved, can be controlled or observed, then their effects will no longer contribute to the random error, and the standard deviation σ of a single observation will be reduced.

In a computer simulation experiment on a given model it is not possible to include more factors for error reduction purposes. The inclusion of more factors requires a change in the model. Once the model has been specified, all the uncontrolled factors have been irretrievably absorbed in the probabilistic specifications for the exogenous inputs.

There are, however, error reduction techniques which are suitable for computer simulation experiments. They are called Monte Carlo techniques. The underlying principle of Monte Carlo techniques is the utilization of knowledge about the structure of the model, properties of the probability distributions of the exogenous inputs, and properties of the observed variates actually used for inputs to increase the precision (i.e., reduce random error) in the measurement of averages for the response variables.

Hammersley and Handscomb [40] have written an excellent book on the subject of Monte Carlo techniques. Some of the techniques they discuss are importance sampling, the use of control variates, methods utilizing correlation (i.e., regression methods and antithetic variate methods), and conditional Monte Carlo. The book also contains an extensive bibliography. An article by Ehrenfeld and Ben-Tuvia [29] describes the application of several Monte Carlo techniques (proportional sampling, fixed sequence sampling, importance sampling, and concomitant information) to certain queueing models.

It is beyond the scope of this paper to include an exhaustive and detailed description of the Monte Carlo techniques that are presently available. However, for illustrative purposes we will describe a Monte Carlo technique that is frequently useful in simulation experiments on a computer.

The technique in question is based on a mathematical result about correlated estimates. Suppose $\bar{X}_1$ and $\bar{X}_2$ are two sample averages which are uncorrelated. Then the standard deviation (i.e., random error) of the sum $(\bar{X}_1 + \bar{X}_2)$ is exactly the same as the standard deviation of the difference $(\bar{X}_1 - \bar{X}_2)$. If, however, a positive correlation between $\bar{X}_1$ and $\bar{X}_2$ is introduced, then the standard deviation of the sum will be greater than before, but the standard deviation of the difference will be less than it was when $\bar{X}_1$ and $\bar{X}_2$ were uncorrelated. The opposite effect is observed when a negative correlation is introduced. In both cases the effect is more pronounced for large magnitude correlations than for small.

In computer experiments we are usually interested in measuring differences in average response for various combinations of factor levels. It is therefore desirable to have our estimates positively correlated. One way of accomplishing this is to use the same sequence of random numbers at each combination of factor levels. (One advantage in dealing with pseudorandom numbers is the convenience with which any particular sequence can be repeated.) Stochastic variates generated from the same set of random numbers are likely to be positively correlated. The result will be a reduced random error in the measurement of differences.

3. The Problem of Size

What we have called the problem of size arises in both real world and computer simulation experiments. It could just as easily be called "the problem of too many factors." In a factorial design for several factors the number of cells required is the product of the numbers of levels for each of the factors in the experiment. Thus, in the three-factor production experiment involving 6 operators, 6 machines, and 5 days of the week a total of $6 \times 6 \times 5 = 180$ cells are required for the full factorial design. Suppose in the single-channel, multi-process waiting line model for a firm that we have five stations or processes and that our experiment will investigate the effects of the factors $E(AT)$, $\text{Var}(AT)$, and $E(ST_j)$, $\text{Var}(ST_j)$ for $j = 1, 2, 3, 4, 5$. We would then have twelve factors. Even if we only used two levels for each of these factors, the full factorial experiment would require $2^{12} = 4096$ cells.

It is clear that the full factorial design can require an unmanageably large number of cells if more than a very few factors are to be investigated. (Notice that this problem is distinct from the problem of stochastic convergence which occurs when an unmanageably large number of *observations per cell* are required for precision.)

If we require a complete investigation of the factors in the experiment, including main effects and interactions of all orders, then there is no solution to the problem of size. If, however, we are willing to settle for a less than complete investigation, perhaps including main effects and two-factor interactions, then there are designs which will accomplish our purpose and which require fewer cells than the full factorial. Fractional factorial designs, including Latin square and Greco-Latin square designs, are examples of designs which require only a fraction of the cells required by the full factorial design.

In any design which utilizes fewer cells than the full factorial there will be some *confounding* of effects. A main effect, for example, might be confounded with an interaction effect, which means that the statistic which measures the main effect is exactly the same statistic which measures the interaction effect.

Thus, the statistic in question can tell us that some effect is present, but it cannot tell us whether the main effect, the interaction effect, or some combination of the two is present. Only if the interaction effect can be assumed to be zero (or at least negligibly small) are we justified in stating that the observed effect is in fact a main effect.

Experimenters are usually most interested in main effects. It is important therefore that main effects not be confounded with other main effects. In practically all of the commonly used fractional factorial designs main effects are confounded with interactions (preferably high order interactions) and not with other main effects. If an experimenter uses one of these designs to measure main effects, he must be willing to assume that the interactions with which the main effects are confounded are zero. Few experimenters are deterred from the use of fractional factorial designs by the necessity of such assumptions.

Although the assumption that a high order interaction is zero is frequently justifiable, we suspect that in many instances the difficulty in interpreting a high order interaction influences the experimenter's willingness to assume it zero.

The problems that arise in obtaining fractional factorial designs by confounding main effects with interactions have proved appealing to mathematical statisticians. As a result much has been written in this area both in books and in articles in the professional journals. Tables of designs can be found in the book by Cochran and Cox [21] and in two of the publications in the Applied Mathematics Series of the National Bureau of Standards [33, 34]. Bonini [7] has an example of a fractional factorial design employed in a computer simulation experiment.

So far the problem of size reduction has been discussed in an analysis-of-variance framework. As was mentioned in the section on analysis of variance, this collection of techniques for data analysis (i.e., the analysis of variance) is appropriate when the factors are qualitative. However, if the factors x_1, x_2, . . . x_k are quantitative, and the response y is related to the factors by some mathematical function f, then regression analysis, rather than the analysis of variance, may be an appropriate method of data analysis. The functional relationship $y = f(x_1, . . . , x_k)$ between the response and the quantitative factors is called the *response surface* [9, 21, 26]. Least squares regression analysis is a method for fitting a response surface to observed data in such a way as to minimize the sum of squared deviations of the observed responses from the value predicted from the fitted response surface.

For an experiment which utilizes regression analysis to explore a response surface a factorial design or a fractional factorial design may not be optimal. Several authors, primarily George Box, have developed designs, called *response surface designs* which are appropriate when response surface exploration via regression analysis is the aim of the experiment. An important advantage of the response surface designs in comparison with comparable factorial designs is the reduction in the required size of the experiment without a corresponding reduction in the amount of information obtained.

Response surface designs have not been given the attention they deserve in most of the books on experimental design. An exception is Chapter 8A in the second edition of the book by Cochran and Cox [21]. Fortunately, there are a number of readable journal articles on response surface designs, including Box and Hunter [12] and Box and Draper [11]. The recent paper by Box and Hunter [44] in this area contains an excellent bibliography.

While we are on the subject of response surface designs, we should mention their usefulness in connection with the sequential nature of computer simulation experimentation. Experimental designs which use analysis of variance as a technique of data analysis are usually based on the assumption of fixed sample size. However, with certain kinds of experiments conducted on an "accumulation-of-information" basis, sequential methods of design and analysis can be utilized and may lead to significant reductions in sample size. Since we are using computers on an "accumulation-of-information" basis, and not planting plots of beans that will mature next year, we may want to take advantage of the savings (in terms of computer time) sequential experiments offer. Sequential sampling methods were designed for testing hypotheses or estimating parameters, "when the sample size is not fixed in advance but is determined during the course of the experiment by criteria which depend on the observations as they occur" [62, p. 365].

Response surface designs can readily be used as sequential experiments. Wald's *Sequential Analysis* [73] is another well-known reference on sequential sampling, and the optimization procedures developed by Kiefer and others [28, 51, 52, 53, 54, 55] appear to offer promise in analyzing data generated by computer models. Chernoff's article entitled, "Sequential Design of Experiments" [15] also considers a number of important aspects of sequential designs.

4. The Problem of Motive

Strictly speaking, the problem of motive is not a problem in the same sense that validity, stochastic convergence, and size are problems. We have included it, however, because a consideration of motivation is important in designing an experiment. The experimenter should specify his objectives as precisely as possible to facilitate the choice of a design which will best satisfy his objectives.

Two important types of experimental objectives can be identified: (1) the experimenter wishes to find the combination of factor levels at which the response variable is maximized (or minimized) in order to optimize some process; (2) the experimenter wishes to make a rather general investigation of the relationship of the response to the factors in order to determine the underlying mechanisms governing the process under study. The distinction between these two aims is less important when the factors are qualitative than it is when the factors are quantitative. Unless certain interactions can be assumed to be zero, the only way to find the combination of levels of qualtitative factors which will produce an optimum response is to measure the response at all combinations of factor levels (i.e., the full factorial design). Even if interactions are assumed negligible in an experiment with qualitative factors, the design is likely to be the same whether the aim is to optimize or to explore.

In an experiment with quantitative factors the picture is quite different. Here, the continuity of the response surface can usually be used to guide us quickly and efficiently to a determination of the optimum combination of factor levels. There are two commonly used methods for finding the maximum of a response surface: the one-factor-at-a-time method and the method of steepest ascent. A detailed description of these two methods can be found in Chapter 8A of Cochran and Cox [21]. Of the two, the method of steepest ascent is likely to be superior in most instances.

When general exploration of a response surface is the aim, it is difficult to identify a "best" experimental design because general exploration is usually a less precisely specified goal than optimization. However, we can state a guiding principle: when the aim of an experiment is to further general knowledge and understanding, it is important to give careful and precise consideration to the existing state of knowledge and to questions and uncertainties upon which we desire the experimental data to shed some light. Perhaps this statement seems trivially obvious, but many an experiment has been ruined by the poor design which resulted from failure to give sufficiently precise consideration to the experiment's goals. An excellent paper on the use of experiments to further general understanding, including the role played by experimental design, is the one by Box and Hunter [44].

5. The Many Response Problem

Before concluding this chapter we should mention one other experimental design problem. We call it the *many response problem*. There are two aspects to this problem: (1) we may wish to observe many different response variables in our experiment, and (2) for any particular response variable we may wish to observe it as a time series (i.e., observe a different value for each month or year or any other convenient time period.)

The many response problem in both its aspects occurs frequently in computer simulation experiments. For example, in the single-channel, multiprocess waiting line model for a firm we could observe the percentage of idle time for each process and the average time per order spent waiting to be served by each process. In this case we would have $2n$ response variables. Furthermore, if seasonal variation and/or trends are incorporated into the arrival rate for orders, we would probably want to observe each of these $2n$ responses as a time series. Another example of the many response problem encountered in computer simulation experiments can be found in the article by Kagdis and Lackner [47].

It is often possible to bypass the many response problem by treating an experiment with many responses as many experiments each with single response. Or several responses could be combined (e.g., by addition) and treated as a single response. However, it is not always possible to bypass the many response problem; often multiple responses are inherent to the situation under study. Unfortunately, experimental design techniques for multiple response experiments are virtually nonexistent. Hopefully, this situation will some day be remedied.

CONCLUSIONS

In the preceding paragraphs we have attempted to relate the problem of designing computer simulation experiments to the literature on experimental design techniques. It goes without saying that the application of experimental design techniques to the design of computer simulation experiments remains an area of research in which there is still a great deal of work to be done.

REFERENCES AND BIBLIOGRAPHY

1. Bailey, N. T. J. *The Elements of Stochastic Processes.* New York: John Wiley and Sons, 1964.
2. Bartlett, M. S. *Stochastic Processes.* London: Cambridge University Press, 1961.
3. Bechhofer, R. E. "A Three Decision Problem Concerning the Mean of a Normal Population," presented at the American Statistical Association Meetings, New York, N. Y., December 30, 1955.
4. Bechhofer, R. E. "A Single Sample Multiple Procedure for Ranking Means of Normal Populations with Known Variances," *Annals of Mathematical Statistics,* **XXV** (1954), 16–39.
5. Bechhofer, Robert E., and Sobel, Milton. "A Single-Sample Multiple Decision Procedure for Ranking Variances of Normal Populations," *Annals of Mathematical Statistics,* **XXV** (1954), 273–289.
6. Blackman, R. B., and Tukey, J. W. *The Measurement of Power Spectra.* New York: Dover Publications, Inc., 1958.
7. Bonini, Charles P. *Simulation of Information and Decision Systems in the Firm.* Englewood Cliffs: Prentice-Hall, 1963.

8. Box G. E. P. "Multifactor Designs of First Order," *Biometrika,* **XXXIX** (1952), 49–57.

9. Box, G. E. P. "The Exploration and Exploitation of Response Surfaces: Some General Considerations and Examples," *Biometrics,* **X** (1954), 16–60.

10. Box, G. E. P., and Behnken, D. W. "Some New Three Level Designs for the Study of Quantitative Variables," *Technometrics,* **II** (1960) 455–474.

11. Box, G. E. P., and Draper, N. R. "A Basis for the Selection of a Response Surface Design," *Journal of American Statistical Association,* **LIV** (1959), 622–654.

12. Box, G. E. P., and Hunter, J. S. "Multi-factor Experimental Designs for Exploring Response Surfaces," *Ann. Math. Stat.,* **XXVIII** (1957), 195–241.

13. Box, G. E. P., and Wilson, K. B. "On the Experimental Attainment of Optimum Conditions," *Journal of the Royal Statistical Society B,* **XIII** (1951), 1–45.

14. Box, G. E. P., and Youle, P. V. "The Exploration and Exploitation of Response Surfaces: An Example of the Link Between the Fitted Surface and the Basic Mechanism of the System," *Biometrics,* **IX** (1955), 287–323.

15. Chernoff, Herman. "Sequential Design of Experiments," *Annals of Mathematical Statistics,* **XXX** (September 1959), 755–770.

16. Chew, Victor, editor. *Experimental Design in Industry.* New York: John Wiley and Sons, 1958.

17. Chu, Kong, and Naylor, Thomas H. "A Dynamic model of the Firm," *Management Science,* **XI** (May 1965), 736–750.

18. Chu, Kong, and Naylor, Thomas H. "Two Alternative Methods for Simulating Waiting Line Model," *Journal of Industrial Engineering* (Nov.-Dec. 1965).

19. Churchman, C. West. "An Analysis of the Concept of Simulation," *Symposium on Simulation Models.* Edited by Austin C. Hoggatt and Frederick E. Balderston. Cincinnati: South-Western Publishing Co., 1963.

20. Clark, C. E. "Importance Sampling in Monte Carlo Analysis," *Operations Research,* **IX** (1961), 603–620.

21. Cochran, W. G., and Cox, G. M. *Experimental Designs.* New York: John Wiley and Sons, 1957.

22. Conway, R. W. *An Experimental Investigation of Priority Assignment in a Job Shop.* The RAND Corp., RM-3798-PR (February 1964).

23. Conway, R. W. "Some Tactical Problems in Digital Simulation," *Management Science,* **X** (October 1963), 47–61.

24. Conway, R. W., Johnson, B. M., and Maxwell, W. L. "Some Problems of Digital Systems Simulation," *Management Science,* **VI** (October 1959), 92–110.

25. Cox, D. R. *Planning of Experiments.* New York: John Wiley and Sons, 1958.

26. Davies, O. L., editor. *Design and Analysis of Industrial Experiments.* New York: Hafner Publishing Co., 1960.

27. Dear, R. E. "Multivariate Analysis of Variance and Covariance for Simulation Studies Involving Normal Time Series," System Development Corporation, FN-5644, November 1961.

28. Dvoretzky, A., Kiefer, J., and Wolfowitz, J. "Sequential Decision Problems for Processes with Continuous Time Parameter. Problems of Estimation," *Annals of Mathematical Statistics,* **XXIV** (1963), 403–415.

29. Ehrenfield, S., and Ben-Tuvia, S. "The Efficiency of Statistical Simulation Procedures," *Technometrics* **IV** (May 1962), 257–275.
30. Eisenhart, Churchill. "The Assumptions Underlying the Analysis of Variance," *Biometrics*, **III**, No. 1 (March 1947), 1–21.
31. Fisher, Ronald A. *The Design of Experiments*. London: Oliver and Boyd, 1951.
32. Fishman, George S., and Kiviat, Philip J. "Spectral Analysis of Time Series Generated by Simulation Models," The RAND Corporation, RM-4393-PR (February 1965).
33. "Fractional Factorial Designs for Factors at Two and Three Levels," U.S. Department of Commerce, National Bureau of Standards, *Applied Mathematics Series 58*, U.S. Government Printing Office, Washington 25, D.C. (September 1, 1961).
34. "Fractional Factorial Designs for Factors at Two Levels," U.S. Department of Commerce, National Bureau of Standards, *Applied Mathematics Series 48*, U.S. Government Printing Office, Washington 25, D.C. (April 15, 1957).
35. Gafarian, A. V., and Ancker, C. J. "Mean Value Estimation from Digital Computer Simulation," System Development Corporation, SP-2005/000/01, (July 16, 1965).
36. Geisler, Murray A. "The Sizes of Simulation Samples Required to Compute Certain Inventory Characteristics with Stated Precision and Confidence," *Management Science*, **X** (January 1964), 261–286.
37. *General Purpose Simulator II*, Program Library, Reference 7090-CS-13x, International Business Machines Corporation.
38. Granger, C. W. J., and Hatanaka, M. *Spectral Analysis of Economic Time Series*. Princeton, N. J.: Princeton University Press, 1964.
39. Graybill, Franklin A. *An Introduction to Linear Statistical Models*. (Vol. I). New York: McGraw-Hill Book Company, 1961.
40. Hammersley, J. M., and Handscomb, D. C. *Monte Carlo Methods*. New York: John Wiley and Sons, 1964.
41. Hicks, Charles R. *Fundamental Concepts in the Design of Experiments*. New York: Holt, Rinehart, and Winston, 1964.
42. Hoel, Paul G. *Introduction to Mathematical Statistics*. New York: John Wiley and Sons, 1954.
43. Hotelling, H. "The Experimental Determination of the Maximum of a Function," *Annals of Mathematical Statistics*, (March 1941).
44. Hunter, William G., and Box, G. E. P. "The Experimental Study of Physical Mechanisms," *Technometrics*, **VII** (1965), 23–42.
45. Jacoby, J. H., and Harrison, S. "Multi-Variable Experimentation and Simulation Models," *Naval Research Logistics Quarterly*, **IX** (1962), 121–136.
46. Jenkins, G. M. "General Considerations in the Analysis of Spectra," *Technometrics*, **III** (May 1961), 133–166.
47. Kagdis, J., and Lackner, M. R. "Introduction to Management Control Systems Research," System Development Corporation, TM-708/000/00 (October 15, 1962).
48. Kahn, Herman, "Use of Different Monte Carlo Sampling Techniques," The RAND Corporation, P-766 (November 30, 1955).
49. Kahn, Herman, and Mann, Irwin. "Monte Carlo," The RAND Corporation, P-1165 (July 30, 1957).

50. Kempthorne, Oscar. *The Design and Analysis of Experiments*. New York: John Wiley and Sons, 1952.
51. Kiefer, J. "Sequential Minimax Search for a Maximum," *Proc. of the American Math. Society*, (June 1953).
52. Kiefer, J. "Invariance, Minimax Sequential Estimation, and Continuous Time Processes," *Annals of Mathematical Statistics*, **XXVIII** (March 1957), 573–601.
53. Kiefer, J., and Sacks, J. "Asymptotically Optimum Sequential Inference and Design," *Annals of Mathematical Statistics*, **XXIV** (September 1963), 705–750.
54. Kiefer, J., and Weiss, L. "Some Properties of Generalized Sequential Probability Ratio Tests," *Annals of Mathematical Statistics*, **XXVIII** (1957), 57–75.
55. Kiefer, J., and Wolfowitz, J. "Stochastic Estimation of the Maximum of a Regression Function," *Annals of Mathematical Statistics*. (September, 1952).
56. Kiviat, Philip J. "GASP—A General Activity Simulation Program," Project No. 90. 17-019(2), Applied Research Laboratory, United States Steel, Monroeville, Pennsylvania, July 9, 1963.
57. McArthur, D. S. "Strategy in research—Alternative Methods for Design of Experiments," *Transactions in Engineering Management*, (1961) 34–40.
58. McMillan, Claude, and Gonzalez, Richard F. *Systems Analysis*. Homewood, Ill.: Richard D. Irwin, Inc., 1965.
59. Markowitz, H. M., Hausner, Bernard, and Karr, H. W. *SIMSCRIPT: A Simulation Programming Language*, The RAND Corporation, RM-3310 (November 1962).
60. Marshall, A. W. "Experimentation by Simulation and Monte Carlo," The RAND Corporation, P-1174 (January 28, 1958).
61. Meyer, Herbert A., editor. *Symposium on Monte Carlo Methods*. New York: John Wiley and Sons, 1956.
62. Mood, A. M. *Introduction to the Theory of Statistics*. New York: McGraw Hill Book Co., 1950.
63. Naylor, Thomas H., and Burdick, Donald S. "Design of Computer Simulation Experiments for Industrial Systems," *Communications of the ACM*, (1966).
64. Parzen, Emanuel. "Mathematical Considerations in the Estimation of Spectra." *Technometrics*, **III** (May 1961), 167–190.
65. Parzen, Emanuel. *Stochastic Processes*. San Francisco: Holden-Day, 1962.
66. Quenouille, M. H. *The Design and Analysis of Experiment*. New York: Hafner Publishers Co., 1953.
67. *SIMPAC User's Manual*. TM 602/000/00 Systems Development Corporation Santa Monica, California, April 15, 1962.
68. Sobel, M., and Wald, A. "A Sequential Decision Procedure for Choosing One of Three Hypotheses Concerning the Unknown Mean of a Normal Distribution," *Annals of Mathematical Statistics*, **X** (1939).
69. Teichroew, Daniel. "A History of Distribution Sampling Prior to the Era of the Computer and Its Relevance to Simulation," *American Statistical Association Journal*, (March 1965), 27–49.
70. Teichroew, Daniel, and Lubin, John F. "Computer Simulation: Discussion of the Technique and Comparison of Languages," Working Paper No.

20, Graduate School of Business, Stanford University, Stanford, California, August 26, 1964.

71. Tocher, K. D. *The Art of Simulation.* Princeton, N.J.: D. Van Nostrand Co., 1963.

72. Tukey, John W. "Discussion Emphasizing the Connection Between Analysis of Variance and Spectras Analysis," *Technometrics,* III (May 1961), 191–220.

73. Wald, A. *Sequential Analysis.* New York: John Wiley and Sons, 1947.

74. Walsh, John E. "Use of Linearized Nonlinear Regression for Simulations Involving Monte Carlo," *Operations Research,* XI (1963), 228–235.

75. Winer, B. J. *Statistical Principles in Experimental Design.* New York: McGraw-Hill Book Co., 1962.

76. Wonnacott, Thomas. "Spectral Analysis Combining a Bartlett Window with an Associated Inner Window," *Technometrics,* III (May 1961), 237–245.

77. Yagil, S. "Generation of Input Data for Simulations," *IBM Systems Journal,* II (1963), 286–296.

78. Yaglom, A. M. *An Introduction to the Theory of Stationary Random Functions.* Englewood Cliffs, N.J.: Prentice-Hall, 1962.

Author Index

Subject Index